This book is a publication of the Curriculum Research & Development Group (CRDG), University of Hawai'i at Manoa, Honolulu.

CRDG Director: Arthur R. King, Jr.
Project Directors: Francis M. Pottenger III and E. Barbara Klemm
Managing Editor: Edith K. Kleinjans
Production: Ann Coopersmith and S. Arthur Reed
Illustrators: Jeffrey Devins, S. Arthur Reed, John Pannel, Lois Johnson, and Byron Inouye
Cover Designer: Darrell T. Asato
Cover Photo: Terry Kerby, Hawai'i Undersea Research Laboratory

Contributors

Edith H. Chave
Keith E. Chave
Mary Gullickson
Will Kyselka

Raymond K. Rounds
Edward D. Stroup
Dorothy Wendt

Content Reviewers and Advisers

Karl H. Bathen, Department of Ocean Engineering, University of Hawai'i
William S. Busch, National Oceanic and Atmospheric Administration, Maryland
Keith E. Chave, Department of Oceanography, University of Hawai'i
John P. Craven, Law of the Sea Institute, University of Hawai'i
George Curtis, Department of Ocean Engineering, University of Hawai'i
Gordon L. Dugan, Department of Civil Engineering, University of Hawai'i
Franciscus Gerritsen, Department of Ocean Engineering, University of Hawai'i
Dale Hazlehurst, Matson Navigation Company, Honolulu
David M. Karl, Department of Oceanography, University of Hawai'i
Terry Kerby, Hawai'i Undersea Research Laboratory, University of Hawai'i
Yu-Chong Lin, Department of Physiology, University of Hawai'i
Fred Mackenzie, Department of Oceanography, University of Hawai'i
Lorenz Magaard, Department of Oceanography, University of Hawai'i
Alexander P. Malahoff, Department of Oceanography, University of Hawai'i

Sherwood Maynard, Marine Option Program, University of Hawai'i
Gary M. McMurtry, Department of Oceanography, University of Hawai'i
Thomas B. Reed IV, Hawai'i Institute of Geophysics, University of Hawai'i
Francis J. Sansone, Hawai'i Institute of Geophysics, University of Hawai'i
Richard S. Shomura, National Marine Fisheries Service, Honolulu (retired)
Barbara Z. Siegel, Department of Public Health Science, University of Hawai'i
Sanford M. Siegel, Department of Botany, University of Hawai'i
Dr. Edward D. Stroup, Department of Oceanography, University of Hawai'i
Everett E. Wingert, Department of Geography, University of Hawai'i
George A. Wilkins, Hawai'i Institute of Geophysics, University of Hawai'i
John C. Wiltshire, Hawai'i Institute of Geophysics, University of Hawai'i

Teacher Reviewers

Katherine H. Aratani, Kamehameha Secondary School, Honolulu (retired)
John Burke, Department of Education, State of Hawai'i
Jonathan D. Fudge, UH Laboratory School, Honolulu
Sandy Hagstrom, Farrington High School, Honolulu
Mary Ann Johnson, Greensboro, North Carolina
Kathy Keeran, Oakland, California
Joseph McQuade, Marblehead, Massachusetts
John Southworth, UH Laboratory School, Honolulu
Dorothy M. Wendt, Waipahu High School, Hawai'i (retired)
Lee Witten, Kamehameha Secondary School, Honolulu

Printed in the United States of America
Distributed by the *HMSS* Project
Curriculum Research & Development Group
1776 University Avenue
Honolulu, Hawai'i 96822
ISBN 0–937049–58–1

The Fluid Earth

Physical Science and Technology of the Marine Environment

HMSS, Hawai'i Marine Science Studies
Third Edition

E. Barbara Klemm

Francis M. Pottenger III

Thomas W. Speitel

S. Arthur Reed

Ann E. Coopersmith

CR DG A Publication of the University of Hawai'i's
Curriculum Research & Development Group
Honolulu, Hawai'i

Contents

Preface

THE FLUID EARTH: Physical Science and Technology of the Marine Environment offers students the opportunity to learn the basic concepts of science by investigating the oceans. They explore the physics, chemistry, and geology of the oceans and learn of their practical applications in ocean engineering. In a companion text, *THE LIVING OCEAN: Biological Science and Technology of the Marine Environment*, they explore the biology and ecology of aquatic environments and their applications in aquaculture and related technologies.

The program was designed, developed, and revised by the staff of the Hawaii Marine Science Studies (HMSS) Project of the Curriculum Research & Development Group of the University of Hawaii under the direction of Francis M. Pottenger III and E. Barbara Klemm.

Since the first experimental edition of the program in 1975, the materials have been used by over 400 teachers. In 1982 the National Science Teachers Association selected HMSS as an "Exemplary Program in Science."

Funds for the project came from the University of Hawaii, the university's Sea Grant program, and other sources.

Introduction for Students

THE FLUID EARTH: Physical Science and Technology of the Marine Environment has been designed to engage you in the activities of science. You will learn the skills, concepts, and methods used by oceanographers and other scientists and engineers who study the ocean. You will learn about the oceans by carrying out investigations, designing experiments, making observations, and interpreting your findings. To succeed in using this text, you will need a laboratory notebook for recording your data and conclusions. Much of what you learn will grow out of the findings recorded in your notebook.

Study Aids

The text contains some aids to study and understanding.

1. When a new science term is defined, it is printed in **boldface**.
2. Cautions and notes are highlighted by **BOLDFACED CAPITAL LETTERS.**
3. Each topic has these parts:
   READING. An introduction to the topic.
   ACTIVITY. A statement of what your are to do in an investigation.
   MATERIALS. A list of supplies and equipment for the activity.
   PROCEDURE. Instructions for doing the activity.
   QUESTIONS. Helps to interpret your findings.

FURTHER INVESTIGATIONS. Suggestions for extending your study by following up related topics.

(W) Indicates a table or figure that is included in the Student Workbook.

Laboratory Safety

These safety precautions apply to all laboratory classes.

1. Wear safety goggles whenever you are working with chemical reagents and Bunsen burners.
2. Wear a laboratory apron when you do laboratory investigations. If you spill chemicals, the apron protects both you and your clothing.
3. Stand when you do laboratory work. Standing prevents spilling chemicals in laps.
4. Always wear shoes with closed tops.
5. If you spill chemicals on yourself or your clothing, rinse immediately with a large quantity of water to dilute and wash away the chemicals.
6. Never taste a chemical without your teacher's permission.
7. If your hair is long, pin it at the back of your head to keep it out of chemicals or flames.
8. Find out where the fire extinguisher, safety shower, and fire blanket are and learn how to use them.
9. Report all accidents to your teacher.

UNIT 1

EARTH AND OCEAN BASINS

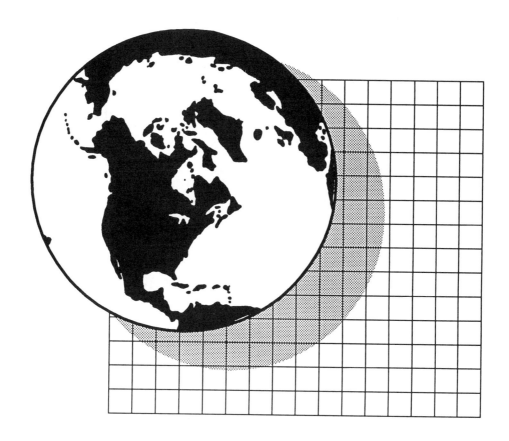

From a vantage place in space, our earth is a water-blue sphere wrapped in white streamers of mist and clouds. All the features we would see on a classroom globe whirl below—oceans, continents, islands, ice caps.

Surprisingly, what we see is, in almost every detail, what cartographers predicted in maps they drew a hundred years ago. How could these earthbound observers sketch the full earth when they could not see features beyond the horizon? How can scientists today create representations of the earth's invisible regions—the bottom of the ocean, the rocky layers of the crust, and the depths of the inner earth? These are questions we turn to first, for no tools are more important to understanding the ocean than maps.

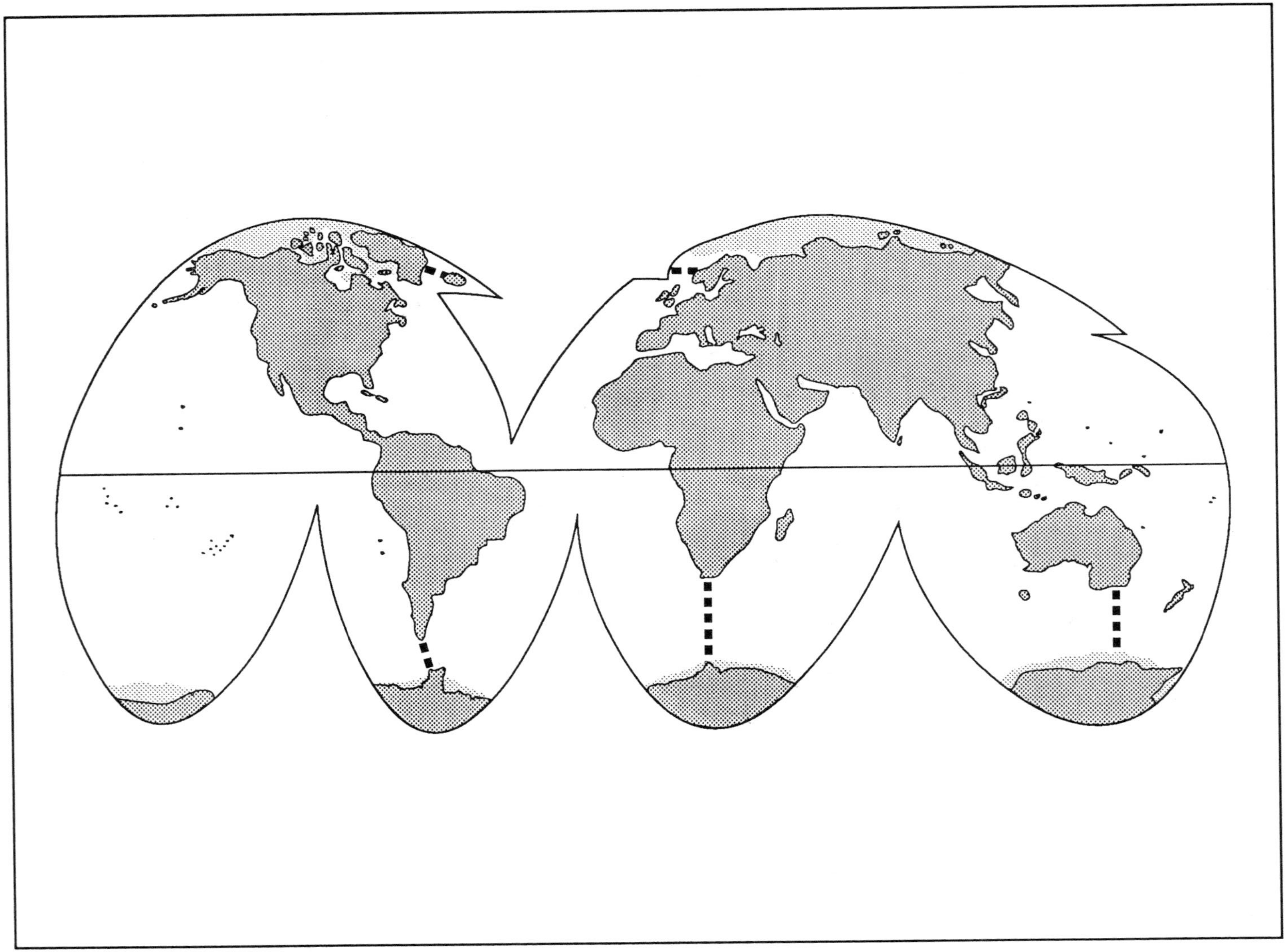

Fig. 1–1. Homolosine-projection map of the world. Continents are recognizable. Oceans appear distorted.

1. Oceans and Continents

All the oceans of the world are connected. You can see this by tracing through the oceans on a map or globe with your finger. Although you can move your finger from one ocean basin to another on these models of the earth, a ship attempting to travel through real ocean waters would be blocked in places by ice. But the waters beneath the ice do connect the ocean basins. Knowing that all the ocean basins of the world join in one continuous ocean, oceanographers speak of the "world ocean."

Because the earth is spherical, a globe represents its surface features more accurately than a map does. But maps are more convenient to use than globes because they can be folded and stored. However, there are disadvantages to using maps. Since maps are two-dimensional representations of the three-dimensional earth, they distort some of the information they display. Flattening the curved surface of a sphere onto a two-dimensional surface changes the way it looks.

The map in Fig. 1–1 shows the entire surface of the earth. This type of map, called a **homolosine** map, distorts the continents as little as possible. It is made by peeling away the surface of a globe as shown in Fig. 1–2. To minimize distortion of the shapes of continents, cuts are made through oceans. Only one continent, Antarctica, is greatly distorted by this process.

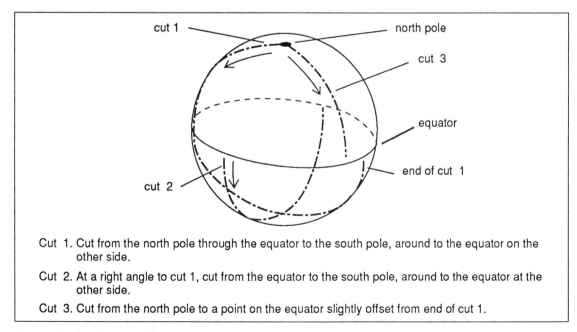

Cut 1. Cut from the north pole through the equator to the south pole, around to the equator on the other side.

Cut 2. At a right angle to cut 1, cut from the equator to the south pole, around to the equator at the other side.

Cut 3. Cut from the north pole to a point on the equator slightly offset from end of cut 1.

Fig. 1–2. Cutting the skin of an orange to construct a homolosine map

Ocean Basins

Traditionally, the world ocean is divided into four major **ocean basins**: the Arctic, the Atlantic, the Indian, and the Pacific.

No natural boundaries entirely separate the four ocean basins. In 1955 the United Nations established the boundaries for oceans and continents that we use in this topic. The ocean boundaries are indicated by dashed lines on the homolosine map of the world in Fig. 1–1. (The map appears in your workbook.) Ocean boundaries are described in Table 1–1.

Seas

Seas are also shown on many maps and globes. The term **sea** arises from tradition and is not used consistently. Some "seas" are enclosed lakes, such as the Caspian Sea and the Sea of Galilee. Some are partially enclosed or isolated sections of the ocean, such as the Mediterranean Sea or the North Sea. The Sargasso Sea is unique in that it has no land boundaries. The word **sea** reflects earlier times, when ships were smaller and much of the world was neither known nor mapped. For ancient peoples, their "sea" was almost their entire world. Such terms as "the seven seas" (referring to all the oceans) and "the south seas" are used in literature but not in maps.

Continents

For our purposes in this topic, we define **continents** as large landmasses, **islands** as smaller landmasses. We will focus on six major continental land areas: Africa, Antarctica, Australia, Eurasia, North America, and South America. By the 1955 United Nations agreement, landmasses are divided according to the political boundaries described in Table 1–2. Note that even though Greenland appears large on some maps, it is not large enough to be considered a continent.

Ice

Ice may cover up to 10 percent of the total surface area of the earth. About 4 percent of the landmasses of the world are ice-covered. These include parts of Greenland, the continent of Antarctica, and the northern areas of North America and Eurasia. Ice covers about 5 percent of the ocean surface. During the winter in each hemisphere the area covered by ice increases; in summer it decreases. Although ice is shown by shading in the homolosine map (Fig. 1–1), we will treat these surface areas as either ocean or land areas.

ACTIVITY

Locate and label the major oceans and continents shown on a world map.

MATERIALS

- pencil or pen
- crayons
- globe showing physical features
- atlas (optional)

PROCEDURE

1. Check your knowledge of continents and oceans. In Fig. 1–1, locate and label the major oceans, continents, and areas covered by ice. Do this without referring to a globe or another map.

2. Correct your own map by checking your answers with a globe or your corrected pretest map.

Table 1–1. Oceans

The **Atlantic Ocean** connects the polar ocean waters. The Arctic Ocean is not included as part of the Atlantic. Many maps label the North and South Atlantic separately.

The **Arctic Ocean** (or Northern Ocean) includes waters north of the North American and Eurasian continents. It is bounded from the Pacific by the Bering Strait and from the Atlantic at about 65°N latitude (just north of Iceland).

The **Indian Ocean** is divided from the Atlantic Ocean by a line drawn from the Cape of Good Hope in Africa to the Antarctic continent. It is divided from the Pacific Ocean by a line running through Indonesia, Australia, and Tasmania to the Antarctic continent.

The **Pacific Ocean**, largest of the ocean basins, by convention is usually separated from the Atlantic by a line drawn between the eastern tip of Cape Horn in South America and the northern end of the Palmer Peninsula in Antarctica.

Table 1–2. Continents

Africa. The continent bordered to the north by the Mediterranean Sea, to the west by the Atlantic Ocean, to the east by the Red Sea and the Suez Canal, and to the east-southeast by the Indian Ocean.

Antarctica. The continent at the south pole.

Australia. The smallest of the continents, located between the Indian and Pacific oceans.

Eurasia. A single, continuous landmass that includes Europe and Asia. Asia includes Saudi Arabia. (On political maps, the islands of Japan, Taiwan, Indonesia, and the Philippines are also considered part of Asia. Europe is usually separated from Asia by a political boundary set from the Caspian Sea north along the Ural Mountains to the Kara Sea. Europe and Asia are thus parts of the Eurasian continent indicated separately only for political reasons.)

North America. The continent that includes Canada, the United States, Mexico, and Central America down to Panama. Islands in the Arctic Ocean such as the Queen Elizabeth Islands are included on North American political maps.

South America. The continent that includes all the countries south of Panama.

3. Color-code your corrected map with crayons to show boundaries of oceans and continents. Attach a legend to the map indicating how you used the colors.

QUESTIONS

1. Explain the difference between two- and three-dimensional views of objects. Use an object in the room to illustrate your answer.

2. Briefly describe the general shape of each ocean basin. Refer to a globe if you have one in your classroom.

3. Describe the boundaries of each ocean. Record major land or water features to the north, south, east, and west of each one.

4. Check your understanding of the terms listed below. Define each term and give an example.
   a. continent
   b. globe
   c. map
   d. ocean basin
   e. political boundary

FURTHER INVESTIGATIONS

1. Make a study of the seas of the world. Locate as many as you can. (There are more than 100 seas, and you may need to use several maps to find them. Also, different maps may not agree. Keep a list of your sources of information.) How do seas differ from oceans? Prepare a world map showing the locations of the seas.

2. Using an atlas and other books, make a study of islands and island groups.
   a. List the ten largest islands by size. Then list the ten most populated islands.
   b. Locate island groups in the Pacific Ocean. Locate the regions referred to as Micronesia, Melanesia, and Polynesia. What major islands and island groups are located in each of these areas?
   c. Locate and list the major islands and island groups in the Atlantic Ocean and in the Indian Ocean.
   d. Compare the oceans in terms of the numbers and sizes of islands in them.

3. Examine atlases and books on geography and cartography (mapmaking) to learn about types of flat maps. Why are different types of maps used? What are the advantages and disadvantages of the main types? Have examples ready to show the class as you continue studying topics in this chapter.

4. Some poems and stories refer to "the seven seas," others to "the south seas." Where are these seas located? Why were they given these names?

2. How Much Water?

For centuries the only available maps of the world were ones drawn by explorers and traders. Maps of the world drawn long ago show us what was then known about our planet. Today we have photographs from satellites to supplement and correct maps drawn from data collected at the earth's surface. **Cartographers** (mapmakers) today can make very detailed and accurate maps of the earth.

As we begin our study of the earth and its ocean basins, we will examine two types of maps commonly used to show the surface areas of the oceans and continents. Fig. 2–1 is an **equal-area map**; Fig. 2–2 is a **cylindrical-projection map**. Mercator-projection maps commonly used in classrooms are a type of cylindrical-projection map.

For this topic, a grid is superimposed on both maps. At the equator each square represents a surface area of about 1,260,000 square kilometers (or 1.26×10^6 km^2).

ACTIVITY

Compare the effectiveness of an equal-area map and a cylindrical-projection map in depicting the surface areas of oceans and continents.

MATERIALS

- globe
- pencil or pen
- colored pencils or crayons
- calculator (optional)

PROCEDURE

1. Compare the equal-area and cylindrical-projection maps shown in Figs. 2–1 and 2–2. Decide which better represents the oceans and continents. Examine a globe before making your decision. In your notebook, record your reason(s) for your decision.

2. Label the map you chose as directed below. Use as a reference Fig. 1–1, the homolosine map you completed in Topic 1.
   a. Label the oceans and continents.
   b. Mark the boundaries of oceans and continents.
   c. (Optional) Use colored pencils or crayons to color-code the map. Make a **map legend** that explains how you used color to convey information.

3. Determine the surface area of each of the oceans and continents. Record your data in Tables 2–1 and 2–2.
   a. Count and record the number of squares covering each ocean and continent. Decide what to do about partial squares. Be prepared to give reasons for your decisions.

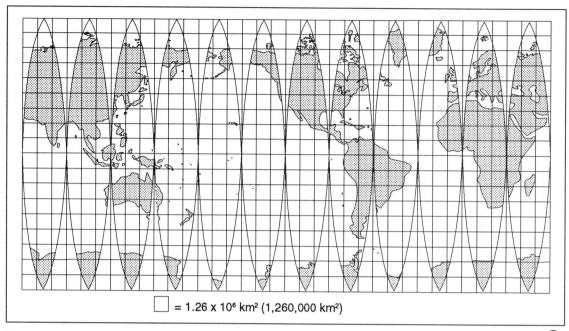

= 1.26 x 10⁶ km² (1,260,000 km²)

Fig. 2–1. Equal-area map with superimposed grid

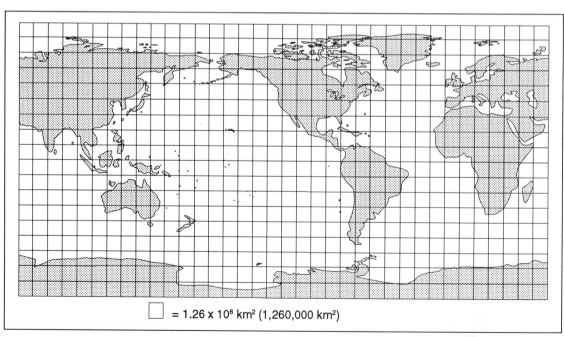

= 1.26 x 10⁶ km² (1,260,000 km²)

Fig. 2–2. Cylindrical-projection map with superimposed grid

8

Table 2–1. Areas of the continents ⓦ

Continent	Counted number of squares		Calculated area (no. of squares x 1.26 x 10^6 km^2)		Rank by size		Accepted value	
	Equal-area	Cylin-drical	Equal-area	Cylin-drical	Equal-area	Cylin-drical	Area (x 10^6 km^2)	Rank by size
Africa								
Antarctica								
Australia								
Eurasia								
North America								
South America								

Table 2–2. Areas of the oceans ⓦ

Ocean	Counted number of squares		Calculated area (no. of squares x 1.26 x 10^6 km^2)		Rank by size		Accepted value	
	Equal-area	Cylin-drical	Equal-area	Cylin-drical	Equal-area	Cylin-drical	Area (x 10^6 km^2)	Rank by size
Arctic								
Atlantic								
Indian								
Pacific								

b. Calculate the apparent area by multiplying the number of squares counted by the surface area of each square (1.26×10^6 km²). Compare your apparent areas with accepted values given to you by your teacher.

4. Rank the continents and oceans in order of size. Rank the largest 1, the next 2, etc. Record your data in Tables 2–1 and 2–2.

5. Calculate the percentages of the surface area of the earth covered by continents and by oceans. Use the data in Table 2–3. Make calculations in your workbook. Recall that

% of area covered by oceans $= \dfrac{\text{area covered by oceans}}{\text{total surface area of earth}} \times 100$

Table 2–3. Percentages of earth's surface ⓦ covered by continents and by oceans

	Accepted area	Accepted percentage
Continents	149 x 10⁶ km²	
Oceans	361 x 10⁶ km²	
Total surface area		

6. Calculate the approximate volume of each ocean. Complete Table 2–4. Use the formula

$$\text{Volume} = \text{area} \times \text{depth}$$

7. Collect and record the values calculated by other students for the surface areas from Tables 2–1 and 2–2. Refer to these data as you answer the questions.

Table 2–4. Depths and volumes of oceans ⓦ

Ocean	Equal- area map			Cylindrical- projection map			Accepted value	
	Area (x 10⁶ km²)	Average depth (km)	Volume (x 10⁶ km³)	Area (x 10⁶ km²)	Average depth (km)	Volume (x 10⁶ km³)	Volume (x 10⁶ km³)	Rank by size
Arctic		1.2			1.2			
Atlantic		3.9			3.9			
Indian		4.0			4.0			
Pacific		4.3			4.3			

QUESTIONS

1. In what ways do an equal-area map and a cylindrical-projection map differ?

2. Compare the data in Tables 2–1 and 2–2. How does an equal-area map compare with a cylindrical-projection map in terms of apparent surface areas for oceans and continents? Is the rank order the same on both maps?

3. Compare the surface areas that you calculated with the accepted areas for continents and oceans in Tables 2–1 and 2–2 that your teacher will give you. Which gives the more accurate measure of the surface area, an equal-area map or a cylindrical-projection map?

4. List the oceans from largest to smallest. To do this, examine the data in Table 2–4 on area, depth, and volume of the oceans.
   a. Which ocean is the largest? Which is the smallest? (Consider each ocean's area, depth, and volume.)
   b. What relationship, if any, is there between an ocean's surface and its depth? Give reasons for your answer.

5. In your own words, describe the sizes and shapes of the oceans and continents.

6. Explain the difference in meaning between each of the following pairs of terms:
   a. apparent surface area — accepted surface area
   b. depth — volume

FURTHER INVESTIGATIONS

1. Calculate the total surface area of the earth. Use the accepted value for the radius of the earth to calculate its total surface area. The formulas for the surface area of a sphere and the radius of the earth are given below. The symbol π stands for **pi**, the ratio of the circumference of a circle to its diameter.

$$\text{Area of sphere} = 4\pi r^2$$
$$\pi = 3.14$$
$$\text{Radius of earth } (r) = 6.38 \times 10^3 \text{ km}$$
$$= 6{,}380 \text{ km}$$

2. Compare old maps showing the way the world was thought to be
   a. when the Phoenicians traded extensively around Africa.
   b. when the Vikings explored the Atlantic.
   c. when Columbus discovered America.
   d. when Cook explored the Pacific.
   How are these maps similar to the maps we use today? How do they differ?

3. Look up references on the planets in our solar system. Find out how much water has been found on the other planets. Use this information to explain why the earth is sometimes called the "Water Planet" and the "Blue Planet."

3. Locating Points on Globes

Because our planet is a sphere, we need two types of imaginary reference lines to locate positions or points on the earth and to make accurate globes, maps, and charts of the earth. These lines are called **parallels of latitude** and **meridians of longitude**. Two of the imaginary reference lines, the equator and the prime meridian, are called **primary reference lines**.

Equator, Hemispheres, Axis, and Directions

The **equator** is an imaginary reference line drawn around the earth halfway between the north and south poles. See Fig. 3–1.

The earth rotates daily about another imaginary line called an **axis**. The north and south **poles** are the two imaginary points where the axis enters and exits from the earth. (For better understanding, imaginary poles are sometimes shown on maps and globes as coming out of the earth.)

The half of the earth to the north of the equator is the **northern hemisphere**; the half to the south is the **southern hemisphere**. (**Hemi** means "half"; thus **hemisphere** means "half-sphere.") The United States (including Alaska and Hawaii) is in the northern hemisphere.

North and south directions are determined by the poles. Movement toward the north pole is northerly in direction. Movement toward the south pole is southerly in direction.

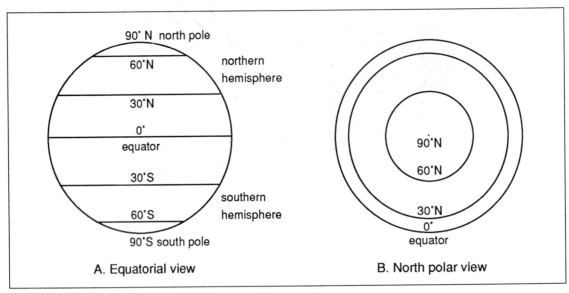

Fig. 3–1. The equator and parallels of latitude form complete circles around the earth.

Parallels of Latitude

Latitude is the distance measured in degrees from 0° to 90° north or south of the equator. **Parallels of latitude** are imaginary reference lines that form complete circles around the earth parallel to the equator and to each other. Every point on a parallel is the same distance from the equator.

The latitudinal distance from the equator to either of the earth's poles is 90°. Degrees of latitude are measured from an imaginary point at the center of the earth. See Fig. 3–2. The equator is 0°; the poles are 90° from the equator.

Except for positions located right on the equator (0°), degrees of latitude are always labeled to tell whether they are north or south of the equator. Any parallel of latitude is described by the number of degrees it is north (N) or south (S) of the equator. Honolulu, Hawaii, for example, is on the 21°N parallel. Sydney, Australia, is on the 34°S parallel.

Meridians of Longitude

Meridians of longitude are imaginary half-circles passing from the north pole to the south pole. They are sometimes called **lines of longitude.** By international agreement, the 0° meridian (also called the **prime meridian**) is drawn through Greenwich, England. The prime meridian is sometimes labeled on maps as the Greenwich (pronounced "grenich") meridian. See Fig. 3–3.

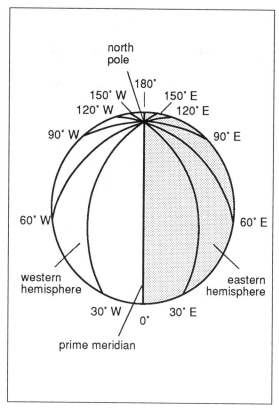

Fig. 3–3. The prime meridian and lines of longitude

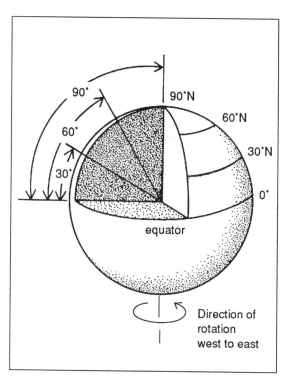

Fig. 3–2. Determining degrees of latitude

Meridians are numbered east and west from the prime meridian. East and west longitude meet at the 180° meridian, which runs through the Pacific Ocean. Thus most of the United States (including Hawaii) lies in west longitude. Only a small portion of Alaska (part of the Aleutian Islands) crosses the 180° meridian into east longitude. Note that the prime meridian (0°) and the 180° meridian divide the earth into eastern and western hemispheres. See Fig. 3–3.

Longitude

Longitude is the distance east or west of the prime meridian measured in degrees from 0° to 180°.

Except for positions located on the prime meridian (0°) or the 180° meridian, all meridians of longitude are given in degrees east or west of the prime meridian. Places to the east of the prime meridian (the right half of the globe in Fig. 3–3) have **east longitude**. For example, Rome, Italy, is located on the 12°E meridian. Places to the west of the prime meridian (the left half of the globe in Fig. 3–3) have **west longitude**. Washington, D.C., for example, is located on the 77°W meridian.

Together the prime and 180° meridians divide the globe into an eastern and a western hemisphere. See Fig. 3–3. Here the western hemisphere is to the left of the prime meridian, the eastern hemisphere to the right.

International Date Line

The **international date line** is an imaginary line running mostly along the 180° meridian. See Fig. 3–4. Events immediately to the right and left of the date line are 24 hours apart. If it is 12 noon on Monday, July 1, on the left side of the international date

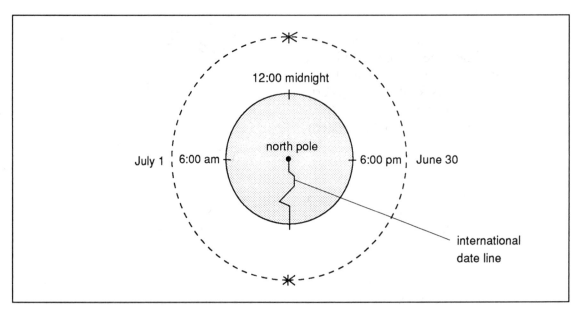

Fig. 3–4. The international date line and time (north polar view)

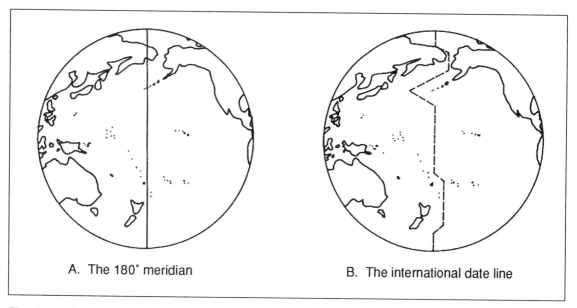

A. The 180° meridian   B. The international date line

Fig. 3–5. The 180° meridian and the international date line

line, it is 12 noon on Sunday, June 30, on the right side. For practical purposes, the international date line was adjusted to allow certain land areas to remain together in the same day and time zones. For example, the extreme eastern tip of Russia, which juts into the Bering Strait, was kept in the easternmost time zone, while the U.S.-owned Aleutian Islands were kept as part of the westernmost time zone. See (B) in Fig. 3–5.

Location

The lines of latitude and longitude form a global grid system as shown in Fig. 3–6. Any point on the globe can be located exactly by specifying its latitude and longitude. This system is essential for ships at sea that cannot locate their positions using landmarks or coastal navigational aids such as buoys or channel markers.

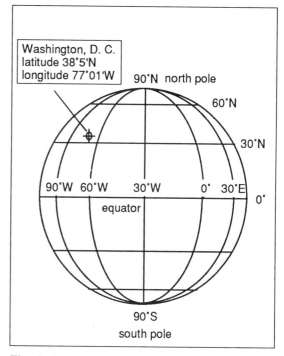

Fig. 3–6. Lines of latitude and longitude form a global grid system.

So that a point on a globe can be located more exactly, degrees are further subdivided into minutes and minutes into seconds. Here **minutes** and **seconds** do not refer to time but to parts of a degree of an angle.

1 degree (1˚) = 60 minutes (60')

1 minute (1') = 60 seconds (60")

The latitude and longitude readings of a place are called its **spherical coordinates**. For example, to state the coordinates of a specific harbor in Honolulu, you would say "latitude 21 degrees, 19 minutes, and 39 seconds north; longitude 157 degrees, 07 minutes, and 30 seconds west."

Both marine and air navigators use latitude and longitude to specify location. They also use the nautical mile as their unit of length or distance. Navigators describe the speeds of ships and airplanes, and meteorologists describe wind speeds, in **knots**. A **nautical mile** is 1 minute of an arc measured along a meridian of longitude or along the equator. These terms have the following values:

1 nautical mile = 1.85 km (1.15 miles)

1 knot = 1 nautical mile per hour

ACTIVITY

Make a globe marked off with reference lines of latitude and longitude.

MATERIALS

- thick-skinned orange
- hot sudsy water
- paper towels
- dipping solution (about 5% bleach)
- wooden skewer
- masking tape
- ballpoint pen
- two 8-1/2 X 11-in sheets of thin cardboard
- drawing compass with pencil
- scalpel
- protractor
- centimeter ruler
- 250-mL beaker (optional)
- rubber band
- toothpicks
- fine felt-tip waterproof pen
- red nail polish

PROCEDURE

1. Make a globe of the earth from a skewered orange as shown in Fig. 3–7.

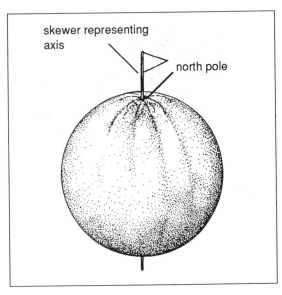

Fig. 3–7. Making a globe from an orange

a. Obtain a thick-skinned orange. Wash it with very hot sudsy water to remove the waxy coat. Rinse and dip in a dilute solution of liquid bleach (about 5% bleach) to retard mold.
CAUTION: Do not splash bleach on your clothes.

b. Dry the orange, then insert a skewer down through its center. Enter at the stem scar and exit on the bottom at a point directly opposite the scar. The skewer represents the axis about which the earth turns.

c. Attach a small flag made of masking tape to one end of the skewer. The flag represents the north pole. Put your team number or your initials on the flag so that you can identify your orange.

2. Make cardboard degree templates as shown in (A) and (B) in Fig. 3–8.

a. Measure the diameter of the globe (orange). Describe in your notebook how you measured the diameter.

b. Determine the radius of the globe.

c. Using a drawing compass with a pencil, make a circle on a piece of cardboard for a hole large enough for the globe to barely slide through. Use scissors to cut out the circle. Discard the inner circular disk.

d. Using a protractor and a centimeter ruler, mark latitude in 30° intervals around the cardboard ring as shown in (A) in Fig. 3–8.

e. Using another piece of cardboard, make a template for longitude as shown in (B) in Fig. 3–8.

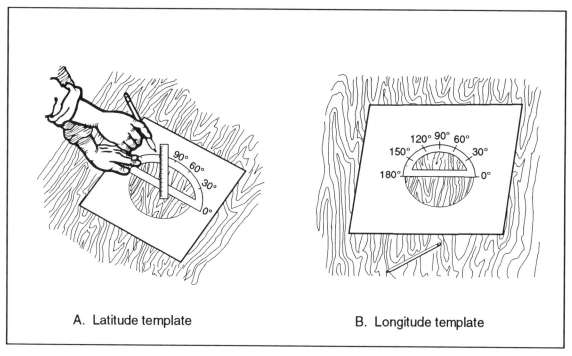

A. Latitude template   B. Longitude template

Fig. 3–8. Using a protractor to mark the templates for latitude and longitude

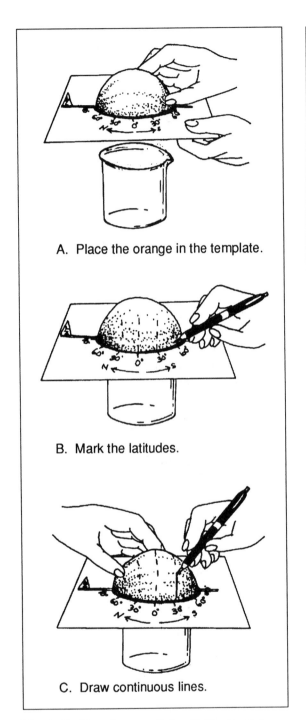

A. Place the orange in the template.

B. Mark the latitudes.

C. Draw continuous lines.

Fig. 3–9. Drawing parallels of latitude on a globe

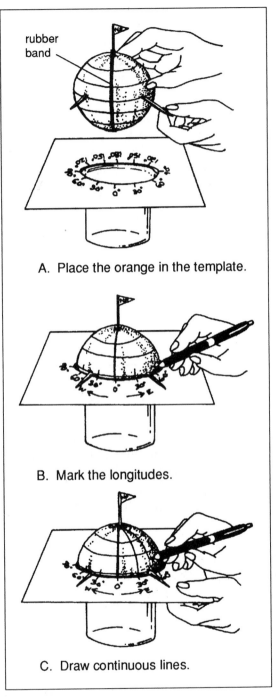

rubber band

A. Place the orange in the template.

B. Mark the longitudes.

C. Draw continuous lines.

Fig. 3–10. Drawing meridians of longitude on the globe

3. Draw the parallels of latitude.
   a. Place the globe in the latitude template as shown in (A) in Fig. 3–9. The skewer should run from 90°N to 90°S on the template.
   b. Using a ballpoint pen, make small marks at 0°, 30°, and 60° intervals on the orange, both north and south, using the template as a guide.
   c. Rotate the globe slightly and make more marks. Continue slightly rotating and marking until you go all the way around the globe. See (B) in Fig. 3–9.
   d. Connect all the marks along each latitude to form continuous lines around the orange. See (C) in Fig. 3–9.
   e. Use a fine felt-tip waterproof pen to mark the equator (0° line) and make it stand out.

4. Draw meridians of longitude on the globe. Refer to Fig. 3–10 as you carry out the steps below.
   a. Connect the poles with a rubber band. The rubber band represents a meridian. Draw a line along the rubber band to mark the globe with a meridian of longitude.
   b. Place the orange in the longitude template so that the equator line is even with the template. The orange can be supported on a beaker. Insert a few toothpicks into the equator line to support the orange. See (A) in Fig. 3–10.
   c. Use a ballpoint pen to make small marks at 30° intervals along the equator as shown in (B) in Fig. 3–10.
   d. Repeat the process of making marks at 30° intervals from the equator to the poles. See (C) in Fig. 3–10.

   e. Select a meridian line. Darken it from pole to pole with a felt-tip pen. Consider this the prime meridian on your globe.

5. Draw a large imaginary continent and an island on the orange globe. Complete the steps below.
   a. Locate the continent so that the primary reference lines pass through it as shown in Fig. 3–11.
   b. Make the continent a simple geometric shape. It should be large enough so that it extends to at least 45°N and 45°S and to at least 45°E and 45°W of the prime meridian.
   c. Locate the island at any convenient place.
   d. Color the continent and the island with red nail polish. Be careful not to obscure the latitude and longitude reference lines.

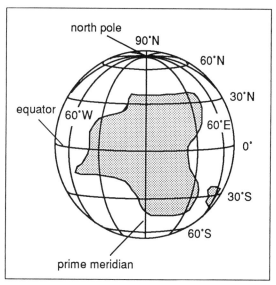

Fig. 3–11. Drawing of a continent and an island on the surface of a globe (oblique equatorial view)

19

e. Make one dot on the continent and one on the island to represent capital cities.

f. Invent names for the continent, the island, their capital cities, and the ocean(s).

6. Locate the outermost boundary points of the continent and the island. Record their coordinates and the coordinates of both capitals in Table 3–1.

7. Keep your orange globe and template for the next topic.

QUESTIONS

1. Which meridian is opposite the prime meridian? State your answer in degrees.

2. What are the approximate coordinates of the two capital cities on your globe?

3. What are the approximate coordinates of the extreme edges of your continent and your island?

4. If you traveled from the capital city of the continent to the island, in what direction would you be traveling?

5. Describe the location of the island in relation to the capital city of the continent.

6. Using the information on the nautical mile, calculate the circumference of the earth along any meridian of longitude.

7. Demonstrate your understanding of these terms. Make a sketch to show the meaning of each term.
a. circle

Table 3–1. Boundary coordinates of an imaginary continent and island (in degrees of latitude and longitude) (w)

Boundary	Latitude		Longitude	
	North	South	East	West
Outermost point of continent				
Location of continent's capital				
Outermost point of island				
Location of island's capital				

b. circumference
c. diameter
d. radius
e. parallel

8. Define each of these terms. Make sketches if necessary.
a. directions (north, south, east, and west)
b. hemisphere (northern and southern, eastern and western)
c. parallel of latitude
d. meridian of longitude
e. pole (north pole, south pole)
f. reference lines
g. primary reference lines
h. location
i. international date line

FURTHER INVESTIGATIONS

1. Why do you think Greenwich, England, was chosen as the prime meridian? Consult references to find out how the prime meridian was selected and when the decision was made.

2. Local time all around the world is set in relation to the time at Greenwich, England (known as Greenwich Mean Time, or GMT). Consult references to learn how clocks are set so that every 15 degrees of meridian represent one hour. Find out what your local time zone is called.

3. Why is it necessary to have a prime meridian? Imagine for a moment that we had no international agreements about where the prime meridian is located. How might this change how we locate places and specify dates and times?

4. List the kinds of businesses that use global maps and timetables for scheduling the delivery or receipt of goods or services. Find out how they use this information.

5. Learn about careers related to cartography and geography. Use library references and career information sources to make a list. What abilities and interests should people have to work in these fields? What kinds of work do they do?

4. Mapping the Globe

To people studying the earth and to travelers, maps are essential tools. There are many types of maps. Each has been developed to serve some special purpose, but each is limited in what it can represent.

In this topic we will investigate how it is possible for cartographers to make flat representations of the spherical and irregular surface of the earth.

A major problem in mapping the earth is finding a way to represent a sphere on a flat surface. Cartographers use many techniques to solve this problem. Each technique has advantages and disadvantages. We will prepare three common types of maps: an orthographic-projection map, a cylindrical-projection map, and an equal-area map.

ACTIVITY

Make an orthographic-projection map, a cylindrical-projection map, and an equal-area map of a globe.

MATERIALS

- two 8-1/2 X 11-in sheets of blank paper
- templates (from Topic 3)
- pencil
- drawing compass with pencil
- orange globe (from Topic 3)
- 8-1/2 X 14-in sheet of blank paper
- scissors
- centimeter ruler
- 8-1/2 X 11-in sheet of thick cardboard
- scalpel
- straight pins or stapler with staples
- red crayon or pen

PROCEDURE

1. Make two *orthographic-projection* maps of your globe. Two views are shown in Fig. 4–1.

a. Make two circles with diameters the same as that of the globe. On a clean 8-1/2 X 11-in sheet of blank paper, trace the inner circles from the templates you made in Topic 3. If you do not have a template, use a drawing compass and pencil to make the circles.

b. In one circle, make an orthographic-projection map that shows the continent and the island when the globe is viewed directly at the equator. Mark the locations of both capitals. (This view is called an **equatorial view**.) (A) in Fig. 4–1 shows an example.

c. In the other circle, make an orthographic-projection map that shows the globe as viewed directly down on the north pole. (This view is called a **north polar view**.) Locate the continent and the island on the map. An example is shown in (B) in Fig. 4–1.

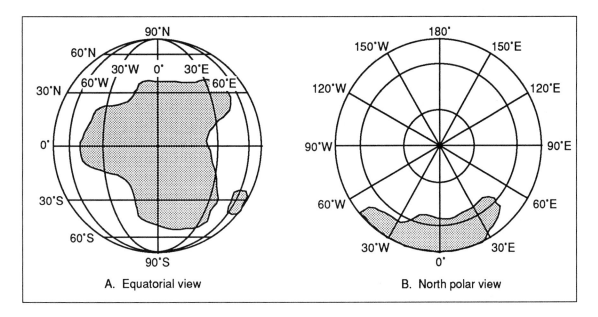

A. Equatorial view   B. North polar view

Fig. 4–1. Orthographic-projection maps

d. Locate and label the following on both orthographic-projection maps:
1) prime meridian (0°)
2) equator (0°)
3) 180° meridian
4) north and south poles
5) meridians of longitude in 30° intervals
6) parallels of latitude in 30° intervals
7) northern and southern hemispheres
8) eastern and western hemispheres

2. Make a *cylindrical-projection* map of your globe.
a. Prepare the cylindrical-projection map. Refer to Fig. 4–2 as you do the following:
1) Roll a sheet of 8-1/2 X 14-in blank paper around the orange globe so that it makes a tight-fitting cylinder.

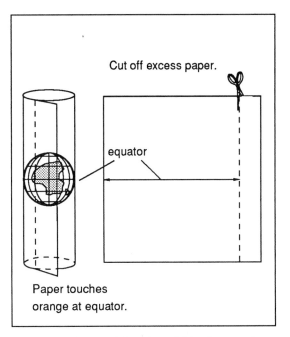

Cut off excess paper.

equator

Paper touches orange at equator.

Fig. 4–2. Determining the width of paper for a cylindrical-projection map

23

2) Make a straight-line cut to remove the excess paper that is not part of the cylinder.
3) Unroll the cylinder. The remaining paper should now be as wide as the circumference of the globe.

b. Mark the prime meridian and the meridians of longitude in 30° intervals on the paper. Refer to (A) in Fig. 4–3 as you do the following:
   1) Fold the paper in half so that the two ends in the direction that the paper was rolled come together. Fold it in half again in the same direction. Open it. Draw light pencil lines down the fold lines.
   2) Label the center line as the prime meridian (0° longitude). The fold on the right is 90°E; the fold on the left is 90°W.
   3) Label meridians of longitude in 30° intervals east and west.

c. Draw the equator on the paper.
   1) Fold the paper in half the other way.
   2) Open it and draw a line along the fold line. Label this the equator (0° latitude).
   3) Your paper should now look like (B) in Fig. 4–3.

d. Project the latitude lines in 30° intervals. Refer to Fig. 4–4 as your teacher demonstrates how to carry out the following steps:
   1) Use the orthographic map (equatorial view) you drew of your globe in Procedure 1.
   2) Line up the equator on the paper with the equator on your orthographic map. The two equators

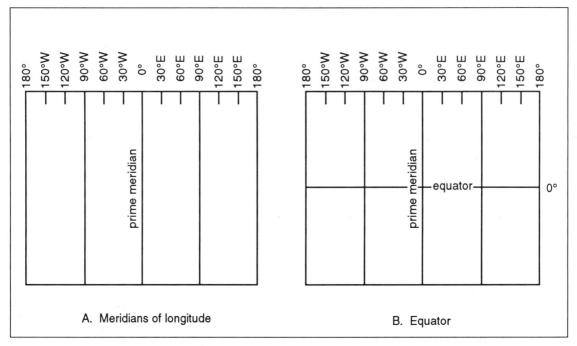

A. Meridians of longitude

B. Equator

Fig. 4–3. Meridians of longitude and equator on paper for a cylindrical-projection map

must form a straight line.

3) Locate the center of your ortho-graphic map (0°, 0°). This is the point where the equator and the prime meridian intersect.

4) Using a centimeter ruler or other straightedge, draw a straight line connecting the center of your orthographic map (0°, 0°) to its outer edge at 30° north latitude (30°N, 90°E).

5) Continue this line until it touches the left edge of the paper. Clearly mark this point. You have just projected 30° north latitude onto the cylindrical-projection map.

6) Following the same steps as above,

project 60°N, then 30°S, then 60°S onto the paper. Mark and label each projected latitude point.

7) Draw the parallels of latitude in 30° intervals on the paper. Extend each line from the projected latitude point across the paper parallel to the equator. Fig. 4–4 shows 30°N completed.

e. Make a cylindrical-projection map of your globe.

1) Locate and mark on the cylindrical-projection map the boundaries of the continent that you drew on your orange globe. Hold the globe so that you view it from the equator as in (A) in Fig. 4–1.

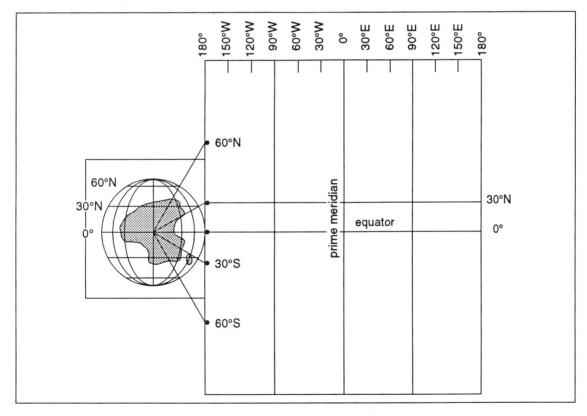

Fig. 4–4. Marking parallels of latitude on a cylindrical-projection map

On the orange globe, locate the points where the boundary line of the continent cuts across the equator. Mark these points on the cylindrical-projection map.

Next, locate the points where the continental boundary line cuts across the prime meridian. Mark these points on the cylindrical-projection map.

Now mark on the cylindrical-projection map each of the farthest boundary coordinate points that you listed in Table 3–1.

2) Connect the boundary points of the continent. If more points are needed, add them by carefully locating and marking where other parallels of latitude and meridians of longitude cut across the continental boundary line.

3) Color the continent red so that it is color-coded the same as the continent on the orange globe.

4) Following the steps given above, draw the island on the cylindrical-projection map.

5) Label the cylindrical-projection map. Use the list of labels in Procedure 1.d.

3. Make an *equal-area* map of the globe.
   a. Draw a horizontal line across an 8-1/2 X 11-in sheet of blank paper to represent the equator. Tape the paper to a sheet of thick cardboard.
   b. With a scalpel, cut the orange into segments along the meridians. Carefully peel skin segments from the orange.
   c. Open the skin segments and staple or pin them flat onto the paper on the cardboard. Make further cuts along the meridian lines if the segments won't lie flat. Be sure the equator on the segments aligns with the equator on the equal-area map as shown in Fig. 4–5.
   d. In pencil, trace the outline of the segments onto the white paper. Mark and label the locations of the parallels of latitude and meridians of longitude.
   e. Remove the orange-peel segments. You now have an equal-area map that shows the globe in segments.
   f. Carefully draw the continent and the island onto the equal-area map.
   g. Label the equal-area map. Use the list of labels in Procedure 1.d.

QUESTIONS

1. Explain why both parallels of latitude and meridians of longitude are needed to locate a specific position on the surface of the earth.

2. Compare the areas of the continent as it is drawn on an orthographic-projection map, on an equal-area map, and on a cylindrical-projection map. How are they different? How are they similar?

3. What are the problems that must be overcome in making a cylindrical-projection map of features on the globe? How does your drawing of the continent on the globe compare with its representation on the cylindrical projection?

4. What are the problems that must be overcome in making an equal-area map of the globe?

5. Compare the advantages and disadvantages of globes, orthographic-projection

26

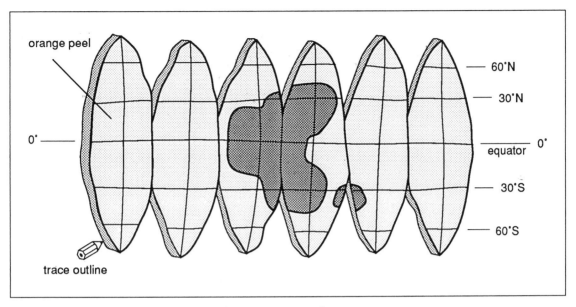

Fig. 4–5. An equal-area map made from orange-peel segments

maps, cylindrical-projection maps, and equal-area maps on the following points:

a. seeing the total surface area of the earth
b. measuring distances between places
c. determining surface areas
d. determining directions
e. determining locations
f. ease of reading

6. Check your understanding of the following terms:

a. map projection (examples are cylindrical, equal-area, and orthographic)
b. map view (examples are equatorial, polar, and oblique view)
c. distortion
d. two-dimensional and three-dimensional views

FURTHER INVESTIGATIONS

1. What other types of projections are used to represent the surface of the earth? How are these projections made? Prepare a demonstration for the class.

2. At sea or on land, how is it possible to use the stars or the sun to determine latitude? If you saw a constellation directly overhead, at what position in the sky would someone 20° to the north of you view it? Using library reference books, prepare a report on navigation.

3. Using library reference books, find out how meridians of longitude are used as aids in establishing standard time on earth. If it were 12 noon now where you are, what time would it be
a. in Washington, D.C.?
b. in Greenwich, England?

5. Seafloor Features

Today we have **bathymetric maps** of the ocean that accurately show ocean depths determined by seismographic techniques. We have data on the elevations and depressions of the ocean floor. By drawing contour lines connecting points of equal depth, oceanographers have found that the floor of the ocean has features like landform features.

Contour Maps

We begin this topic by interpreting contour maps to learn the major features of the ocean floor. To envision these features, we will use colors to represent different elevations and shades of blue to show changes in depth.

To prevent confusion between dryland and seafloor features, we will use maps that show features above sea level as positive numbers (such as 10 and 20) and features below sea level as negative numbers (such as −10 and −20). On our maps measurements are in meters.

Three-Dimensional Maps

By far the most realistic maps are **contour maps** and three-dimensional **raised relief maps**. See Fig. 5–1. These maps use colors and shades to convey information about features. **Landform models** can also be sculpted to show the effects of erosion, thus making the landforms look more realistic.

Detailed, accurate maps and models of geological features are used by scientists to explain how the features of the earth form and how they change over time. In this

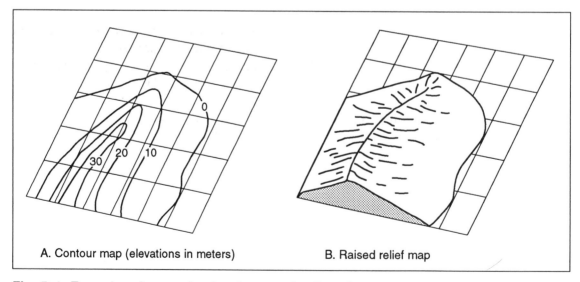

A. Contour map (elevations in meters)   B. Raised relief map

Fig. 5–1. Examples of maps showing the same landform feature

activity we will use two-dimensional maps and three-dimensional models to learn about the major landform features and seafloor features of the earth.

ACTIVITY

Interpret contour maps of seafloor and coastal features.

Construct a raised relief map of common underwater features.

Hypothesize how features form and change over time.

MATERIALS

For contour map

• colored pencils, crayons, tempera paints

For relief map

• colored construction paper
• carbon paper
• ballpoint pen
• scissors
• scraps of cardboard
• straight pins
• white glue

For landform model (optional)

• eight 8-1/2 X 11-in sheets of cardboard
• 25 X 35-cm sheet of cardboard
• scalpel
• papier-mâché (prepared in class)
• 8-1/2 X 11-in sheet of cotton cloth
• 1,000-mL beaker or 1/2-gal milk carton
• white glue diluted 1:1 with water
• oven or fan (optional)
• wooden skewer
• 1/4-in or 1/2-in brushes
• tempera paints (blue, green, white, brown, and black)
• jars and lids (for paints)

PROCEDURE

1. Read the descriptions of features listed in Table 5–1.

2. Refer to Table 5–1 as you identify features shown on the contour maps, Figs. 5–2 to 5–10.

   a. Examine each map to determine whether sea level, the zero (0) elevation contour line, is given. If it is, mark it with a colored pencil.

   b. Locate the contour lines of dry landform features with elevations above sea level. Using crayons, pencils, or paint, color-code the map to show differences in elevation. Save blue for seafloor contours.

   c. Locate the contour lines of features below sea level shown as negative numbers. Color-code the map in shades of blue to show differences in depth.

   d. Study the shapes of the contour lines, then identify and label features on the maps.

3. Construct a color-coded relief map from one of the contour maps.

   a. Use the 8-1/2 X 11-in enlargement in the Student Workbook of the map you have chosen or been assigned. If necessary, label the enlarged map.

   b. Decide how to color-code the relief map with colors from a package of construction paper. Choose your colors to show increasing depths of water or increasing elevations of land. The color scheme you select should provide meaningful information about the area. Be ready to justify your choices.

Table 5–1. Common features of the seafloor and coastline

Abyssal plain. A flat region of deep ocean basins.

Alluvial fan. A broad, sloping deposit of sediments at the mouth of a river or at the foot of a submarine canyon or a river canyon.

Atoll. A ring-shaped coral reef surrounding a lagoon. It may have low sand islands. Atolls rest on submerged volcanic islands.

Bank. A navigable shallow area of the ocean caused either by elevation of the seafloor or by submergence of a landmass.

Bay. An inlet of the sea; an indentation in the shoreline, often between headlands or capes.

Cape. A large point or extension of land jutting into a body of water. A cape may be a peninsula or a hook of land.

Channel. A deeper part of a river or harbor that is navigable. The word is sometimes used to name a broad strait, for example, the English Channel.

Cliff. A very steep or overhanging land feature.

Coast. A strip of land bordering the sea. A coast is affected by marine waves and wind.

Continental shelf. The land forming the shallow seafloor extending outward from the edge of a continent; submerged part of a continent extending outward 15 km to 50 km to the **continental slope**.

Continental slope. The sloping front of a continental shelf; the place where the continent ends. These are long slopes, often 20 km to 40 km wide or more. The bottom of the continental slope is the **continental rise**.

Continental rise. The area of the continental shelf between the continental slope and the deep seafloor where sediments from the continent accumulate.

Delta. An alluvial deposit at the mouth of a river.

Estuary. A river mouth or channel, or the drowned seaward end of a valley where fresh water from land mixes with seawater. River flow in some estuaries continues across the continental shelf, carving out a submarine canyon.

Guyot. A seamount with a flat top. Guyot tops are always below the ocean surface. Also called a **tablemount**.

Table 5–1 (continued). Common features of the seafloor and coastline

Headland. A cape or other landform jutting into the ocean. It is usually high above water and prominent when viewed from the sea. It gets its name from the practice of sailors using such features to take their bearings or "headings."

Island. A landmass smaller than a continent and surrounded by water.

Island chain. A group of islands formed by the same geological process (also called an **archipelago**).

Isthmus. A narrow strip of land connecting two larger landmasses.

Lagoon. A shallow body of relatively quiet water almost completely cut off from the open ocean by coral reefs, barrier islands, or barrier beaches.

Ocean basin. A large depression in the earth's crust that holds the water of an ocean.

Ocean ridge. A long, continuous mountain range on the seafloor. Ocean ridges are often of volcanic origin at a point or line of separation in the earth's crust.

Ocean trench. A deep cut or trench in the seafloor, usually close to where continental shelves and seafloors meet.

Peninsula. A piece of land almost completely surrounded by water. It is usually connected to a larger land body by a narrow land strip called a **neck** or an **isthmus**.

Point. The narrow tip-end of a cape, headland, peninsula, or other land feature jutting into a body of water.

Reef. A shallow rock or coral formation, often exposed at low tide. A **fringing reef** forms along the shore; a **barrier reef** is an offshore coral ridge.

Seamount. An isolated undersea hill or mountain. It is usually in the form of a cone.

Shoal. An area of the ocean, such as a sandbar, that is too shallow to navigate.

Sound. A wide waterway connecting two larger bodies of water. It may be a body of water between the mainland and an offshore island.

Strait. A long, narrow water passage connecting two larger bodies of water.

Submarine canyon. A deep canyon cut into the continental shelf and slope, often at the mouth of a large river.

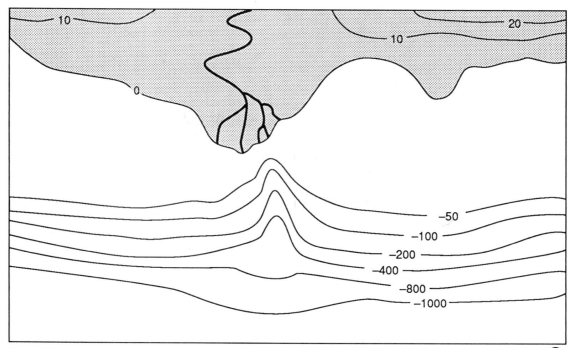

Fig. 5–2. Contour map A (elevation and depth in meters) (W)

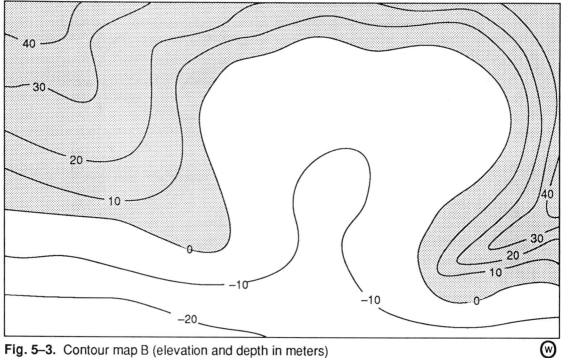

Fig. 5–3. Contour map B (elevation and depth in meters) (W)

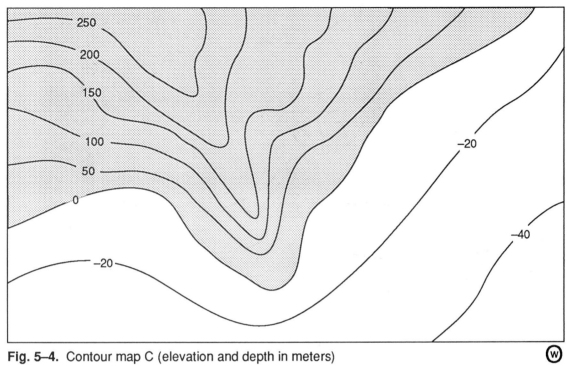

Fig. 5–4. Contour map C (elevation and depth in meters)

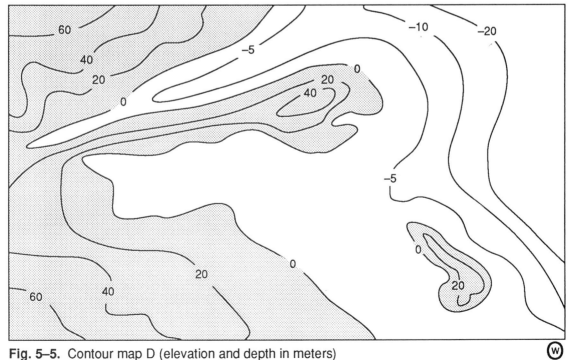

Fig. 5–5. Contour map D (elevation and depth in meters)

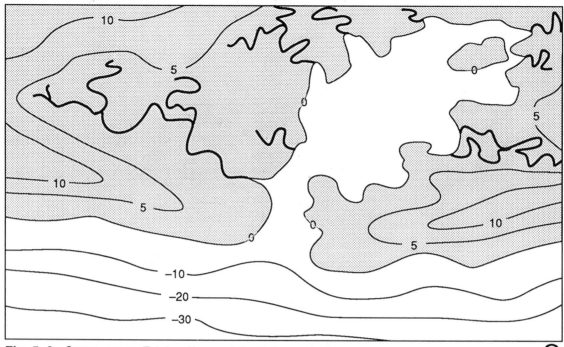

Fig. 5–6. Contour map E (elevation and depth in meters) ⓦ

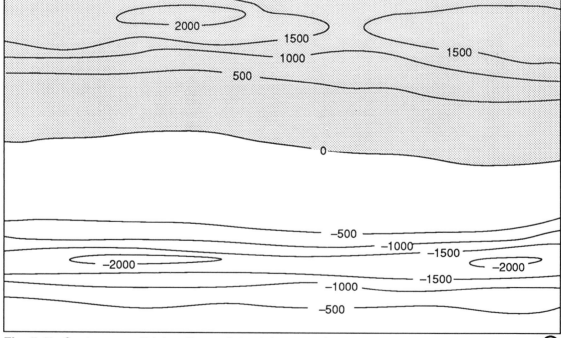

Fig. 5–7. Contour map F (elevation and depth in meters) ⓦ

34

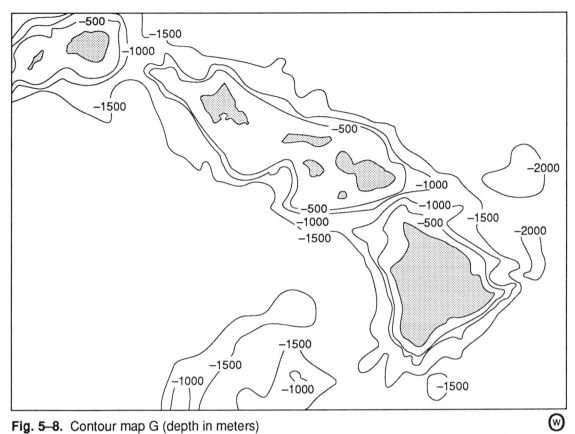

Fig. 5–8. Contour map G (depth in meters) Ⓦ

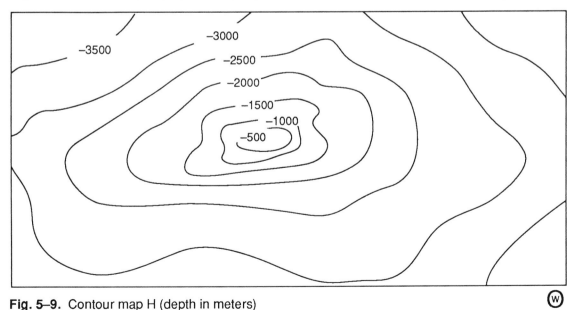

Fig. 5–9. Contour map H (depth in meters) Ⓦ

35

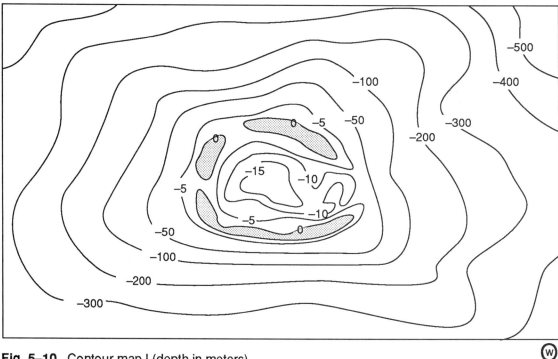

Fig. 5–10. Contour map I (depth in meters)

c. Place carbon paper inked side down on the construction paper under the enlarged contour map.

d. Prepare a template out of colored construction paper for each elevation line. Pressing hard with a ballpoint pen, carefully trace the elevation line onto the construction paper. Also trace the elevation line for the next higher contour so that later you will know exactly where to position the higher-contour template. Label the elevations of both contour lines.

e. Use scissors to cut out the lower elevation line on each of the contour templates. Work slowly and carefully.

f. Stack the colored contour templates in order of increasing elevation. Use the elevation lines drawn on each template to position the next higher template.

4. Construct the relief map to accurate vertical scale.

a. Make cardboard risers to put between the contour templates to provide the proper vertical scale for the model. Determine how high each riser should be. To do this, first decide what elevation interval is to be represented by each thickness of cardboard. See Fig. 5–11 for an example.

b. Assemble the relief model. Glue or pin the risers to the contour templates. Working from the lowest to the highest elevation, carefully position each contour template and its risers.

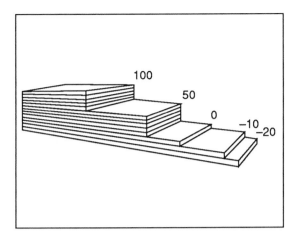

Fig. 5–11. Stacked cardboard contour templates

c. Glue the assembled relief map to a cardboard base.

d. Label the model to identify the features represented. Include a legend showing the elevations. Write your name(s) and the date on the model.

5. (Optional) Construct a papier-mâché model of the landform.

a. Cut out and assemble a cardboard relief map using scraps of cardboard for the risers. Follow Procedure 3, using corrugated cardboard and a scalpel. Work slowly and carefully. To avoid making slash marks in the table, put a sheet of cardboard under the template you are cutting.

b. Prepare papier-mâché by carrying out the steps below. Your teacher will give you additional information.

1) Tear newspaper into strips.

2) Soak newspaper strips in water for a few hours or overnight to soften the paper.

3) Use a blender to make a slurry of paper and water. Never fill the blender more than half-full. Run the blender on low speed.

4) Filter the water from the slurry through a piece of cloth. Wring out the water. Save the pulp.

5) Mix pulp with diluted white glue so that it has a smooth, medium-firm, claylike consistency. Use this firm mixture for the first coat on the model.

6) Make a thinner, moister papier-mâché for the finishing coats. Add a more diluted glue solution to the pulp.

c. Coat the cardboard relief map with firm papier-mâché. Fill in all exposed spaces between contour templates and the exposed cut ends of the corrugated cardboard. Make a smooth, natural slope between the templates. See Fig. 5–12.

d. Dry the first coat and the filling. If possible, put the model in a 120°C oven for an hour. Otherwise, use fans or lights to hasten drying.

e. Apply a finishing coat of thinner papier-mâché over the entire model. Using a wooden skewer or the handle of a fine brush, stroke wet papier-mâché in an upward movement to sculpt valleys and erosion effects.

f. Dry the model thoroughly. To prevent warping, place weights uniformly on the model.

g. Paint the model. Color-code features on the map using shades of colors to show changes in elevation. Allow the paint to dry.

h. Label the model. Identify the features. Include a legend showing the elevations. Put your name(s) and the date on the model.

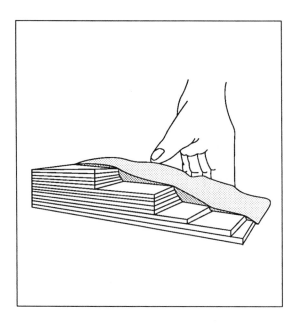

Fig. 5–12. Coating the cardboard relief map

6. Make accurate drawings of the relief map or model. Show all the contours
   a. looking straight down from the top.
   b. from the north looking south.
   c. from south to north.
   d. from east to west.
   e. from west to east.

7. Display each model together with its contour map and your drawings from Procedure 6.

QUESTIONS

1. Compare a relief map, a contour map, and a shaded contour map. Make a table showing the advantages and disadvantages of each.

2. Discuss the physical feature you have modeled. Suggest its relationship to the following:

   a. navigation
   b. economic value
   c. ecological value
   d. aesthetic value

3. Using all your models and contour maps, form hypotheses to explain
   a. how these seafloor features formed.
   b. how the seafloor features might change over time.

4. Check your understanding of the following terms:
   a. contour line   d. model
   b. elevation   e. physical feature
   c. landform   f. sea level

FURTHER INVESTIGATIONS

1. How well do official or popular names of shoreline features agree with the technical terms for geological features? (For example, Diamond Head is both a volcanic feature and a headland.) Examine maps and charts for examples. Look particularly at local shoreline features.

2. Construct an accurate relief map or model of your local shoreline.
   a. Obtain a nautical chart showing your local shoreline.
   b. Using tracing paper, construct one contour map or a series of contour maps.
   c. Carefully mark contour elevations and lines of latitude and longitude.
   d. Following the lines on your contour map(s), construct and assemble contour templates to form a relief map.
   e. Sculpt with papier-mâché.
   f. Label features and lines of latitude and longitude.

3. To construct a larger map, use either of these methods:
   a. Put the map on an overhead projector. Project it onto a large sheet of paper. Trace the contour lines.
   b. Prepare a series of relief maps, each carefully marked with lines of latitude and longitude. Assemble the series of relief maps in a large box. Sculpt with papier-mâché.

4. What kinds of businesses or government agencies produce and sell topographic maps and nautical charts? List places where you can obtain maps and charts. Use the yellow pages in the telephone book. Check with your librarian.

5. Visit a place that sells maps and nautical charts. Find out who buys them and how they use them.

6. Compare a topographic map and a nautical chart of the same region. How do these maps differ? For what purposes is each intended?

6. Mapping the Seafloor

Centuries ago sailors ventured into unknown oceans to discover new lands. They had no accurate charts or maps to guide them to new places or back to home ports. Imagine how relieved they were to see land after enduring the hardships at sea for months! Land meant safety from the dangers of the sea, relief from hard work aboard ship, and fresh food and drinking water.

Seeing land, however, meant new dangers because a ship could run aground in unfamiliar shallow waters. Sea captains had to be cautious. They sent sharp-eyed sailors to the crow's nest at the top of the mast or to the bowsprit at the forward part of the ship to look for dangerous shoals, reefs, and rocky outcroppings. But they all knew that visual sightings do not always detect hazardous underwater features, particularly if the water is choppy or murky. Anxious to avoid running aground, they measured the ocean depths, using a process called **sounding**.

Depth Soundings

The earliest soundings were made with a handline of rope weighted at one end. Sticky tallow was often smeared on the weight to pick up sand and other sediments from the seafloor. The weight was then dropped overboard and the rope allowed to run free until the weight reached the bottom. The length of the line let out was an approximate measurement of the water depth. See Fig. 6–1. Simple handline soundings are still used today, but they are reliable only in calm, shallow areas near continental shelves, in inland seas, and near midocean islands.

The first successful deepwater soundings were made with large balls of twine. A heavy weight was attached and tossed overboard, pulling twine from the ball until it hit bottom. Then the ball of twine was cut from the weight and the twine that had run out. The remaining ball of twine was weighed to determine how much had been lost. Because the weight of a length of twine was known, the depth of the ocean at that point could be determined quite easily.

After the twine method came a wire-sounding machine that used a single strand of piano wire running over a measuring

Fig. 6–1. Sounding with a weighted handline

pulley. But handlines, twine, and wire pulleys required slowing or stopping the vessel. Making deepwater soundings took a lot of time, so they were done only every hundred kilometers or so. Nevertheless, enough sounding data were accumulated to create maps that gave a rough idea of the shape of the seafloor.

ACTIVITY 1

Construct contour lines and interpret a **nautical chart** using **bathymetric** data. (**Bathy** means "deep" or "depth"; **metric** refers to measuring.)

MATERIALS

• world map, globe, or atlas
• colored pencils
• centimeter ruler

PROCEDURE

1. Fig. 6–2 is a chart of the Maug Islands. Using the latitude and longitude information given on the chart, locate this island group on a map of the world. Describe its location in your notebook. If you were to go there, would you have to take warm clothes? Explain why.

2. The Maug Islands are three volcanic islands. In your notebook, describe each island, including its size and elevation above sea level.

3. Locate the deepest sounding on the chart. Draw a box around the number.

4. Using a light color, circle all depths 30 m or less. Draw the 30-m bathymetric contour line so it goes around all the depths less than 30 m. See Fig. 6–3.

5. Repeat Procedure 4 using darker colored pencils for
a. the 60-m contour line.

b. the 90-m contour line.
c. the 120-m contour line.

6. Lightly shade in the intervals between the contour levels using the shades you selected for each depth. Make a depth color key on the side of the chart.

7. Suppose you were on a sailing ship that **draws** (extends below the waterline) 4 m. You want to sail your ship safely into the protected waters in the center of the Maug Island group and drop anchor.
a. Study the chart to learn about each channel that leads from the open ocean into the protected central water. Describe each channel in terms of depth and hazards to navigation.
b. Decide how you would sail from open ocean into the center of the island group. With the ruler, mark a straight line on the map in your workbook showing the course you would choose.

QUESTIONS

1. Would the Maug Islands be considered an atoll or a mountainous island group? How did you decide your answer?

2. If you heard that centuries ago a pirate ship loaded with gold had run aground and sunk trying to reach protected waters within the Maug Islands, where would you look for the treasure? Give reasons for your answer.

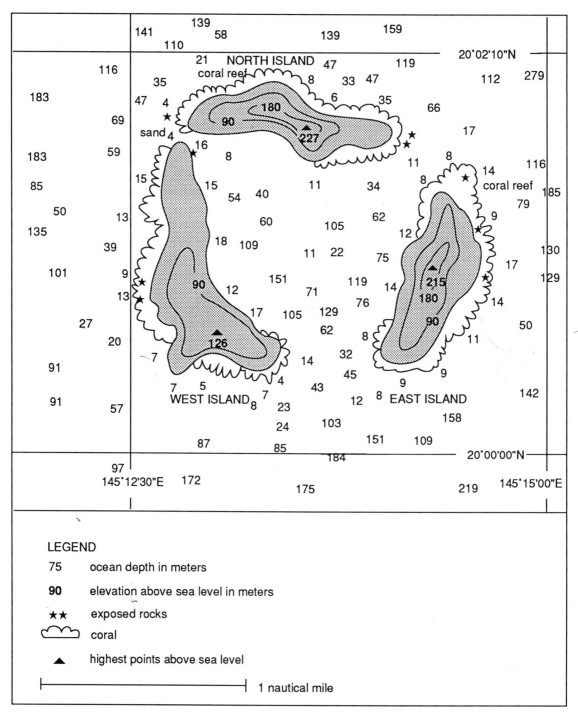

Fig. 6–2. Modified nautical chart of the Maug Islands. **A nautical chart** is a map used for navigation. (W)

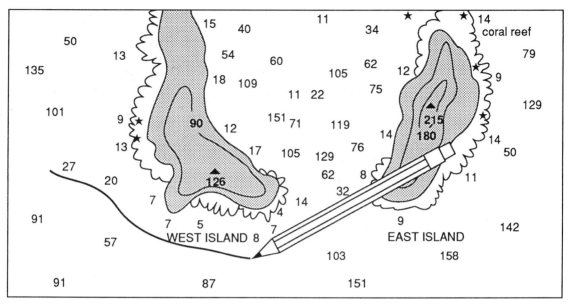

Fig. 6–3. Drawing the 30-m contour line

Sonar Soundings and Seafloor Profiles

Modern oceanographers use sophisticated **remote-sensing** techniques to gather data. The data are then plotted on charts and maps and used to create models that help us understand what seafloor features are like.

A major advance in the ability to measure ocean depths was made in the 1930s when **echo-sounding sonar** devices (also called fathometers) replaced sounding lines. The word **sonar** is formed from the term **so**und **na**vigation **r**anging. Sonar works by sending out pulses of sound waves from a ship. Instruments record the time it takes for the sound waves to travel to the bottom, reflect, and return to the ship. See Fig. 6–4. Because the velocity of sound in seawater is known to be about 1,460 m/sec, the depth can be calculated. The velocity of sound in seawater varies

with the temperature and salinity in different regions of the ocean, and these variations must be taken into account when depth determinations are being made. Sonar devices are so inexpensive and easy to operate that they are commonly used even on small outboard motorboats.

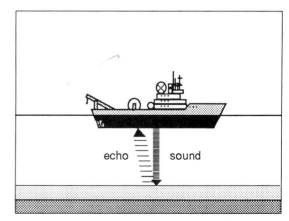

Fig. 6–4. Echo soundings can be made while a ship is under way.

43

The great advantage of using sonar is that a vessel can keep moving at normal speed while soundings are made. Recording a series of soundings on a strip of paper or making a computer printout produces a two-dimensional visual **profile** of the seafloor, called an **echogram** or **sonograph**. See Fig. 6–5.

To map the seafloor, research vessels cross the ocean making sonar profiles along carefully navigated parallel courses called **transect lines**. After many profiles are made, they can be cut out of cardboard or wood and assembled in order. A three-dimensional model of the seafloor can be constructed by filling the spaces between the profiles with modeling material. See Fig. 6–6.

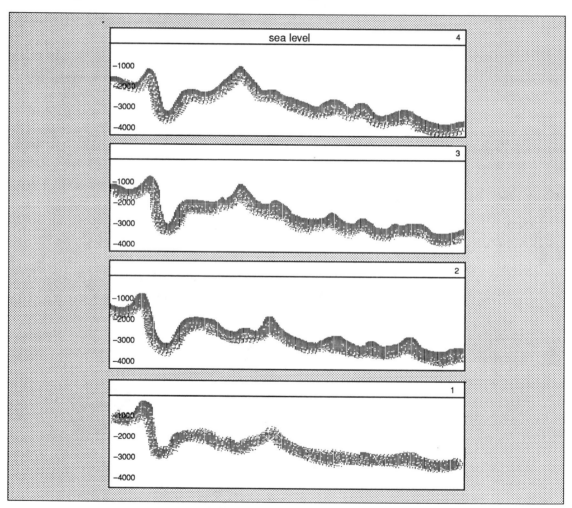

Fig. 6–5. Echograms are two-dimensional images of seafloor features along a transect line. The profile series shown here illustrates data obtained from parallel transects made several kilometers apart.

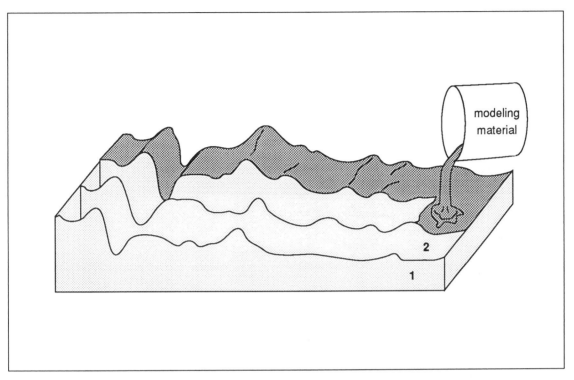

modeling
material

2

1

Fig. 6–6. A three-dimensional model of the ocean floor constructed by assembling a series of parallel profiles

ACTIVITY 2

Construct a profile drawing from data along a transect line.

MATERIALS

- materials from Activity 1
- 3/4-in X 8-in paper strip
- centimeter ruler
- three-dimensional seafloor model
- cardboard box
- paper
- masking tape
- paper with 1/2-in grid
- wooden skewers

PROCEDURE

1. Construct a profile drawing of the Maug Islands (Fig. 6–2). Follow the steps below and look at the examples in Fig. 6–7. The map used in this example is similar to contour map I shown in Fig. 5–10 in Topic 5.

   a. On the chart of the Maug Islands shown in Fig. 6–2, extend the line you drew in Activity 1, Procedure 7.b., so that it becomes a transect line cutting across the entire chart, including a portion of any of the islands. See the example in (A) in Fig. 6–7.

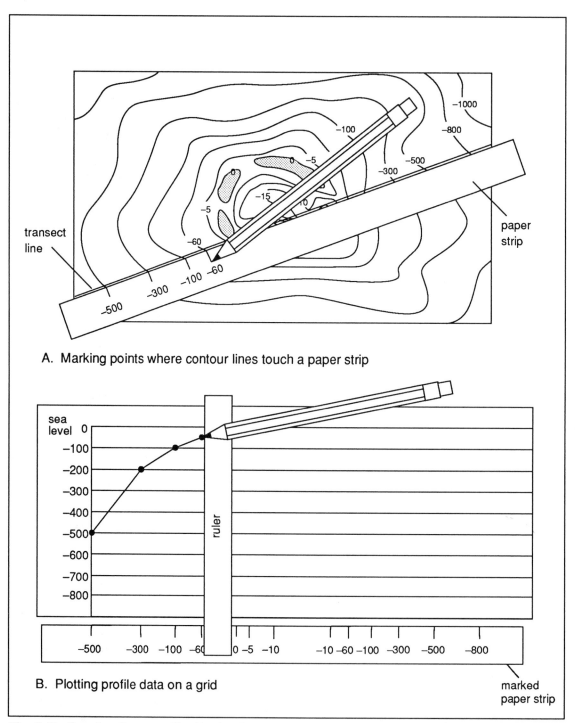

A. Marking points where contour lines touch a paper strip

B. Plotting profile data on a grid

Fig. 6–7. Constructing a profile drawing from a transect line drawn on a contour map

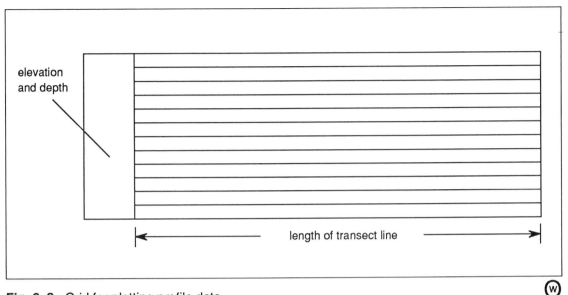

Fig. 6–8. Grid for plotting profile data

b. Lay a paper strip along the transect line as shown in (A) in Fig. 6–7. Mark the strip at each point where the edge of the paper strip touches a contour line.

c. Record the depth or height of each contour mark on the strip.

2. On the grid in Fig. 6–8, plot the depths and elevations from the chart. Follow the example shown in (B) in Fig. 6–7.

a. Label each axis. The horizontal axis represents the distance across the transect line. Note that the chart in Fig. 6–2 gives a scale for distance. The vertical axis represents the depths below sea level and the elevations above sea level in meters.

b. Plot each depth and elevation marked on the paper strip. Hold the strip along the horizontal axis of the grid and make a dot corresponding to each contour line marked. Read the depth or elevation marked on the strip, beginning with the first mark on the left. Move your pencil straight up from the mark on the bottom to the appropriate level on the grid and make another mark at the corresponding depth or elevation. Use a ruler to help you stay directly above the mark on the horizontal axis.

3. Draw the profile by connecting all the depth and elevation marks.

4. Examine the shape of the profile.

a. Identify and label the seafloor and landform features in each profile.

b. Compare several profiles made from the same chart.

c. What differences do you see in the profiles? How would you explain these differences?

5. Simulate using sonar to make ocean soundings, then construct seafloor profiles from the data.

   a. Place a three-dimensional seafloor model into a box. Use one of the models you made in Topic 5.

   b. Cover the top of the box with paper. Tape the paper in place.

   c. Place the paper with 1/2-in grid on top of the paper cover. See Fig. 6–9.

   d. Mark a straight line across the grid paper to represent a transect line.

   e. At regular intervals along the transect line, insert a sharp probe such as a skewer.   Keep the probe vertical, being careful not to let it slide down a slope on the model.

   f. For each location, measure the distance in centimeters that the probe is inserted.   This is equivalent to the seafloor depth.

   g. Record each depth at its proper location on the grid.

   h. Use the data to make a profile of the seafloor feature(s) along the transect line. Use the steps in Procedure 2 and a grid like Fig. 6–8.

   i. Examine, identify, and label the seafloor features on the profile.

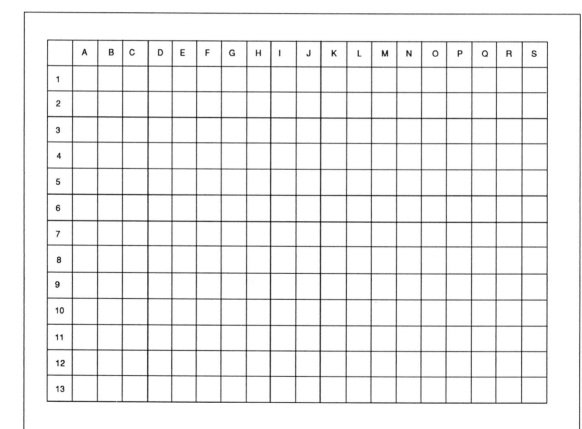

Fig. 6–9. Grid for plotting depth data   Ⓦ

Swath Mapping

Maps and models produced from single-beam sonar profiles lack the precision and detail needed for modern oceanography. Most are made from relatively sparse data based on profile lines spaced from 1 to 10 km apart. Without more data, mapmakers can only guess what features lie between the sample lines.

In the 1970s, a whole new seafloor-mapping technology was developed called **swath mapping**. Instead of sampling depth along a line as does single-beam sonar sounding, swath mapping makes many measures of depth within a two-dimensional area of the seafloor. On a single transect the area sounded may be 10 to 60 km wide and as long as the distance traveled by the ship. One swath-mapping device called **multibeam sonar** sends out and tracks up to 16 closely spaced sonar beams at a time. See Fig. 6–10. Computers translate the multiple echoes, assemble data from parallel transects, and then draw a detailed bathymetric contour map of that section of the seafloor. Another swath-mapping device called **side-scanning sonar** uses computers to translate the multiple echoes into detailed three-dimensional **images** of seafloor features. The images look like photographs taken from an airplane. The difference is that sound waves, not light waves, are used to produce the images.

Swath bathymetric maps and images are produced by placing the strips of data together. Details in swath maps are so clear that small-scale features such as faults, craters, landslides, and the paths of sediments flowing through submarine canyons can be clearly identified. Features as small as 10 m across can be detected. To get an idea of the significance of this, imagine that your town is submerged under several thousand meters of water. Using swath technology, scientists in a ship at the surface could not only produce a bathymetric map of your town that accurately represents the locations of all its natural and manmade features, but also make photograph-like images of structures as small as single-car garages and outdoor swimming pools.

Scientists are using the detailed swath-mapping techniques and image-mapping tools to learn more about the processes that form such seafloor features as underwater volcanoes and island chains and cause sediment erosion and deposition. Furthermore, swath-mapping technology has made it possible to locate potentially valuable mineral resources on the seafloor. We will investigate the mining of seafloor minerals in Unit 4, Chemical Oceanography.

Staking Claims in the Ocean

Traditionally, nations considered the ocean to be open to everyone, a doctrine known as **freedom of the sea**. Ocean resources historically were available for the taking on a "first-come, first-served" basis.

Today, in an effort to find fuel, food, and minerals for use by a world population of about 6 billion people, nations must look to ocean resources. In doing so, they are staking claims to the oceans and to the seafloor. Nearly 40% of the ocean has been claimed.

These claimed regions are called **zones**. One particularly important zone is the **territorial sea**. Traditionally, coastal nations

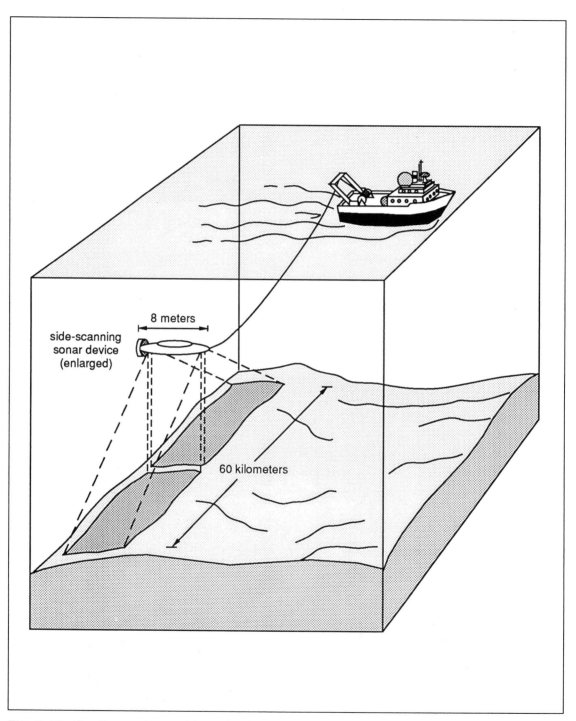

side-scanning
sonar device
(enlarged)

8 meters

60 kilometers

Fig. 6–10. Swath mapping enables scientists to collect data over a large area of the seafloor.

50

claimed a territorial sea of 3 nautical miles. See Fig. 6–11. They exercised full control of this zone but allowed nonmilitary commercial ships to pass through these waters. Many nations today claim a 12-nautical-mile territorial sea, and a few claim a 200-nautical-mile territorial sea. Increasing the width of the territorial sea from 3 to 12 nautical miles means that more than 100 straits would become entirely territorial seas with no central belt of international waters. Examples of straits that would be affected are the Strait of Dover, the Bering Strait, and the Strait of Hormuz. In 1958 the United Nations agreed upon a **Law of the Sea** that included "transit passage" provisions for ships, submarines, and even airplanes.

Today the concept of an **Exclusive Economic Zone** (EEZ) has been adopted by more than 70 nations that claim sovereign rights to all resources, living or nonliv-ing, up to 200 nautical miles from shore. See Fig. 6–11. In 1983 the United States became the fifty-ninth nation to declare its 200-nautical-mile EEZ. Included in the U.S. EEZ are large regions around the continental margins plus areas around all the islands under U.S. jurisdiction. This area is larger than the land area of the United States. See Fig. 6–12. By 1990 two federal organizations, the U. S. Geological Survey and the National Oceanic and Atmospheric Administration, plan to complete swath mapping and assessment of the living and nonliving resources of the U.S. EEZ. A major difference between the new EEZ frontier and previous frontiers on land is that these new seafloor areas and waters can be owned only by federal and state governments, not by individuals.

In 1982 a new **Law of the Sea Convention** (LOSC) was written by the United Nations. It is the most comprehensive docu-

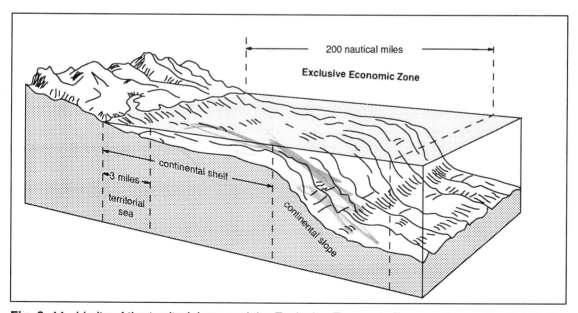

Fig. 6–11. Limits of the territorial sea and the Exclusive Economic Zone on the continental shelf

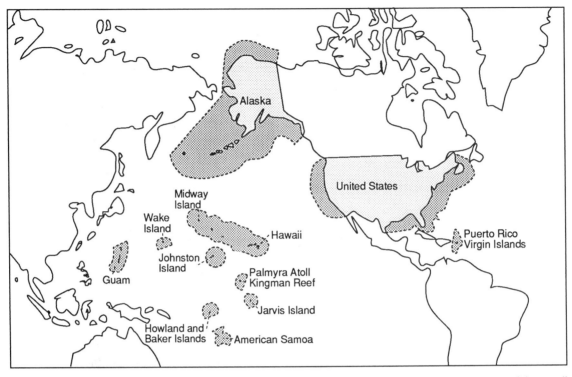

Fig. 6–12. Regions in the Exclusive Economic Zone (EEZ) extend 200 miles seaward from all states and territories of the United States.

ment to date governing use and management of the oceans. LOSC acknowledges the 12-nautical-mile territorial seas, with special provisions for international straits, and allows for the 200-nautical-mile EEZ. All waters beyond the EEZs of nations are called **high seas**, and the seabed and subsoil beneath are called "**The Area.**" All resources of the high seas and The Area are the "common heritage" of all mankind; that is, they belong to all nations, even ones with no seacoast. LOSC proposes that the United Nations administer the high seas and The Area, and that all nations share their ocean technologies and the wealth obtained from those technologies. The Law

of the Sea treaty has not yet been ratified by enough nations to become binding international law. The United States has neither signed nor ratified the treaty.

QUESTIONS

3. Explain how mapping with single-beam sonar differs from swath mapping.

4. Examine Fig. 6–12 showing the zones claimed by the United States.
   a. What is the width of the territorial sea claimed by the United States? Coastal states have jurisdiction of resources within this area.
   b. The United States claims a 200-nauti-

cal-mile EEZ. What is the width in kilometers of the area under the jurisdiction of the U.S. government?

c. Is the continental slope included in the EEZ? See Fig. 6–11.

d. If the continental shelf were wider than 200 nautical miles, what portions would be included in the EEZ? Under the Law of the Sea, what parts might come under international jurisdiction?

5. Examine the EEZ claimed by the United States. See Fig. 6–12.

a. How might the circular areas in the Pacific Ocean be explained?

b. How might the straight line in the EEZ just to the west of the Aleutian Islands be explained?

6. Under an EEZ claim, how much new territory could a nation claim if it

a. has only one coastline that is 1,000 km long?

b. were a circular island with a land area of 1 km²?

Satellite Oceanography

Satellites are essential to mapping and measuring the oceans. Satellites equipped with communication devices and power sources make global communication possible by telephone and television. Now ships and airplanes can be linked to land stations and to each other. Navigation is more advanced because satellite communication systems help to determine exact latitude and longitude. Computers record seafloor measurements and locations, then plot the data onto maps.

Some satellites are equipped with cameras that continuously make photographs of the earth's surface and relay them to receiving stations. The satellite weather maps in newspapers are a familiar example. For oceanographers and others who work or travel on the ocean, satellites provide up-to-date information about storms and other weather conditions at sea.

Seasat, the first satellite dedicated to oceanography, was launched in 1978. See Fig. 6–13. It allowed reseachers to detect and map seafloor features around Antarctica and other areas rarely visited by ships.

Seasat mapped seafloor features indirectly by measuring sea height. It sent out pulses of electromagnetic radiation that reflected off the ocean surface, giving precise measurements of the distances between the satellite and the ocean at different points. These measurements showed that the surface of the ocean is uneven. Depressions in the surface suggest the presence of massive seafloor features, such as midocean ridges and seamounts, that increase gravitational pull. Bulges in the surface are evidence of deep seafloor trenches and fracture zones, which decrease the gravitational pull.

Although satellites cannot yet give us precise information about small areas of the seafloor, they provide oceanographers with information about global phenomena such as cloud and ice formation, wind patterns, and surface temperatures. Interpreting all the data collected by modern oceanographic research ships and satellites occupies many researchers and complex computer systems full-time.

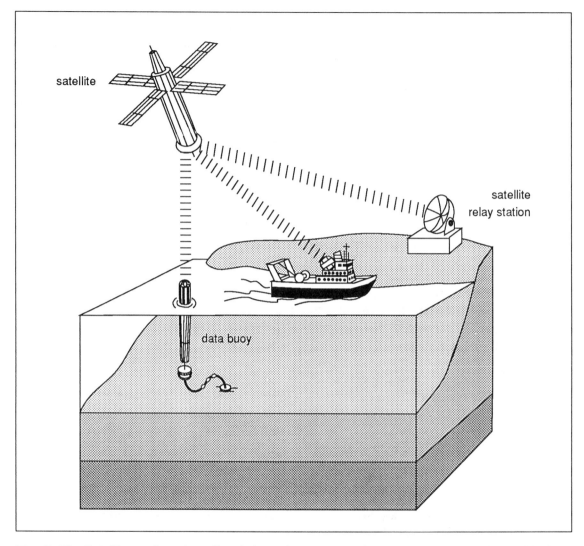

Fig. 6–13. Satellites collect data directly from the ocean and link oceanographic ships with data-collecting buoys.

FURTHER INVESTIGATIONS

1. Construct a three-dimensional model of the Maug Islands. Make a raised relief map or a papier-mâché model using the procedures in Topic 6.

2. Construct a three-dimensional model of a section of a coastal area from topo-graphic maps and nautical charts of the region.

3. In the profile drawing you made in Activity 2, note that the horizontal measurement is in nautical miles, but the vertical measurement (height and depth) is in meters. This way of measuring mag-

nifies the vertical distance and is called **vertical exaggeration.** Draw two new profiles using a vertical scale
a) in hundreds of meters.
b) in kilometers.
Which of the drawings is most accurate or realistic? Why do we use vertical exaggeration in profile drawings?

4. Advances in seafloor mapping have made it possible to locate sunken ships. Using library references, read and report to the class on
   a. the search for the *Titanic*, including how it was discovered and how it was explored with research submersibles and remotely operated vehicles.
   b. modern efforts to locate sunken treasure.
   c. searches for the recording devices from airplanes downed at sea and efforts to retrieve these devices.

5. An interesting biological discovery was made by marine technicians from careful examinations of unusual sonar data. In some regions of the ocean, it appeared that the level of the ocean bottom changed at different times of the day. Groups of small marine organisms were identified whose bodies scatter sonar sound waves. They are collectively called the **DSL** for **d**eep-**s**cattering **l**ayer. These animals spend the day in deep water and migrate nearer to the surface at night, causing the sonar readings to change. Commercial fishermen use fathometers to locate large schools of fish. Read and report to the class on the uses of fathometers and sonar in fishing.

7. Layers of the Earth

Modern maps and globes of the earth show the geological features of the continents and ocean basins. To understand how these features formed and how they change, we need to understand the processes that formed the earth itself.

Formation of the Solar System

Scientists theorize that our solar system formed about 4.6 billion years ago. Particles of dust were pulled together by gravity until they formed a huge solar cloud. As particles within the cloud were attracted toward a center of gravity, many of them collided, causing friction that began to heat up the solar mass. Some particles underwent radioactive decay, further heating up the solar mass. Finally, the temperature at the center reached millions of degrees, hot enough that hydrogen atoms began to fuse. Thus our sun became a star fueled by nuclear fusion in its core.

Many millions of kilometers from the center of the solar cloud, other smaller clouds of particles formed the planets in our solar system. When the earth formed, friction and radioactive decay also heated the center of our planetary mass, but the mass was too small to start nuclear fusion. Our earth became a molten planet rather than a hot, fiery sun.

Density Layering

As our planet became a molten mass, layers formed. The most-dense material, containing iron and nickel, settled to the **core** in the center. Less-dense matter, con-taining iron-rich silicates (compounds of silicon and oxygen), formed the vast interior **mantle**. The least-dense materials, such as common granite and basalt rock, rose to the surface, cooled, and formed the earth's solid, stony **crust**.

Volcanic eruptions through the stony outer crust continued to release heat and pressure from the molten center of the earth. Each eruption brought gases, water vapor, ash, and **lava** (molten material) to the surface from the interior. When the earth's surface cooled enough, the water vapor condensed into liquid. Thus our oceans formed. (In Unit 4, Chemical Oceanography, we will investigate how the oceans became salty and how they too have changed over time.) Volcanic activity is still reshaping the surface features of our planet.

Fig. 7–1 shows an idealized cross-section of the outer layers of the earth. The solid outer crust of the earth is composed of two distinctly different types of material, the less-dense continental crust and the more-dense oceanic crust. Both types of crust rest on solid upper-mantle material. The upper mantle in turn floats on a denser layer of mantle that is plastic, much like thick, molten tar.

The earth's crust changes continually to balance the amounts of lighter and denser material. Erosion or glacial melting reduces continental mass; volcanic eruptions increase it. When a continent loses mass, it floats higher on the mantle; when it gains mass, it sinks lower.

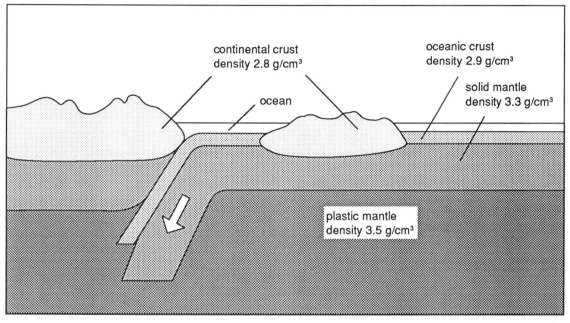

Fig. 7–1. An idealized drawing showing the densities of the earth's crust and upper mantle ⓦ

QUESTIONS

1. How is heat produced? Give examples.

2. Why do you think the temperature rose more at the center than at the edges when the solar cloud formed?

3. What evidence do we have that our planet was once a molten mass and that it continues to release heat today?

Evidence for Density Layering

Scientists needed evidence to support the hypothesis that the earth's interior is composed of layers of materials of different densities. **Density** is the amount of mass in a given volume of material.

$$Density = mass/volume = g/cm^3$$

The densities of some materials–granite and basalt, for example–can be determined in the laboratory from rock samples by measuring their mass and volume. Fig. 7–2 shows the basic procedures for determining mass and volume of a rock specimen. For precise measurements of the density of different kinds of rock material, pure specimens must be used.

From direct laboratory measurements of surface rocks, scientists have determined that the average density of the earth's surface is about 2.8 g/cm³. Indirect evidence indicates that the earth as a whole has a density of about 5.5 g/cm³. Thus the interior of the earth must be denser than the crust.

There is evidence that materials within the earth form distinct layers, each with a

57

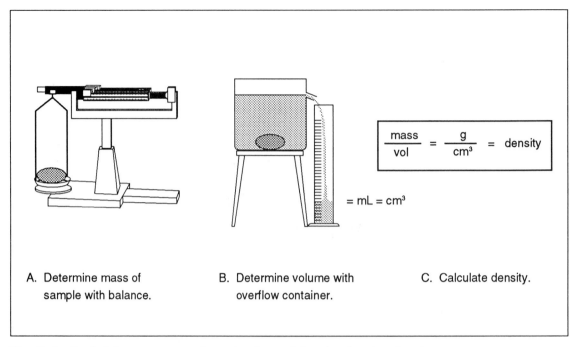

A. Determine mass of sample with balance.

B. Determine volume with overflow container.

C. Calculate density.

$$\frac{mass}{vol} = \frac{g}{cm^3} = density$$

$= mL = cm^3$

Fig. 7–2. Basic laboratory procedures for determining the density of rocks

different density. Most of this evidence comes from observations of **seismic waves**, the vibrations generated by earthquakes or explosions. As seismic waves travel through the earth, changes in wave patterns indicate where the waves are **reflected** (bounced back) or **refracted** (changed in direction) in the earth's interior. Careful measuring of changes in the velocity of these waves as they travel through the earth has provided information about the number of layers, their thickness, and their composition. These data also indicate the probable **physical state** of each layer – whether it is a solid, a liquid, or a tarry, plastic substance.

Scientists are still unable to get samples of materials from deep within the earth to test. However, they can compare data from seismographic observations with data from simulated laboratory tests on materials of known chemical composition. They can also construct and test computer models of the physical features of the earth. From these data, scientists have inferred that our earth is made of layers of material of different densities.

ACTIVITY
Diagram the layers of the earth and study their physical characteristics.

MATERIALS
• 8-1/2 X 11-in sheet of paper
• drawing compass with pencil
• centimeter ruler

58

PROCEDURE

1. Fold the paper in half to form a crease. See Fig. 7–3. Open the paper and lay it sideways.
   a. Make a dot on the crease at the bottom edge of the paper to represent the center of the earth.
   b. Lay a centimeter ruler along the crease with the zero at the dot. Place the point of a drawing compass on the dot.

2. Draw semicircles to represent the approximate layers of the earth, starting from the innermost layer.
   a. Draw the inner core of the earth. Keep the point of the compass on the center dot. Use the ruler to set the pencil to a 2.6-cm radius. See (A) in Fig. 7–3. Then draw a semicircle with this radius. See (B) in Fig. 7–3. Material within this inner core is thought to be a solid mass of very dense iron and nickel.
   b. Draw the next layer, the outer core. Put the pencil at the 7.0-cm mark on the ruler and draw a semicircle with this radius. This second layer is the outer core, a region thought to be made of a liquid material also rich in iron and nickel.
   c. Add the next layer, the mantle. Set the pencil on the compass to a radius of 12.7 cm and draw another semicircle. Evidence shows that the lower portion of this layer is solid and very dense. The middle portion of the mantle is plastic and partially molten. The silicate materials here are thought to be so close to their melting point that they flow like thick tar. The least-

dense outer layer of the mantle is solid. See Fig. 7–1.
   d. Draw the earth's rigid outer crust. Set the radius of the compass to 12.8 cm. The crust includes two types of stony material: the continental crust and the oceanic crust. The least dense is the continental crust, composed mostly of granite high in aluminum silicates. Its average thickness is 35 km. The denser oceanic crust, about 5 km thick, is composed of basalt, which is high in iron and magnesium. Ocean water lies in basins formed from the oceanic crust on the bottom and the continental crusts on the sides. The average depth of ocean water is 3.8 km.

3. Complete Table 7–1 using the information in Fig. 7–1 and Procedure 2.
   a. Record the estimated average density, the probable chemical composition, and the physical state of each layer.
   b. Calculate the thickness of each layer. Each centimeter in your diagram represents about 500 km.

QUESTIONS

4. What happens to the density of the materials in the earth as depth increases? How does the density of each layer affect its location with respect to other layers?

5. How large would a globe of the earth be if you let 1 cm represent the thickness of the continental crust? What would be the radius of this globe?

6. What is the average depth of the ocean?

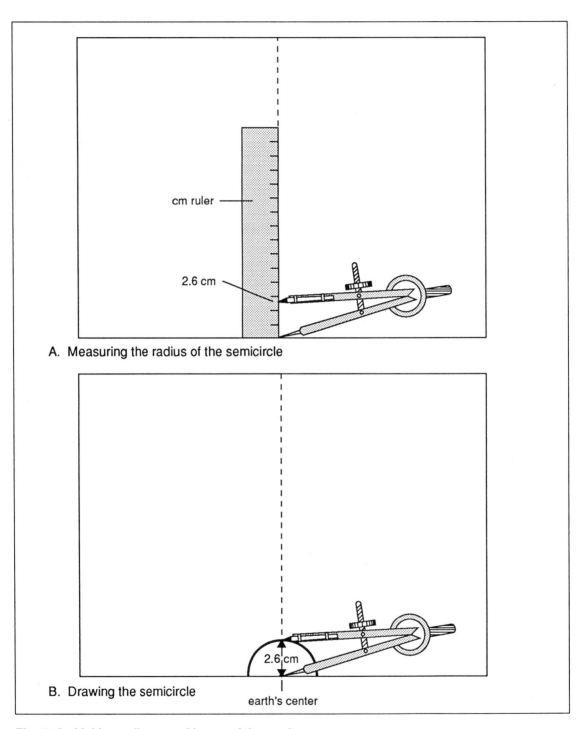

A. Measuring the radius of the semicircle

2.6 cm

B. Drawing the semicircle

earth's center

Fig. 7–3. Making a diagram of layers of the earth

60

Table 7–1. Physical characteristics of the layers of the earth   (w)

Layer of the earth	Estimated average density	Thickness in kilometers	Physical state	Probable chemical composition
Continental crust				
Oceanic crust				
Mantle	4.5 g/cm³			
Outer core	9.0 g/cm³			
Inner core	11.5 g/cm³			

If you were to include this on your diagram from Procedure 2, how thick would the ocean be?

7. Distinguish between direct and indirect evidence. Give an example of each. How valid is indirect evidence? Should indirect evidence be considered acceptable for testing a hypothesis?

8. Check your understanding of the following terms:
   a. hypothesis
   b. physical state
   c. density

9. Note that the density of the upper, solid mantle is 3.3 g/cm³ and the density of the middle, plastic mantle is 3.5 g/cm³. In Table 7–1 the average density of the mantle is given as 4.5 g/cm³. How do you explain these differences?

FURTHER INVESTIGATIONS
1. Construct a model of the earth showing its layers and their properties.

2. Calculate the volume and percentage of total volume of each of the layers of the earth. Ask your teacher for assistance in making the calculations. Prepare a table of your results and report to the class.

3. Ask a librarian to help you find references on hypotheses and theories related to the formation of the universe, our solar system, and the oceans. Report your findings to the class.

4. Find information and report to the class about the Moho, the boundary between the oceanic crust and the mantle below it. The term *Moho* is an abbreviation for "Mohorovic discontinuity".

8. Earth's Moving Plates

Many of the important discoveries about the structure of the earth were made by scientists who found evidence in the oceanic crust for regular patterns of crustal movement. As we will see, these movements are thought to be related to convection currents in the mantle.

An example of a convection current in liquids is shown in Fig. 8–1. In the beaker, hot water rises at the point where heat is applied, goes to the surface, then spreads out and cools. Cooler liquid sinks to the bottom at places where there is less heat. The rising up, spreading out, and sinking of gas, liquid, or molten material produces **convection currents**.

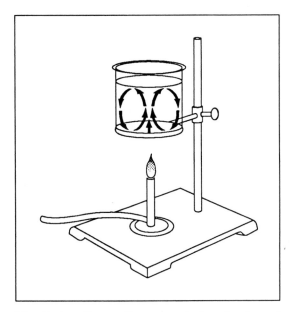

Fig. 8–1. Convection currents in a beaker of liquid

Cracks in the Earth's Crust

The solid crust acts as a heat insulator for the hot interior of the earth. Below the crust, in the mantle, is the molten material called **magma**. Tremendous heat and pressure within the earth cause the hot magma to flow in convection currents. Periodically it rises to the surface, cracks the crust, erupts as lava, steam, or ash, and releases heat. The lava cools to form new rock on the oceanic or continental crust.

A worldwide system of great cracks in the oceanic and continental crust has been mapped. These cracks divide the crust into rigid **plates**, huge sections of the earth that move relative to each other. See Fig. 8–2.

Movements of the Earth's Plates

There are four major kinds of movements of the plates in the earth's crust:
1. **subduction**, when one plate plunges beneath another
2. **collision**, when two continental plates are shoved together
3. **seafloor spreading**, when two plates are pushed apart
4. **transform faulting** (also called transverse fracturing), when two plates slide past each other

Subduction is the downward movement of an oceanic plate into the mantle. Locate the Nazca and South American plates (Fig. 8–2), then follow the process of subduction shown in Fig. 8–3. The Nazca Plate plunges under the South American Plate at a rate of 2 to 3 cm per year. As the

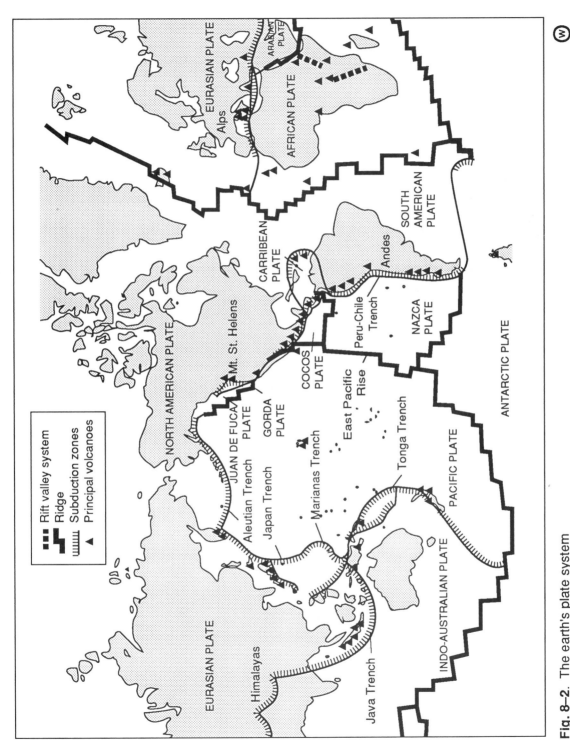

Fig. 8–2. The earth's plate system

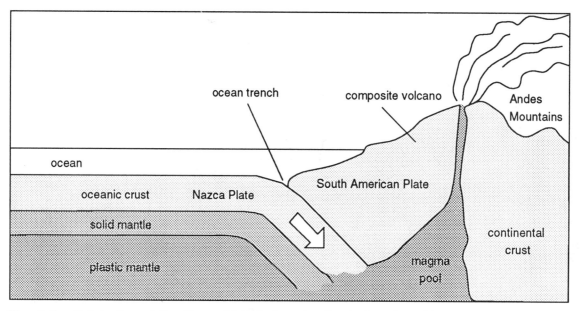

Fig. 8–3. Subduction of the Nazca Plate below the South American Plate forming composite volcanoes

oceanic crust enters the mantle, pressure breaks the crustal rock, heat from friction melts it, and a pool of magma develops. This thick magma, called **andesite lava,** consists of a mixture of basalt from oceanic crust and granite from continental crust. Forced by tremendous pressure, it eventually flows along weaker crustal channels toward the surface. The magma periodically breaks through the crust to form great, violently explosive **composite volcanoes,** steep-sided, cone-shaped mountains like those in the Andes at the margin of the South American Plate.

Ocean trenches form at the regions where one plate moves downward beneath another. These trenches are deep (up to 10.8 km), narrow (about 100 km), and long (from 800 to 5,900 km), with very steep sides. Places where subduction occurs are also sites of **deep earthquakes** caused by rocks slipping over other rocks deep in the mantle.

Subduction pulls the seafloor steadily downward, as if it were a giant conveyor belt. **Continental collision** occurs if two plates carrying continents collide and the subduction is interrupted. Because continental crusts are composed of low-density material, they do not sink. So when the continents collide, the crust moves upward, and the crustal material folds, buckles, and breaks. Many of the great mountain ranges were formed by the collision of continents.

Fig. 8–4 illustrates the continuous process of plate movement over very long periods of time. (A) shows how a subduction zone forms when oceanic crust slides under continental crust. (B) shows how the collision of two continental crusts interrupts the subduction process and forms a new mountain chain. (C) shows how the oceanic crust continues sliding under the continental crust, forming a new subduction zone and a new submarine trench, and how two continental crusts begin to fuse.

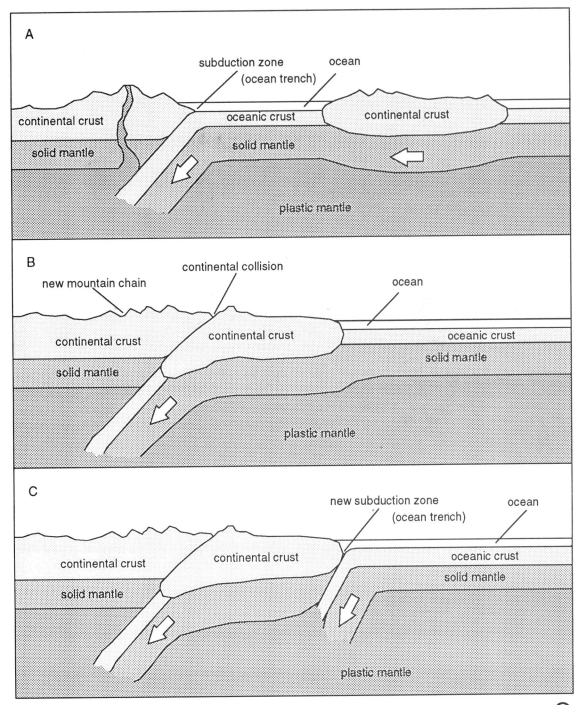

Fig. 8–4. Subduction and continental collision

Seafloor Spreading and Transform Faults

While one boundary of an oceanic plate is being pushed down into the mantle by subduction, new material is coming up at the opposite boundary by a process called **seafloor spreading**. See Fig. 8–5. Great cracks develop in the ocean floor where hot magma rises to the crustal surface and forms midocean **ridges** or **rises**. As the lava cools, it forms new seafloor features such as **rift valleys**, **seamounts** (volcanic peaks that extend more than 1 km above the seafloor), and **abyssal hills** (volcanic peaks that extend less than 1 km above the seafloor). The outpouring of material continues as the oceanic plates pull apart. Crustal movement related to this spreading causes frequent **shallow earthquakes** with distinct seismic wave patterns. In fact, earthquake data were used to help map active oceanic ridge systems.

Today we know that midocean ridges and rises are the largest continuous features on the earth. They are tens of thousands of kilometers long, running through and connecting most of the ocean basins. Oceanographic data reveal that seafloor spreading is slowly widening the Atlantic Ocean, the Red Sea, and the Gulf of California. Similar spreading on land is also causing a large rift valley in Africa that may eventually split that continent.

As we might expect, spreading does not occur evenly along a ridge. Perpendicular breaks or fracture zones, called **transform faults**, occur when the sections of the plates slip by each other and displace segments of the midocean ridges. See Fig. 8–5. Great tension can build up before slippage occurs and causes shallow earthquakes. People living near the San Andreas Fault, a transform fault in California, regularly experience such quakes.

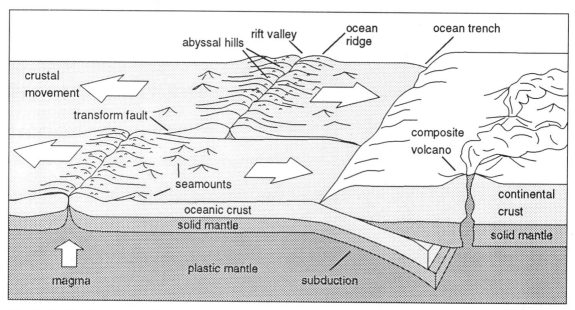

Fig. 8–5. Seafloor spreading and the formation of transform faults

ACTIVITY

Interpret information about the earth's moving plates from the map in Fig. 8–2.

MATERIALS

- pencil
- crayons or colored pencils (red, green, yellow, orange)
- world map

PROCEDURE

1. On the map in Fig. 8–2, put a star on the plate where you are now.

2. Locate ridges (the areas of seafloor spreading) and color them green.

3. Locate areas of subduction and color them red.

4. Locate the areas where composite volcanoes are occurring and color them yellow.

5. Find Iceland and the region where the Mid-Atlantic Ridge comes to the surface and pushes the Eurasian and North American plates apart. In this area volcanic activity and earthquakes happen at the surface. Color this region orange.

QUESTIONS

1. How many plates are there?

2. Which plate are you on?

3. Which plates, if any, carry no continents?

4. What kinds of structures are found at the boundaries of plates?

5. Follow the areas of seafloor spreading around the map. What do you notice about the relationship between them and how far around the earth they extend?

6. Why are the lines representing the midocean ridges jagged rather than smooth? What type of movement explains this irregularity?

7. Locate the areas of seafloor spreading at the boundaries of the Pacific Plate. In what direction does spreading seem to be driving the plate?

8. Mount St. Helens, a volcano in Washington state, erupted violently a few years ago. What might account for the eruption of this mountain? How was the volcano probably formed?

9. Locate the **island arcs** that form the Aleutian Islands, Japan, and the Philippines. What processes might have formed them? Explain.

10. In what direction does the Indo-Australian Plate seem to be moving? Describe what is happening at the northern boundary of this plate.

11. Inspect Fig. 8–2 to find other locations where continents have collided. What mountain ranges were formed?

12. San Francisco is approximately 10,000 km from Tokyo. The Japan Trench is gobbling up crust at the rate of 3 cm a year. How many years will it take until San Francisco collides with Tokyo?

13. Scientists use the term **plate tectonics** to refer to the theory that major structural features on the earth's surface form as crustal plates move. How could convection currents of materials within the earth be related to the theory of plate tectonics?

Hot Spots

Some volcanoes form over stationary **hot spots** in the middle of plates. See Fig. 8–6. Magma flowing from these volcanoes is called **basalt lava**. It is high in iron and magnesium. This lava flows like hot, thick syrup, gradually forming **shield volcanoes** shaped like domes with gently sloping sides. These volcanoes are much less explosive than the composite volcanoes formed at regions of subduction. Some shield volcanoes begin on the ocean floor and, with repeated eruptions, grow slowly until they reach the surface of the water and form islands. Peaks of some of these islands reach 3.6 km above sea level in regions where the ocean is 7 km deep, making them the largest mountains on earth as measured from their bases on the seafloor to their summits. Almost all of the mid-Pacific and mid-Atlantic islands formed in this way.

Over time, as the plate moves or twists, a volcano that was over the hot spot moves away, ceases to erupt, and becomes extinct. New islands in the **island chain (archipelago)** form as other parts of the oceanic crust move over the hot spot. See Fig. 8–6. **Erosion** (wearing away) and **subsidence** (sinking of the earth's crust) eventually cause older islands to sink below sea level. **Atolls**, groups of islands that ring a shallow lagoon, form when coral reefs grow on top of submerged volcanoes. Found even deeper are **guyots**, which are extinct, flat-topped, eroded volcanoes 1,800 to 3,000 m below the ocean surface.

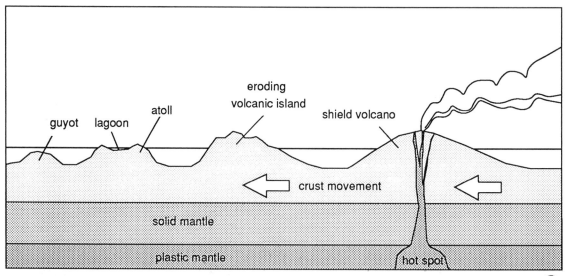

Fig. 8–6. Formation of volcanic islands

QUESTIONS

14. Examine Fig. 8–2 and locate volcano symbols that are not associated with regions of subduction (composite volcanoes).
    a. How did these volcanoes form?
    b. What are the differences among shield volcanoes, composite volcanoes, and the types of volcanoes found in Iceland?

15. If we assume that a hot spot is stationary and that the plate moving over it is forming an island chain, what is the likely minimum depth of the hot spot?

16. What is the relationship between erosion and subsidence?

FURTHER INVESTIGATIONS

1. Find Figs. 7–1, 8–3, 8–4, 8–5, and 8–6 in your Student Workbook. Choose appropriate colors and color-code each of the layers of the earth in these figures. Use the same colors for the color key in each figure.

2. Using all the models and maps from Topics 4 and 5 and information from this topic, develop hypotheses to explain how each kind of oceanic feature formed and changed over time.

3. Evidence from mineral, geological, and fossil records indicates that about 225 million years ago the earth was vastly different than it is today. There was just a single landmass, a supercontinent called **Pangaea**, after the Greek goddess of the earth. At that time there was only one large ocean. Between Eurasia and Africa was the ancient Tethys Sea, the site of the present Mediterranean Sea. Pangaea gradually began to break apart. About 180 million years ago two distinct sections had formed. The one on the north, called **Laurasia**, eventually gave rise to North America and Eurasia. The other, called **Gondwanaland**, later gave rise to Africa, South America, India, Australia, and Antarctica.
    a. Find references showing the timing and patterns of continental drift.
    b. Cut out paper outlines of the continents, arrange them into the ancient continents, then move them gradually to simulate the formation of the present continents and oceans. Make outlines of the arrangements 200 million, 180 million, 135 million, and 65 million years ago.
    c. Predict what the earth will look like 20 million years from now.

4. Iron particles, which are magnetic, orient themselves in relation to the magnetic pole of the earth. The earth's magnetic pole changes from time to time. Rocks formed by the cooling of lava in midocean ridges have different magnetic alignments, depending on the direction of the magnetic pole when they cooled. Find references that explain how the rate of seafloor spreading and the age of the oceanic crust may be determined by magnetic patterns frozen in the rocks.

5. It appears that not all of the oceanic crust is subducted and returned to the mantle when oceanic and continental

plates collide. Very small amounts, called **ophiolites**, become embedded in the edges of continents. These fragments contain rocks typical of the seafloor, with a high content of rich metallic ores that contain copper, iron, and magnesium. Find references and prepare a report explaining how these regions may have formed and how the resources are used.

6. Read books or view videotapes to learn more about the theory of plate tectonics and continental drift. Make a series of diagrams showing changes in the ancient oceans.

7. Using library references and career information systems, make a list of occupations related to geology. What abilities and interests must a geologist have? What kind of education and training? What is the employment outlook?

8. Invite a geologist to speak to the class about local geology. What is known about the land you live on? What is the evidence?

UNIT 2

WAVES AND BEACHES

Waves—mysterious, terrifying, relentless, beautiful—agents of destruction and balm to the spirit. One day they are hurricane-driven mountains of water crushing ships and pulverizing shorelines. A week later they are swells forming breakers on a distant beach where agile surfers guide their boards. One day waves rip and pry the proud rocks from the land, carrying them into the deep. A day or a season later they return these same rocks, broken and humbled, as beach-building sand.

Tsunamis rise unexpectedly from the sea and level whole towns. True tidal waves of the moon and sun gently lift and carry ships in and out of harbors. To land-dwellers, waves are the most striking feature of the ocean. We turn to them next.

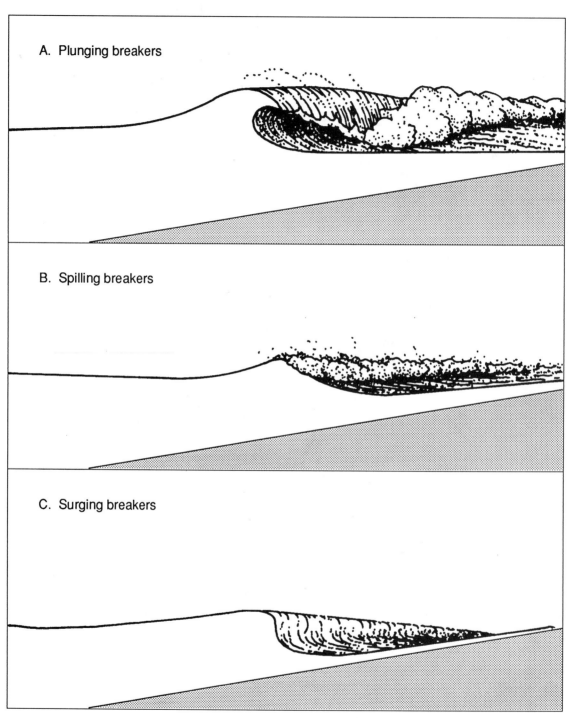

A. Plunging breakers

B. Spilling breakers

C. Surging breakers

Fig. 1–1. Types of breaking waves

1. Watching Waves

The best way to learn about waves is to observe them. You need not go to a beach; you can observe waves on windy days on a lake or a river. On a smaller scale, you can see waves in swimming pools, puddles, and other bodies of water. In this topic we concentrate on ocean waves.

Surf Zone

The **surf zone** is the area near shore where waves break. How far from shore a wave breaks depends on the length of the wave and the depth of the water. How a wave breaks depends largely on the steepness of the bottom slope, whether the slope is smooth or irregular, and whether the bottom is composed of shifting sands or solid rock. **Surf** usually contains a mixture of several types of breaking waves.

Waves may break more than once as they advance to shore. Each time a wave breaks, it gives up energy, becoming smaller and shorter as it continues into shallower water.

Types of Breaking Waves

Three types of **breaking waves** may be seen: plunging breakers, spilling breakers, and surging breakers. Combinations often occur. Each is shown in Fig. 1–1.

Plunging breakers, shown in (A) in Fig. 1–1, form where there is a moderately steep, sloping bottom. "Plungers" form tubes or curls that cascade water in a circular motion downward into the trough and break with a forceful crash, rapidly releasing energy. Air trapped inside the curl of the wave may "explode," forming geysers of white water as the wave collapses. If the bottom is very steep, the top of the wave may break over the lower half, forming a **collapsing wave** with no curl.

Surfers like the high-speed ride they can get on a plunging breaker as they drop steeply down its front with the chance of "getting locked in the tube." Bodysurfers sometimes catch rides on plungers that break in water less than a meter deep. Neither bodysurfers nor board surfers try riding collapsing waves. Plunging breakers can seriously injure swimmers because the waves literally pound them against the beach.

Spilling breakers, shown in (B) in Fig. 1–1, form where the bottom slopes gradually. "Spillers" advance to shore with a line of foam tumbling steadily down their front. Unlike plungers, they break slowly over considerable distances. Surfers can get their longest rides on spilling waves.

Surging breakers, shown in (C) in Fig. 1–1, form when large waves suddenly hit bottom in shallow water. Examples are tsunami waves and tidal bores, which look like walls of white water advancing toward shore. Surging waves can cause great damage when they run up the beach.

Estimating Wave Height

You can estimate the height of the surf using one of the following methods:

Method A. You may judge the relative height of the waves as compared to a surfer, a boat in the water, or some other reference.

For example, if a surfer appears as tall as your thumb and the surf about twice that, the wave is about twice the surfer's height. See Fig. 1–2.

Method B. If it is safe to do so, walk down the slope of a beach until the top of the breaker and the distant horizon are aligned. When these are aligned, the vertical distance from your eye level to sea level is about the height of the wave. Measure the vertical distance from your eye to the level of the water returning to the sea. See Fig. 1–3.

QUESTIONS

1. If the surfer shown in Fig. 1–2 is 2.0 m tall, how high is the wave?

2. If the girl shown in Fig. 1–3 is 1.5 m tall and is standing 0.5 m above sea level, how high is the wave?

3. What are some of the safety precautions that
   a. a spectator should keep in mind when observing waves from the shoreline?
   b. a surfer or body surfer should keep in mind when riding waves?

4. Check your understanding of each of the following terms:
   a. breakers
   b. surf
   c. surf zone

ACTIVITY

Observe and describe waves.

MATERIALS

- notebook or pad
- camera (optional)
- watch (optional)
- protective clothing as needed
- sunscreen (optional)

PROCEDURE

1. Plan to observe the ocean at your favorite beach site. If you do not live near the ocean, observe waves formed as winds blow over a lake or a river. Keep in mind that wave-watching activities usually cannot be scheduled very far ahead because wave conditions change so rapidly. Plan to spend about 30 minutes to observe wave conditions.

2. Read the suggested observations in Table 1–1 to guide you as you begin to observe waves. Do not expect to observe all the phenomena at any one place or at any one time.

3. Go to a safe vantage point, sit quietly, and watch the waves. Make as many observations as you can.

4. After watching the waves, record your observations.

5. In class, share your observations and opinions. Also describe things you noticed that are not included in the list of suggested observations.

6. Remember your observations as you study waves and beaches in this unit.

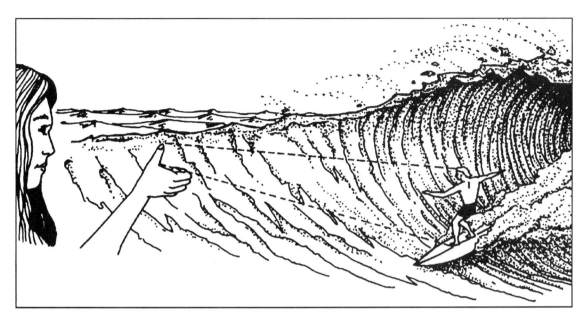

Fig. 1–2. Estimating wave height from a known object in the water

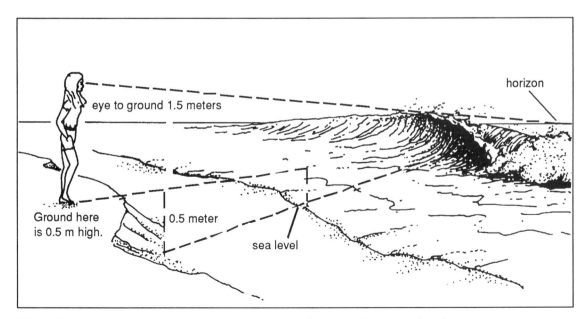

Fig. 1–3. Estimating wave height by knowing your height above sea level

75

Table 1–1. Suggested observations for wave watchers

1.   What shapes do waves have? Sketch the shapes of the waves you observe.

2.   How do waves change in shape and size as they come toward shore?

3.   In what direction(s) do waves move? Is there a pattern to their movement? At what angle(s) do waves approach the shoreline?

4.   What colors are waves? How do colors vary in different types of waves?

5.   How do waves compare in height? Where in relation to the shore are the largest waves found? Do the largest waves always form at the same place?

6.   Are the waves arriving on shore always the same height? If not, is there any pattern in how the wave heights change?

7.   How many times do waves break before they reach the shore? Do all waves break at the same place? Do they all look the same as they break?

8.   Close your eyes. Listen to the sounds and rhythms of waves as they approach and break on shore. How might listening for the sounds of waves be important to your safety?

9.   Again, close your eyes. What do you smell? Can you detect seaweeds?

10. Look for protruding rocks, seawalls, or offshore islands. How do these affect the waves?

11. Watch as waves break on sandy beaches, on rocks, or on seawalls.
     a. How high up on the shore does the water go when the waves break?
     b. Where have the highest waves broken recently on the shore? Look for wet areas, for marks on the sand, for litter or seaweeds washed onto the beach, for salt crystals on rocks, and for limpets and periwinkles on the rocks.

12. Is the tide in or out? Notice whether seaweeds or oysters on rocks, walls, or pilings are exposed. Observe whether waves advance up to the highest **swash marks** (small sand patterns formed as waves recede).

Table 1–1 (continued). Suggested observations for wave watchers

13. Watch the advance and retreat of waves on shore. How much of the water in the wave actually returns to the ocean? Are there times when the amount of water rushing onto the beach seems greater than other times? When does this happen?

14. Notice the patterns formed in sand as waves advance and retreat. Look also for evidence of sand being sorted by color or size along the beach. Sketch your observations.

15. Notice the shape and slope of the beach. Does the beach slope gradually or abruptly to the sea? Does it have sudden steplike drops? Is the beach wider in some areas than in others? Do you see any evidence of erosion?

16. Do waves advance evenly up the slope of the beach? Are there regular indentations (**cusps**) where the waves advance farther up the beach?

17. Does the beach appear to be eroding or enlarging? Look for sandbars and spits. If a stream empties out on the beach, does it flow directly into the sea, or is it diverted or closed off by sand? How do waves seem to be associated with beach erosion or replacement?

18. Observe how experienced swimmers, surfers, and boaters enter the water. How do they maneuver through waves? Are there any areas they seem to avoid? What are the areas like where they enter? What are the areas like that they avoid? Where do they return to the beach?

19. What living organisms are there in the surge zone? How have living organisms adapted to living in areas of heavy wave action?

20. Look for the following minor beach features:
    a. **rills**: very small channels formed in the beach as a wave retreats.
    b. **ripplemarks**: wavelike patterns in the sand formed by currents.
    c. **laminations**: sand grains sorted by wave action or layers of sand, often of different colors, formed by winds.

FURTHER INVESTIGATIONS

1. Collect or prepare a series of photographs showing as many features as you can about waves.

2. Look for examples of waves in paintings and prints. Explain what you think the artist has shown.

3. Talk with someone who draws or paints waves. If possible, arrange a demonstration for the class. Learn how an artist captures the movement, color, and transparency of waves.

4. Listen to music depicting waves, then describe your impressions from the music.

5. List as many words as you can that describe waves.

6. Read a book, a short story, or a poem that describes waves or a great storm at sea. Tell how the author is able to make the reader visualize waves.

7. Interview a surfer or consult references to determine how surfers describe waves and surfing. If possible, invite an experienced surfer to speak to the class.

8. Find out how a professional surfing photographer takes pictures of waves and of people surfing.

9. Return periodically to the beach to observe waves. Note the direction waves are coming from, their height, and their period. See Topic 2. Keep a recording of the date, the weather conditions, the direction and speed of the wind, and the condition of the beach.

10. Predict wave conditions at different times of the year and under different weather conditions.

11. Find out if any of your friends, relatives, or neighbors have had an experience with a "big wave" or know of any unusual events related to waves. Write these down. Make a class collection.

12. Hold a contest in class to see who can tell the "tallest tale" or the most exaggerated story about a big wave or waves. This kind of storytelling is in the tradition of the Able Bullpop Stormalong stories—sea stories about a sailor whose ship was so tall that the top of its mast caught a spark from the sun.

2. Wave Properties

Open-ocean waves appear to change endlessly, much to the delight of wave watchers. Oceanographers and ocean engineers who want to study waves must understand the common, basic properties of waves. To do this, they use the idealized profile of a simple wave shown in Fig. 2–1 and the terms listed in Table 2–1.

Different waves may have different **speeds**. Most ocean waves move at 20 to 40 mph, and certain kinds move as fast as jet planes.

Calculating Wave Properties

We can calculate the speed (C) of a wave from its wavelength (L) and period (T) using the formula

$$C = L \div T$$
Speed = wavelength ÷ period

Knowing that a wave has a wavelength of 20 m and a period of 4 sec, we can calculate its speed as follows:

$$C = 20 \text{ m} \div 4 \text{ sec}$$
$$C = 5 \text{ m/sec}$$

QUESTIONS

1. A wave has a length of 24 m/wave and a period of 4 sec/wave. What is its speed?

2. Demonstrate mathematically that the correct formula for wavelength is

$$L = C \times T$$
Wavelength = speed × time

3. A wave has a speed of 3 m/sec and a period of 20 sec/wave. What is its wavelength?

4. Demonstrate mathematically that the formula for period is

$$T = L \div C$$
Period = wavelength ÷ speed

5. The speed of another wave is 4.2 m/sec. Its wavelength is 12.6 m. What is its period?

6. Demonstrate mathematically that the formula for frequency (F) is

$$F = 1 \div T$$
Frequency = 1 ÷ period

7. What is the frequency of a wave with a period of 0.1 sec/wave?

8. If the frequency of a wave were 0.2 wave/sec, what would be its period?

9. Demonstrate mathematically how you would find the speed of a wave from its frequency and wavelength.

10. A diagram of a wave is shown in Fig. 2–2. Use this figure to answer the following questions:
    a. What is the height of the wave?
    b. What is the wavelength?
    c. Can you calculate the frequency of

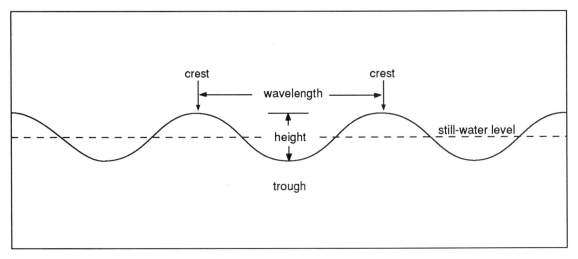

Fig. 2–1. Profile of a simple wave

Table 2–1. Wave terms and formulas

Still-water level. Water level when surface is flat and smooth with no waves. Still-water level is slightly lower than halfway between the crest and trough because crests are usually steeper and narrower than troughs.

Crest. The highest point of a wave.

Trough. The lowest point of a wave below the still-water mark.

Wave height (H). The vertical distance from crest to trough.

Wavelength (L). The horizontal distance from crest to crest. (L = meters/wave.)

Wave period (T). The time in seconds that it takes for one complete wave (from crest to crest) to pass a fixed point. (T = seconds/wave.)

Wave frequency (F). The number of wave crests that pass a fixed point per unit of time, usually in seconds. (F = waves/second.)

Wave speed (C).* The speed of the wave in a certain direction expressed as distance per unit of time. (C = distance/second or C = L ÷ T.)

* The letter **C** is used for speed, referring to the scientific term **celerity**.

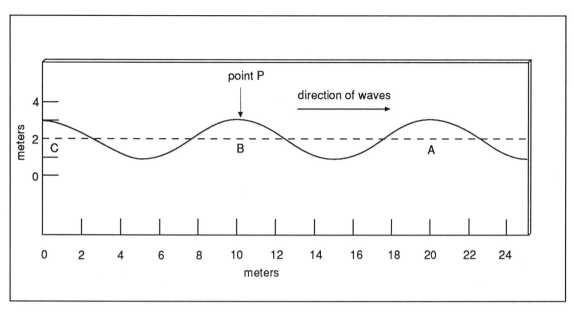

point P

direction of waves

meters

4

2

0

C

B

A

0   2   4   6   8   10   12   14   16   18   20   22   24

meters

Fig. 2–2. Diagram of a moving wave

the wave from this information? If so, what is it? If not, what is needed?

11. Fig. 2–2 shows three wave crests moving to the right. When the crest of wave A passed point **P**, the watch read 0.00 sec. When the crest of wave B passed point **P**, the watch read 10.00 sec.
a. What is the period of the wave?
b. What is the speed of the wave?
c. What is the frequency of the wave?

12. Check your understanding of the following terms:
a. period   e. height
b. wavelength   f. crest
c. speed   g. trough
d. frequency   h. profile

3. Wave Sets

In open-ocean conditions, sets of waves intersect, cutting across each other. These **wave sets**, also called **wave trains**, are groups of waves of the same wavelength that travel together. The wave patterns produced when two or more wave sets intersect are called **interference patterns**. Interference patterns formed by two sets of waves can be seen by tossing two pebbles close together into a pond and watching how the waves intersect.

Interfering wave sets can produce exceptionally high waves when the crests of two waves come together. Very deep wave troughs form when the troughs of two waves come together. This combining is called **wave reinforcement**. Recent reports of giant troughs have been added to reports of giant waves at sea. Both are capable of damaging—even sinking— ships.

Along the shore, surfers refer to the highest wave in a set as the "clean-up wave." **Surf beats** are regular series of low waves followed by several high waves within a 2- or 3-minute period. These are caused by wave interference patterns.

Scientists study waves in **wave tanks**. They can obtain pictures showing the properties of the waves they produce. A variety of techniques, including photography, are used to study wave properties

---

ACTIVITY

Make profile pictures of wave trains generated in a long wave tank and analyze them.

MATERIALS
- long wave tank
- sponges
- 2 meter sticks
- 2 sets of paddle stops
- masking tape
- 2 wave paddles
- several sheets of construction paper
- scissors
- watch

PROCEDURE

1. Set up a long wave tank as shown in Fig. 3–1. Fill about two-thirds with water. Put sponges at one end of the tank.

2. To control the amount of energy used in generating waves, tape a paddle stop across the top of the tank to limit the distance the paddle can move. Begin this activity with the paddle stop 5 cm from the backstop.

3. Generate wave pulses by moving the wave paddle back and forth rhythmically.

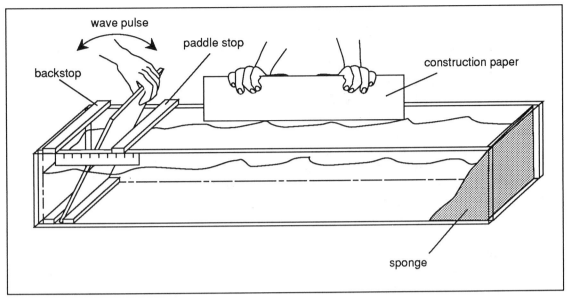

Fig. 3–1. Making a watermarked wave profile picture in a long wave tank

a. Make two or three wave pulses. Observe the waves you generate. These are called **progressing waves** because they move forward down the wave tank.

b. Compare the movement of one wave and of a set of waves or wave train. Generate one wave and carefully observe its movement down the wave tank. Then generate a set of 4 to 6 waves. Carefully observe the first and last waves of the set.

c. Compare the speed (distance/time) of a single wave and of a wave set. Remove the sponge, then repeat Procedure (b). Count the seconds it takes for the wave(s) to move the length of the long wave tank, **reflect** off the end, and return to the paddle.

d. Simulate a **seiche**, the oscillating (back-and-forth surging) movement on the surface of a lake or other land-locked body of water. Begin with still water. Make one or two waves. Observe how many times the waves move back and forth across the wave tank, reflecting off the ends.

e. Observe how progressing waves form standing waves. **Standing waves** do not advance but appear to move up and down in place. To make them, increase the number of waves to 20 or 30 until standing waves form.

4. Make watermarked profile pictures of waves generated in the long wave tank. See Fig. 3–1.

a. Obtain a sheet of construction paper about half the height and two-thirds the length of the wave tank.

b. Hold the construction paper lengthwise by its corners close to the back side of the wave tank and just above the water level.

c. Once the water is still, have your partner generate waves at a frequency of two pulses per second.

d. Just before the first wave reaches the far end of the wave tank, dip the paper quickly in and out of the water. The watermarks on the paper will show the profile of the waves at the instant the paper was dipped into the water.

e. Immediately trace the profile of the waves in pencil.

f. Label the profile as shown in Fig. 3–2 with the following:
   1) paddle-stop setting (cm)
   2) wave frequency (number of waves per second)
   3) type of wave (progressing, standing, and so on)

g. Analyze each watermarked profile for wavelength and wave height.
   1) Determine the wavelength as shown in. Fig. 3–2. Record wavelength above the line.
   2) Measure the distance from the trough to the wavelength line. Record the wave height as shown in Fig. 3–2.
   3) Record your measurements in Table 3–1.

5. Make watermarked pictures of waves generated with different pulse rates and paddle-stop settings. Repeat Procedure 4, using the combinations given below. Record data in Table 3–1.
   a. Frequency = 1 wave/sec, paddle-stop setting 5 cm
   b. Frequency = 1 wave/sec, paddle-stop setting 10 cm
   c. Frequency = 2 waves/sec, paddle-stop setting 10 cm

6. Modify the long wave tank so that it has a paddle at each end. See Fig. 3–3.

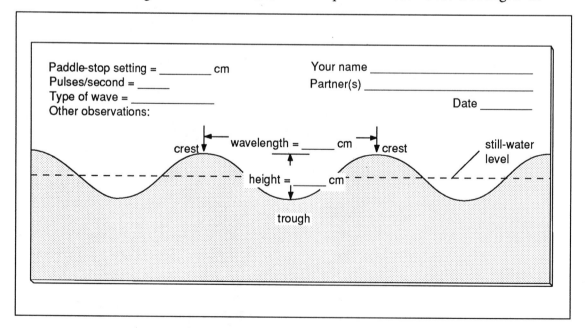

Fig. 3–2. Analysis of a watermarked wave profile picture

Table 3–1. Effects of frequency and amount of energy on wavelength and wave height Ⓦ

		Number of wave pulses/sec (frequency)	
		1	2
Paddle-stop settings (cm) (amount of energy)	5	L = _____ H = _____	L = _____ H = _____
	10	L = _____ H = _____	L = _____ H = _____
		L = wavelength (cm) H = wave height (cm)	

7. Produce profiles of the left and right wave sets and of the interference pattern formed when the left and right wave sets intersect.

   a. Produce a profile of the left wave set. Start with the paddle stop 5 cm from the backstop. Generate a wave set with five pulses of the left wave paddle with a frequency of one pulse per sec. Make a watermarked profile picture and label it as you did in Procedure 4. With scissors, cut out the profile of the crests.

   b. Generate a wave set with five pulses of the right wave paddle. Set the paddle stop 5 cm from the backstop. Make a profile of the right wave set with a different frequency.

   c. Produce a profile of the complex interference pattern formed when wave sets intersect. Simultaneously generate wave sets from each end of the tank. Keep the settings and frequency the same as for (a) and (b) above. Make a watermarked picture. Cut out the profile.

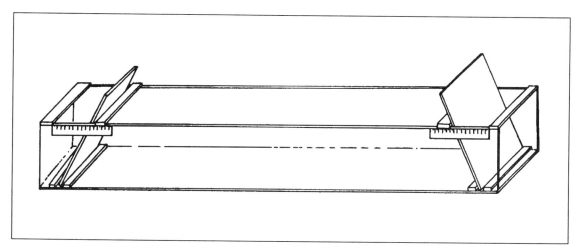

Fig. 3–3. Long wave tank with two paddles

8. Compare the interference pattern profile with the left wave set profile and the right wave set profile.
   a. Look for waves on the interference pattern profile that are about the same size and shape as the waves in either the left or the right wave set profile. Slide the cut-out profiles of the wave sets from Procedure 7 over the interference pattern profile.
   b. Decide whether the component left and right wave set patterns can be distinguished in the more complex interference pattern.
   c. Notice whether there is any regular pattern to the occurrence and height of waves in the interference pattern. Decide how the regularity might be related to the component left and right wave trains. Compare wave height and wavelength.

9. Repeating Procedures 7 and 8, simulate interference patterns created by wave sets with different wave heights or periods. Change the paddle stop and the pulse frequency. Make watermarked pictures of the separate wave trains and of their complex interference patterns. Analyze each interference pattern for its component wave set.

QUESTIONS

1. What happens to the first wave in a wave set as it moves down the long wave tank?

2. If you generate a wave set consisting of four waves, how many waves reach the far end of the long wave tank?

3. What is a seiche? How might a seiche be a problem for boats in an enclosed harbor?

4. What happens to the size of waves when crests from two wave sets come together? When two troughs coincide? When the crest of one wave and the trough of another wave coincide? Make sketches to show your answer.

5. Would you agree with a surfer who claims that waves always come in sets of seven? If yes, explain how this is possible. If no, explain why you disagree.

6. Explain the difference between these pairs of terms:
   a. standing wave and progressing wave
   b. reflected wave and seiche

7. Standing waves form in the ocean under natural conditions when two wave sets of the same height travel in opposite directions. Explain how it is possible to simulate standing waves in a wave tank.

8. Suppose that you are aboard a ship in the open ocean being bounced around by waves of different sizes coming from different locations.
   a. Explain this in terms of wave sets and interference patterns.
   b. What might the wave pattern look like as all the wave sets shown in Fig. 3–4 converge on the central square? Draw the pattern in the center square.
   c. What do the wave sets look like after they pass each other? Draw each wave pattern in the correct square.

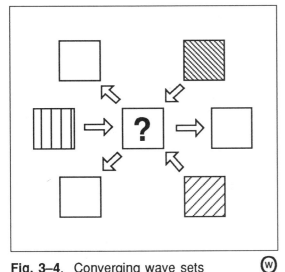

Fig. 3–4. Converging wave sets ⓦ

FURTHER INVESTIGATIONS

1. Construct your own **wave bottle**. Use two immiscible liquids (ones that do not mix readily, such as water and oil). Tint only the water with food coloring. Fill the bottle until it just overflows. Cap the bottle, allowing no air bubbles inside. To produce waves, rock the bottle back and forth.

2. Interview a naval architect, someone from the Army Corps of Engineers, a harbor pilot, or a harbor official.
   a. Learn how knowledge about waves is used in designing ships, harbors, and waterfront properties.
   b. Find out what kinds of abilities, interests, and educational training are needed to work in these career fields.

3. Use library references to find out how recreational equipment is designed to compensate for wave properties. Consider surfboards, kayaks, wave skis, sailboards (windsurfers), and sailboats.

4. Wind Waves

Winds are the primary source of energy for waves. Light winds blowing over calm water ruffle the surface. As the winds continue to blow, ripples begin to appear, then grow into waves.

Most ocean waves are produced by the force of the wind. The force of the wind is influenced by

1. its **duration**, the length of time it has been blowing.
2. its **fetch** (an old sailors' term), the distance over which the wind is blowing.
3. its average **speed** over the fetch.

Imagine that a wave tank is a large section of the ocean. A hair dryer represents the source of wind, either a storm or constant winds such as the "prevailing westerlies." From this simulation we can see how wind-generated waves begin as ripples, become chop, grow to wind waves, and finally become swells. See Fig. 4–1.

Sea States

Wave conditions at sea are called **sea states**. Refer to Fig. 4–1 and to Table 4–1 as you read about the development of waves.

When light winds start to blow across an undisturbed surface of water, they produce friction that drags the water into ripples. **Ripples** are small wavelets averaging about 8 cm high.

Chop is the sea state that develops when winds push ripples into waves about 1 m high. When these conditions occur, winds will be increasing in velocity.

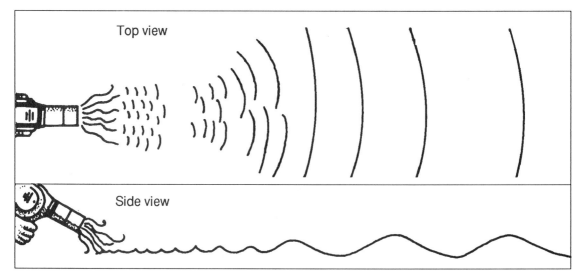

Fig. 4–1. Simulation of developing wind-generated waves

Table 4–1.   National Weather Service visual estimates of winds, waves, and sea conditions

Beaufort force	Sea state	Described sea conditions	Estimated wave height (m)	Description and estimated wind speed (knots)
0	ripples	Sea smooth and mirrorlike.	0.00	Calm (0 – 1)
1	ripples	Scale-like ripples without foam crests.	0.08	Light air (1 – 3)
2	chop	Small, short wavelets; crests have a glassy appearance and do not break.	0.15	Light breeze (4 – 6)
3	chop	Large wavelets; some crests begin to break; foam of glassy appearance. Occasional white foam crests.	0.61	Gentle breeze (7 – 10)
4	chop / seas	Small waves, becoming longer; fairly frequent white foam crests.	1.22	Moderate breeze (11 – 16)
5	seas	Moderate waves, taking a more prononced long form; many white foam crests; there may be some spray.	1.82	Fresh breeze (17 – 21)
6	seas	Large waves begin to form; white foam crests are more extensive everywhere; there may be some spray.	3.05	Strong breeze (22 – 27)
7	storm waves / seas	Sea heaps up and white foam from breaking waves begins to be blown in streaks along the direction of the wind; spindrift begins.	4.27	Near gale (28 – 33)
8	storm waves / seas	Moderately high waves of greater length; edges of crests break into spindrift; foam is blown in well-marked streaks along the direction of the wind.	5.49	Gale (34 – 40)
9	storm waves / seas	High waves; dense streaks of foam along the direction of the wind; crests of waves begin to topple, tumble, and roll over; spray may reduce visibility.	7.01	Strong gale (41 – 47)
10	storm waves / seas	Very high waves with long overhanging crests. The resulting foam in great patches is blown in dense white streaks along the direction of the wind. On the whole, the surface of the sea is white in appearance. The tumbling of the sea becomes heavy and shocklike. Visibility is reduced.	8.84	Storm (48 – 55)
11	storm waves / seas	Exceptionally high waves that may obscure small- and medium-sized ships. The sea is completely covered with long patches of foam lying along the direction of the wind. Everywhere the edges of the wave crests are blown into froth. Visibility reduced.	11.28	Violent storm (56 – 63)
12	storm waves / seas	The air is filled with foam and spray. Sea completely white with driving spray; visibility very much reduced.	13.72	Hurricane (64 – 71)

Storm waves begin to form when there are winds of gale-force intensity, more than 70 km/hr. Such waves may not be very high if the storm is of short duration or if the fetch is short. The longer the storm duration and fetch and the greater the intensity of the storm, the higher the waves. Several short-duration storms following each other and blowing in the same direction may also increase wave height dramatically. Large storm waves may reach 14 m or higher.

Hurricanes, also called **typhoons** or **tropical cyclones**, are violent storms with winds exceeding 105 km/hr. They may form huge waves over 14 m high. A hurricane is a circular wind field with winds over 200 km/hr. Winds may reach fetches of 240 to 345 km from the center of the storm.

Sea is a term used to describe a confused mixture of waves that is often observed from ships. Seas may include ripples, chop, wind waves, storm waves, and swells. Seas are characterized by waves of differing heights coming from many directions. See Fig. 4–2.

Swells are waves that have traveled beyond their generation area or fetch. They need no further wind to push them onward. Swells may be generated by storms or prevailing winds, such as tradewinds, which blow over long fetches for long durations. Swells may carry the energy of storms thousands of kilometers, for example, from the Antarctic to Alaska.

Fig. 4–2. Storm waves

QUESTIONS

1. What factors determine the size of waves?

2. Suggest a reason why the length of the fetch is important in wave size.

3. What are the two principal conditions under which swells form?

4. What role do ripples play in wave formation?

5. How might a hurricane-force wind develop very large waves?

6. What is meant by each of the following terms?

   a. swell   e. storm wave
   b. ripple   f. hurricane
   c. chop   g. sea state
   d. sea

Ocean Wave Organization

Open-ocean waves are organized in a variety of ways, including wave trains, cross seas, developing seas, and fully developed seas. A **wave train** or wave set is a group of progressing waves of about the same wavelength moving in the same direction at about the same speed. Ocean swells travel at relatively evenly spaced distances and are examples of wave trains. We simulated wave trains and sets in Topic 3.

Cross seas are the interference patterns formed when two or more wave trains intersect. Waves may cross each other at different angles, or they may come from the same direction but have different wavelengths and periods. Because of these differences, shorter waves are superimposed on longer waves.

Developing Sea

A **developing sea** means that waves are growing larger, but waves do not continue to grow indefinitely. When the waves have stopped growing, the sea state is described as fully developed sea. A **fully developed sea** is one where the energy supplied by the wind is equal to the energy lost in breaking waves. Table 4–2 shows properties characteristic of fully developed seas in winds of 10, 20, 30, 40, and 50 knots. A **knot** is a unit of speed used in maritime references. It is equal to 1 nautical mile per hour or 1.15 statute (land) miles per hour or 0.51 m per sec.

Predicting Waves

Wind speed tells only part of the story. Remember, it takes time to make fully developed waves. To become fully developed, a wave must be pushed by the wind over a long fetch. Table 4–3 shows how long a time and how long a fetch are required by winds at the same speed to produce a fully developed sea.

Probable wave size for winds of given speed, fetch, and duration have been determined by ocean engineers from simulations in very long wave tanks. Table 4–3, for example, shows that if winds of 20 knots (37 km/hr) blow for 10 hr over a fetch of 75 nautical miles (86.25 mi or 138.75 km), the seas would develop to an average wave height of 1.6 m (5 ft). About 10% of these waves will be twice as high (about 3 m).

Marine forecasts issued by the National Weather Service include reports of offshore swell heights and predictions of changing winds and sea states. They also predict the time of arrival and the approximate size of large waves generated by storms at sea. People in coastal areas can

Table 4–2. Characteristics of fully developed wind waves

Wind speed (knots) *	Average wave characteristics			
	Height (meters)	Length (meters)	Approximate speed	
			(knots)	(meters/second)
10	0.27	9	9	5
20	1.6	33	17	8
30	4.3	77	26	13
40	8.5	136	35	18
50	14.6	212	43	22
*1 knot = 1.15 mi/hr = 1.85 km/hr = 0.51 m/sec				

Table 4–3. Predicting wave size for mature and fully developed seas

Wind conditions			Probable wave size			
Speed (knots)*	Duration (hours)	Fetch (nautical miles)**	Average height		Highest 10%	
			(meters)	(feet)	(meters)	(feet)
10	2.4	10	0.27	0.9	0.55	1.8
15	6	34	0.76	2.5	1.52	5
20	10	75	1.6	5	3.0	10
25	16	160	2.7	9	5.5	18
30	23	280	4.3	14	8.5	28
40	42	710	8.5	28	17.3	57
50	69	1,240	14.6	48	30.1	99
* 1 knot = 1.15 mi/hr = 1.85 km/hr = 0.51 m/sec						
** 1 nautical mile = 1.15 mi = 1.85 km						

thus be warned in time to take precautions against potentially destructive storm waves. The National Weather Service cooperates with the World Meteorological Organization in making weather charts and marine forecasts available to ships, planes, and coastal areas throughout the world. Ships and planes at sea cooperate in reporting wind speeds, sea states, and other weather data to centralized weather agencies. Additional weather information is obtained from weather satellites.

QUESTIONS

7. If a marine forecast predicts that winds will rise from calm (no winds) to 25 knots overnight, what kinds of changes can be expected in offshore waves?

a. Estimate how long (time) the winds must blow and over what distance (fetch) to produce fully developed seas. Refer to Table 4–3.

b. If time and fetch are long enough to form fully developed seas in 25-knot winds, what are the properties of the waves? Use the terms *height*, *length*, and *speed* to describe them. Refer to Tables 4–2 and 4–3.

8. Use Tables 4–2 and 4–3 to compare the following:

a. the speeds of long waves (212 m) and short waves (9 m)

b. the heights of long waves and short waves

c. the fetch required to produce a fully developed sea of short and long waves

d. the characteristic conditions of waves produced by light breezes and storms.

9. Calculate the frequency of the waves listed in Table 4–2 using the equation

$$F = C \div L$$
Frequency = speed ÷ wavelength

10. What is meant by the following terms?
a. fully developed sea
b. developing sea
c. probable wave size

ACTIVITY

Simulate wind-wave formation, movement, and effect on exposed coasts.

MATERIALS

- cardboard
- scissors or knife
- masking tape
- plastic sheeting or trash bag
- clothespins
- water
- variable-speed fan or hair dryer
- 4 L washed sand of mixed grain sizes
- centimeter ruler
- toothpicks

PROCEDURES

1. Build a beach simulation tank as shown in Fig. 4–3.

a. Make a frame at least 12 cm high to fit on the top of the table you will be using. Use cardboard strips taped together with masking tape, notched wood, or a large cardboard box cut to size.

b. Line the frame with plastic sheeting or a heavy-duty trash bag. Fold the sheeting as needed for smooth fit on bottoms and sides. Hold it in place with clothespins or masking tape.

c. Fill tank with water to about 5 cm. (Wait until Procedure 3 to add sand.)

2. Simulate a storm with strong winds blowing over the open ocean. See Fig. 4–4.

a. Set up a high-speed fan or hair dryer. **CAUTION:** Do not let cord, hair dryer, or fan get wet or fall into the water.

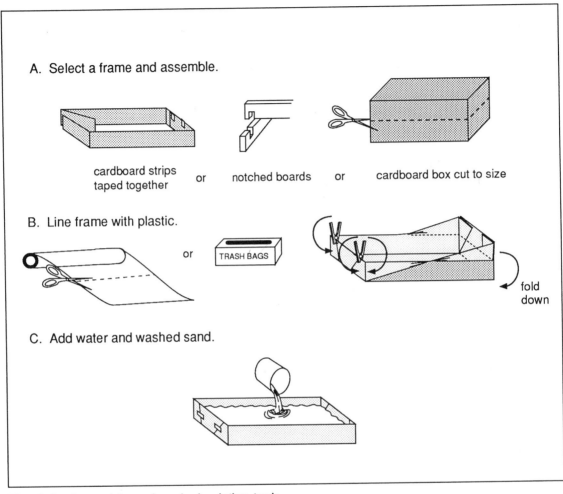

A. Select a frame and assemble.

cardboard strips taped together   or   notched boards   or   cardboard box cut to size

B. Line frame with plastic.

or   TRASH BAGS

fold down

C. Add water and washed sand.

Fig. 4–3. Assembling a beach simulation tank

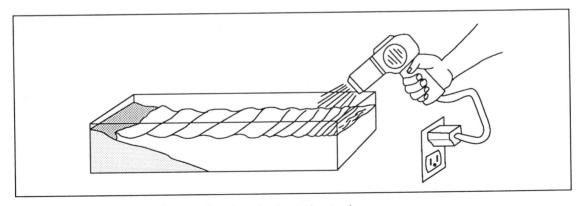

Fig. 4–4. Simulating wind waves in a beach simulation tank

b. Position the fan so that it blows down at an angle of 10° to 30° onto the surface of the water. Turn the fan to high speed.

c. Observe wind-wave formation. Move around the beach simulation tank to find the best angle for observing the waves.

d. Compare waves at the source, in the middle, and at the other end of the tank. Sketch your observations.

e. Identify and label ripples, chop, storm waves, and swells.

3. Make a simulated sandy beach at one end of the tank.

a. Add sand and form it into a gently sloping beach that rises at the far end to about 5 cm above the waterline.

b. Place toothpicks in the sand every 5 cm along the shoreline. The **shoreline** is where water and sand meet.

c. Make "before" sketches of the profile view and the top view of the beach.

Use the diagrams in Fig. 4–5 as a guide.

4. Simulate the effects of summer and winter wind-wave action on the beach.

a. Begin by simulating **winter waves**, short-period, high, choppy waves. (They can occur at any time of year.) Turn the fan to high speed to generate short-period wind waves that reach the beach.

b. Observe both how the waves form and how they interact with the beach.

c. After about 5 minutes, turn off the fan. Make "after" sketches of the top and profile views of the beach. Include in these sketches the location of the waterline and the toothpicks. Use arrows to indicate the direction of sand movement.

d. Compare your "after" sketches with your "before" sketches. Describe changes in the beach.

e. Repeat Procedures (b), (c), and (d),

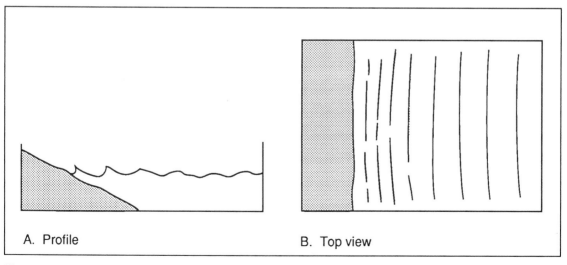

A. Profile   B. Top view

Fig. 4–5. Profile and top views of a beach simulation tank

this time simulating **summer waves**, long-period, low swells that also can occur at any time of year. Begin again with a smoothly sloping beach and new "before" sketches. Turn fan on lowest speed.

NOTE: If you are unable to vary the fan speed enough to generate noticeably different summer and winter waves, use a wave paddle to generate waves. Rock it about once per second for summer waves and more energetically (about three times per second) for winter waves.

5. Simulate wave interaction on the **windward** coast facing the **prevailing winds**, which are the winds most common to an area, and on the **leeward** coast on the opposite side of the island, protected from the prevailing wind. See Fig. 4–6.

   a. Rearrange the sand to simulate an island located about two-thirds of the way down the length of the tank. The island should be about 5 cm higher than the waterline and narrow enough so that water can flow freely around all sides. Mark the shoreline with toothpicks.

   b. Make accurate profile and top view sketches of the island. Show its height, width, and the slopes of the beaches.

   c. Turn the fan on high speed and adjust it to generate wind waves that travel to the island.

   d. After 5 minutes, turn off the fan. Observe and sketch the effects of wind waves on the windward and leeward coasts of the island.

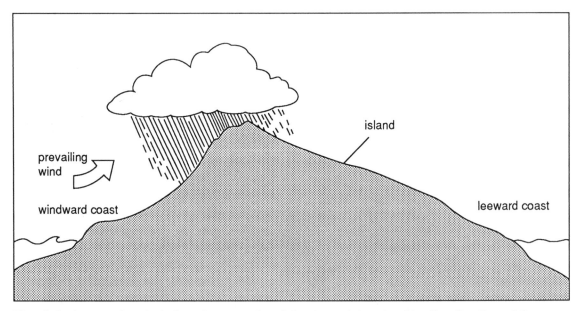

Fig. 4–6. Leeward and windward coasts of an island are determined by the direction of the prevailing wind.

QUESTIONS

11. Assume that the water closest to the fan in Fig. 4–4 is a storm center. In the open ocean, what do you suppose waves are like close to the center of a storm with high winds? How do these waves change as they move farther and farther away from the storm?

12. Compare summer and winter waves in wavelength, wave height, and wave period. Which type of wave causes more beach erosion?

13. Compare the width and slope of a beach formed by summer waves with the width and slope of a beach formed by winter waves.

14. How do winds and waves shape the windward and leeward beaches of an island? See Fig. 4–6.
    a. Are the waves higher on the windward or leeward coast?
    b. Which side of the island is more eroded?

15. When waves interact with a sandy beach, what happens to the sand? What evidence supports your observation?

16. Define each of the following terms:
    a. prevailing winds
    b. windward coast
    c. leeward coast
    d. summer wave
    e. winter wave

FURTHER INVESTIGATION

Study changes at a nearby beach over several months. Locate several favorable positions for observing the width and slope of the beach. Record the locations of these positions so you can return to them. Either take photographs or make sketches on graph paper. Look for effects of summer and winter waves.

5. Waves and Wave Depth

Most waves are formed by wind blowing over the surface of water. If the wind speed is great enough and the wind blows long enough over a large enough area, waves become fully developed. When the wind stops, they become swells. When swells reach a shore, they change into breaking waves. See Fig. 5–1 and Table 5–1. At one of the world's most famous surfing spots, Waimea Bay in Hawaii, ocean swells reaching shore sometimes crest and break at heights of 10 m or more.

We can understand how swells change into breaking waves by watching a surfer waiting for a good wave. The passing swells do not move the surfer toward shore; they move the surfer in a circular fashion, first up and forward, then down and back to a place near the original position. Neither the surfer nor the water advances toward shore. How does this occur?

Wave Energy

Swells are **deep-water waves**, meaning that the ocean depth is greater than half their wavelength (D > 1/2 L). Wave energy extends only to a depth of half the wavelength (D = 1/2 L). In open ocean the energy of a swell does not touch the seafloor.

As the energy passes through water, it sets water particles into orbital motion as shown in (A) in Fig. 5–2. Notice that water particles near the surface move in orbits with diameters approximately equal to the wave height. Deeper in the water, the orbital diameter decreases. Below a depth of

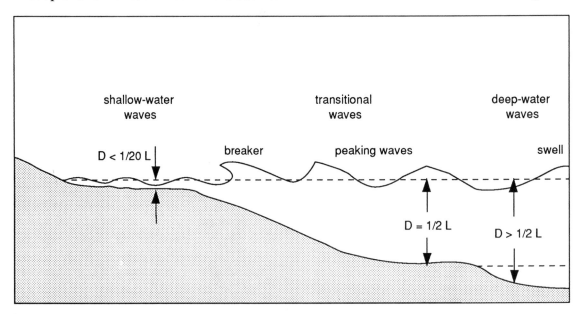

Fig. 5–1. Waves change as they approach shore

Table 5–1. Terms relating waves to water depth

D = Depth of water. ***L*** = Length of wave. ***H*** = Height of wave.

Deep-water waves. Waves traveling across a body of water where depth is greater than half the wavelength (D > 1/2 L), including all wind-generated waves moving across the open ocean.

Transitional waves. Waves having wavelengths greater than twice but less than 20 times the water depth (D < 1/2 L but D > 1/20 L), including wind-generated waves that have moved into shallower water.

Shallow-water waves. Waves traveling in water where depth is less than one-twentieth the wavelength (D < 1/20 L), including wind-generated waves that have moved into shallow nearshore areas, tsunamis (seismic waves) generated by disturbances in the ocean floor, and tide waves generated by the gravitational attraction of the sun and moon.

Breaking shallow-water waves. Unstable shallow-water waves that begin to break when the ratio of wave height to wavelength is 1 to 7 (H/L = 1/7), the crest peak is steep (less than 120˚), or the wave height is three-fourths of the water depth (H = 3/4 D).

Breaking deep-water waves. Unstable deep-water waves that begin to break when the seas are confused or when the wind blows the crests off waves, forming white-caps.

---

half the wavelength (D = 1/2 L), water is unaffected.

When the wave energy reaches bottom — that is, when the orbiting water particles begin to drag along the seafloor and the circular orbit is flattened — the swells become **transitional waves.** See (B) in Fig. 5–2. This occurs when the water depth is less than one-half the wavelength (D < 1/2L). The water particles are pushed up off the bottom, forming a higher, steeper wave called a **peaking wave.** Because of the friction of the water particles on the seafloor,

the top of the wave begins to move faster than the deeper parts. The front surface of the wave gradually becomes steeper than the back surface.

When the water depth is less than one-twentieth the wavelength, it becomes a **shallow water wave** (D < 1/20 L). The top of the wave travels so fast that it begins to spill over and fall down the front surface and becomes a **breaking wave.** This occurs when

• the crest of the wave forms an angle less than 120˚,

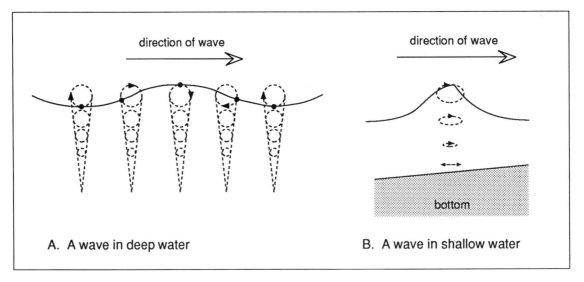

direction of wave

direction of wave

A. A wave in deep water

B. A wave in shallow water

bottom

Fig. 5–2. Movement of water particles inside deep-water and shallow-water waves

- the height is greater than one-seventh of the wavelength (H > 1/7 L), or
- the wave height is three-fourths of the water depth (H = 3/4 D).

There are several types of breaking waves. Their forms depend on the characteristics of the incoming waves and on features of the seafloor. The most common breaking wave is a spilling breaker that develops where the coastal seafloor is a gradual, almost-flat slope. Spilling breakers form when fast-moving particles at the top of a steep wave spill over slower-moving particles at the bottom. Plunging breakers form when low swells with long wavelengths roll to shore. The entire crest curls over, traps air in a tube, and breaks with a large splash. If the bottom is very steep, a plunging wave becomes a collapsing wave when the curl breaks onto the lower part of the wave.

Surfing is actually coasting down the steep front face of an advancing shallow-water wave. Because the front surface of the advancing wave is moving upward, the surfboard always remains at about the same position on the wave as the surfer moves toward shore. Surfers who go "over the falls" are in danger as they are swept up and back by the motion of the water, then over and down the lip of the wave. They can be pinned under water for a minute or more by the downward pressure of the plunging water.

At Waimea Bay, where the ocean floor rises abruptly, rounded deep-water swells change abruptly to steep-crested waves when they move into the shallow area. The swells, which originate in storms in the North Pacific during the winter, arrive with long wavelengths and long periods—as much as 22 to 30 sec. But when the swells touch bottom, the fast-moving water in back piles on top of the water in front, forming spectacular breakers. See Fig. 5–3. Experienced surfers ride breaking waves up to 7 or 8 m high, but they do not venture out when the surf is running 10 m or more.

ACTIVITY

Simulate deep-water waves and shallow-water waves in a long wave tank.

MATERIALS

- long wave tank and paddle
- 2 blocks of wood
- wooden board to support wave tank (if the tank is on the floor)
- water for the wave tank
- centimeter ruler
- 2 pieces of construction paper for water-marked wave pictures
- 4 corks
- 30 cm of monofilament line
- 2 small lead sinkers
- sand granules
- felt-tip marker or grease pencil
- detergent, one drop

PROCEDURE

1. Set up the long wave tank as shown in Fig. 3–1 in Topic 3.

2. Simulate a shoaling (sloping) shoreline by elevating one end of the tank. If the tank is on a table, put blocks under the table legs at one end. If it is on the floor, put a long, wide board under the tank and raise one end of the board with blocks.

3. Simulate deep-water, transitional, and shallow-water waves in the wave tank.
   a. Put water into the tank. Measure and record the water depth at the deep end, in the middle, and at the shallow end.
   b. Follow the steps in Procedures 4 and 5 in Topic 3 for generating waves. Experiment with paddle settings and pulse rates to generate deep-water, transitional, and shallow-water waves. As you plan, recall that for deep-water waves $D > 1/2\ L$.
   c. Make and analyze watermarked profile pictures of the deep-water, transitional, and shallow-water waves.
   d. Compare the shapes of the crests of deep-water waves with the shapes of the crests of shallow-water waves.

4. Observe the movement of particles in deep-water waves ($D > 1/2\ L$) and shallow-water waves ($D < 1/20\ L$).
   a. Place two free-floating corks on the water, one over the deeper section, the other over the shallower section.
   b. Tie sinkers to the two other corks so that the corks hang near midwater level. Put one cork in the deep section, the other in the shallow section.
   c. Sprinkle some sand granules into the deep section and some into the shallow section.
   d. Generate waves.
   e. Observe the movements of the corks and the sand.
   f. With a marker or a grease pencil, trace onto the side of the tank the movements of the corks and the sand at the surface, at midwater, and at the bottom.
   g. In your notebook, make sketches showing the water movement in deep-water and shallow-water waves. Interpret your observations using the concepts in this topic.

QUESTIONS

1. Describe what happens to a wave as it changes from a deep-water to a shallow-water wave.
   a. How does the shape of the wave crest change?

Fig. 5–3. Spectacular breakers at Waimea Bay, Hawaii

b. How does the wavelength change?

c. How does the speed of the wave change?

d. How does the movement of water in the wave change at the surface? In midwater? At the bottom?

2. What features of a wave would a surfer look for in deciding which one to catch? Base your answer on what you know about changes in waves with depth.

3. By observing waves, what can you tell about water depth and the seafloor?

FURTHER INVESTIGATIONS

1. Invite an experienced surfer to the class to describe
   a. how surfers position themselves to catch rides on waves.
   b. how surfers decide which wave to choose to ride.
   c. what surfers do to catch the ride to shore.

2. Ask experienced surfers and boaters how they use knowledge about shallow-water wave movements as a navigational aid to detect shallow or underwater rocks.

3. Use references to find how surfboards are designed
   a. for different kinds of waves and wave conditions, and
   b. for differences in surfers' height, weight, and strength.

6. Wave-Coast Interactions

As waves move toward shore, they change from deep-water swells to shallow-water breaking waves. Constant pounding by waves erodes and changes coastal features. To observe and describe changes caused by wave-beach interactions, we must learn to recognize typical coastal features.

ACTIVITY 1
Identify typical coastal features.

PROCEDURE
Locate and label each of the coastal features in Fig. 6–1. Use the terms in Table 6–1.

QUESTIONS
1. Using terms from this activity, describe the features of the beaches formed from summer and winter waves in Topic 4:
   a. a "summer" beach
   b. a "winter" beach

2. List the coastal features that are defined with respect to changes in the level of the tide.

3. Name the parts of a sandy beach from the backshore line to the water's edge.

Table 6–1. Common coastal features (Letters refer to features shown in Fig. 6–1.)

Backshore. The zone of the beach between the foreshore and the point on the coastline where the beach berms are. Only storm waves reach the backshore. (O)

Bar. An embankment of sand, gravel, or other particles deposited in shallow water by waves and currents; may be submerged or emerged. Also called a **sandbar**. (N)

Beach. The zone of loose sand, gravel, and other material that extends landward from the low waterline, either to the line of permanent vegetation or to where there is a marked change in substrate. Also called **shore**, including the backshore and the foreshore. (B)

Berm. Nearly horizontal part of the backshore of the beach formed by the erosion of material by wave action. Some beaches have no berms. (L)

Breaker. An unstable wave that is breaking on shore or over a reef or other object. Breakers include spilling, plunging, collapsing, and surging waves. (T)

Table 6–1 (continued). Common coastal features

Breaker zone. Area where deep-water waves touch bottom and become shallow-water waves, changing from rounded swells into unstable peaked waves. (R)

Coast. A strip of land of indefinite width (up to several miles) extending from the shoreline inland to the first major change in land features. Also called **coastal area**. (A)

Coastline. The indefinite line that forms the boundary between the coast and the shore. (F)

Dunes. Ridges or mounds of loose, windblown material, usually sand. (J)

Foreshore. That part of the shore (beach) between the upper limit of the wave wash and the water's edge. Also called **intertidal zone**. (P)

High tide. The highest water level of each rising tide. (H)

Low tide. The lowest water level of each falling tide. (I)

Nearshore (inshore). An indefinite zone extending seaward from the shoreline to beyond the breaker zone. (C)

Offshore. The direction seaward of the breaker zone. (E)

Onshore. The direction landward from the water. (D)

Peaking wave. A wave that has begun to change from a rounded swell to a higher, steeper, and less-stable pointed wave. (U)

Plunge point. The point at which a plunging wave curls over and falls. (S)

Rip feeder channel. A drop-off parallel to the beach formed at the final breaking point of waves just before they rush up the beach. Also called **trough**. (M)

Shoreline. Usually the line formed when the water touches the beach at high tide. (G)

Scarp. A steep slope along a beach caused by wave erosion. (K)

Surf zone. The area extending from where waves begin to peak to the highest uprush of the waves. (Q)

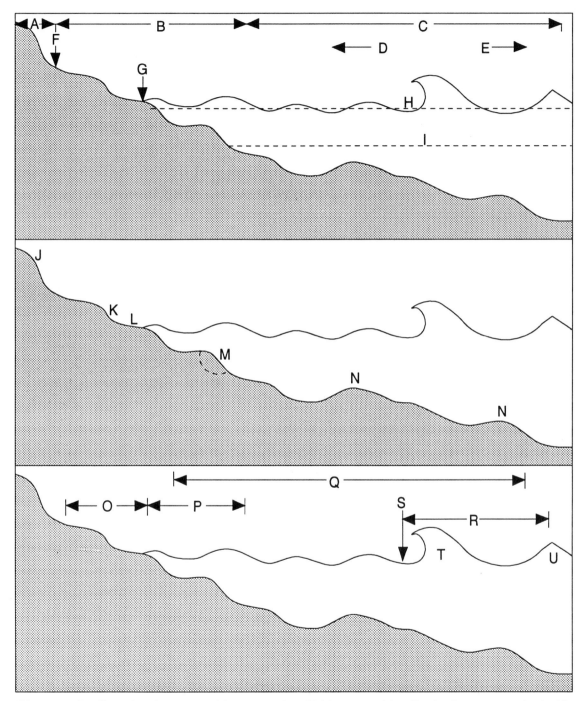

Fig. 6–1. Profiles of typical coastal features. See Table 6–1 to identify the features marked with letters. Ⓦ

Wave Patterns

Waves form distinct patterns as they move toward shore and interact with coastal features. Some of the most common wave patterns are listed in Table 6–2.

ACTIVITY 2

Observe patterns formed by waves interacting with coastal features.

MATERIALS

• beach simulation tank (See Fig. 4–3)
• water
• sponges
• wave paddle
• 4 L washed sand, mixed grain sizes under 2 mm
• 8 to 10 dense objects for simulating coastal features (coral pieces, rocks, rubber stoppers, etc.)

PROCEDURE

1. Set up the beach simulation tank and wave paddle. See Topic 4, Fig. 4–4, and follow Procedure 1.

2. Determine how natural and engineered coastal features affect the formation of wave patterns.
   a. See Fig. 6–2 for suggested simulations.
   b. Change only one coastal landform feature at a time. Sketch profile and top views before and after generating waves.
   c. Shape sand to make beach features. Use pebbles, rocks, and other dense objects to form offshore natural and engineered features.
   d. Generate waves for about 5 minutes.
   e. Observe the wave patterns that are created. Make sketches showing both wave patterns and beach profiles.

Table 6–2. Wave patterns

Converging waves. The higher waves formed when the crests of two waves merge; a wave interference pattern.

Diffracted waves. Wave crests in a wave train that spread out, decreasing in height and in energy.

Parallel waves. Sets of waves traveling together in the same direction with crests about equally distant from each other.

Radiating waves. Sets of waves that move outward in concentric rings away from the generating source.

Reflected waves. Waves that have bounced off an object.

Refracted waves. Waves that bend, changing somewhat in direction because part of the wave trough touches bottom and slows down.

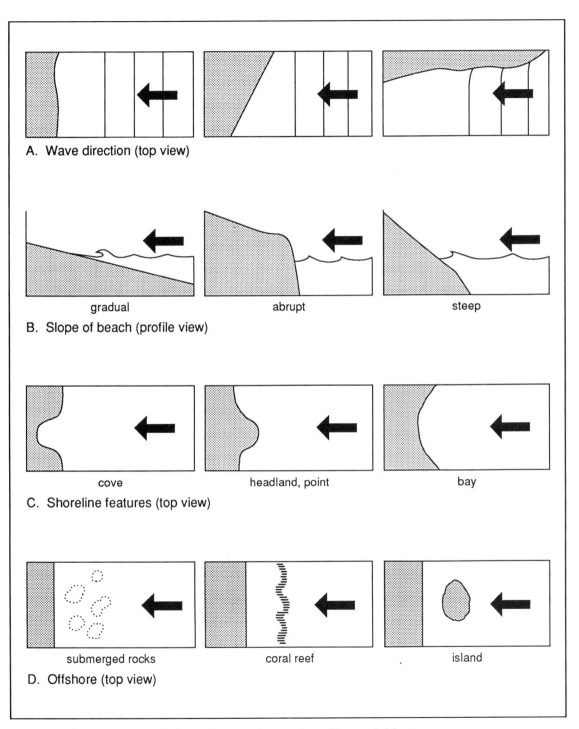

A. Wave direction (top view)

gradual   abrupt   steep

B. Slope of beach (profile view)

cove   headland, point   bay

C. Shoreline features (top view)

submerged rocks   coral reef   island

D. Offshore (top view)

Fig. 6–2. Suggested simulations of waves interacting with coastal features

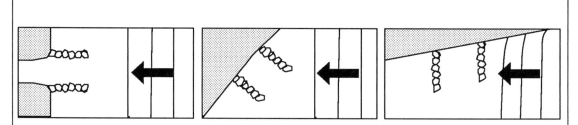

A. Jetties: usually constructed in pairs extending into the ocean. Often built at the mouth, or entrance, of a bay or river.

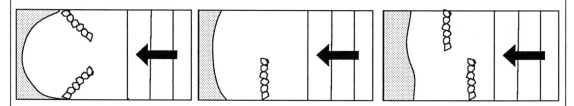

B. Harbors: constructed to provide a safe anchorage for boats along an open coastline where no natural harbors exist.

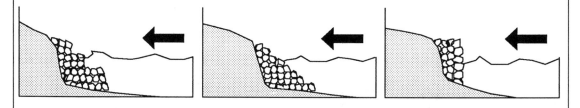

C. Seawalls: built at the shoreline separating land from water. Shaped like steps or like sloping or vertical walls. Also called revetments.

Fig. 6–3. Suggested simulation of engineered coastal features

3. Label sketches. Indicate types of wave patterns with the terms *reflection*, *refraction*, *diffraction*, and *convergence*.

4. Determine how engineered coastal features affect the formation of wave patterns.
   a. See Fig. 6–3 for suggestions.
   b. Repeat Procedures 2 and 3.

QUESTIONS

4. How can you account for the observation that, no matter what the direction of incoming waves, they become more parallel to the shoreline as they approach land?

5. What effects would a sudden shallow area (for example, a concave shoreline) or a sudden deeper area have on incoming shallow-water waves?

6. Discuss the saying "The points always draw waves." (A **point** is a narrow piece of land projecting into the ocean.)

7. Some sailors use waves to detect an island long before they can see it. How is this possible?

Currents

A **current** is a flowing body of water. An ocean current is much like a river of water. **Longshore currents** flow roughly parallel to the beach. **Rip currents** flow toward the sea, forming the typical pattern shown in Fig. 6–4.

At the beach, a rip current usually begins when longshore currents flowing toward each other meet, then flow together back to the sea. A rip current can also form

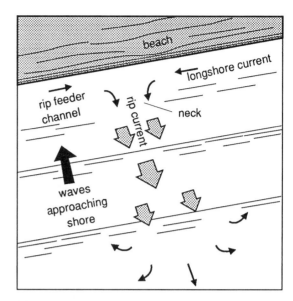

Fig. 6–4. A rip current

when the water flows over a bar or reef, perhaps from an incoming high tide or large waves, and then flows back to sea through a gap or low area in the bar or reef. Waves do not break in this gap because of its depth.

A rip current is stronger at its neck, where the currents merge and flow back to sea through a deeper channel. The strength and speed of a rip current dissipate as it heads out to sea, where the channel becomes wider or shallower.

Waves are usually smaller but choppier in the area of a rip current. Because a rip current carries sediment out to sea, water in the rip current may appear lighter than surrounding water.

An **eddy** is a circular motion of water on the surface. The interaction of longshore currents and eddy currents with coastal features produces nearshore circulation patterns.

Sand Transport

Sand transport is the movement of sand by waves and currents. We have already simulated summer and winter waves and studied their effects on a gently sloping sandy beach. Depending on how waves and currents interact with coastal features, sand may be carried away from beach areas and deposited elsewhere.

The study of wave and beach interactions contributes to our understanding of the processes of **erosion** (loss) and **accretion** (buildup). Although sand erosion is often a problem, sand accretion can also be a problem; for example, a sandbar can block boat channels, and sand deposits can fill harbors.

As sand is moved by waves and currents, it is sorted by size and density. Knowledge of this sorting process is useful in understanding such beach formations as **sand dunes, sandbars, spits,** and **barrier beaches.** A spit, shown in Fig. 6–5, is like a curved sandbar, except that it is connected to the beach at one end.

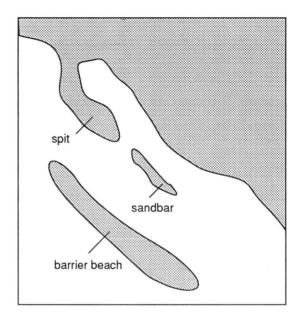

Fig. 6–5. Sandbar and spit

ACTIVITY 3

Study the formation of currents and the effects of coastal features on them.

Simulate the movement of sand by waves and currents and determine how sand transport is affected by coastal features.

MATERIALS

- beach simulation tank and materials from Activity 2
- small pieces of paper of uniform size (for example, the circles from a hole punch)

PROCEDURE

1. Generate parallel waves. Look for evidence of currents and of sand transport.

   a. Begin with a smoothly sloping sandy beach and generate waves for about 5 minutes. Float small pieces of paper on the surface. Note their movements as evidence of surface currents. Look for sand movement as evidence of bottom currents.

   b. Sketch both profile and top views. Indicate current patterns with arrows. Label sandbars, spits, and other features.

   c. Test the effect of shoaling, the steepness of the bottom. Raise one end of the tank. Repeat Procedures (a) and (b). Sketch your observations.

2. Determine how various types of shoreline features affect sand transport and the formation of currents.

a. Changing one coastal feature at a time, simulate various types of shorelines. Refer to suggestions on simulating features in Figs. 6–2 and 6–3. Sketch profile and top views before and after generating waves for about 5 minutes.

b. Look for evidence of currents and of sand transport. Notice the movement of sand and other objects carried by waves or currents. Indicate currents with arrows in your sketches.

c. Sketch the final location of sand. Look for evidence of sand sorting. Describe the sorting by sand color or size (fine, medium, coarse).

3. Label each of your sketches as follows:
   a. Identify the types of currents you have observed (longshore, rip currents, eddies).
   b. Label the sandy beach features (berms, sandbars, trenches, and so on). Indicate where the sandy beach eroded and where it built up.

QUESTIONS

8. How can longshore currents or rip currents affect swimmers? How do swimmers know they are in a current? What should they do?

9. How might you spot a rip current before you get into it?

10. What are some of the natural defenses a beach has against erosion by waves, currents, and storms?

11. How do seawalls, breakwaters, and jet-ties affect sand transport?

12. How do summer waves and winter waves affect the formation of sandbars? Make sketches.

13. Compare the simulated harbor designs. Where are sand deposits likely to form?

14. In your own words explain each of the following terms:
    a. landforms
    b. shallow-water waves
    c. deep-water waves
    d. coastal features
    e. breaker

FURTHER INVESTIGATIONS

1. Look for evidence of currents at your favorite beach site. If possible, take photographs.
   a. Notice whether swimmers tend to drift parallel or perpendicular to shore.
   b. Study wave action for evidence of rip currents. Waves are smaller and choppier and rarely break in a rip current. How might this be explained?
   c. Look for evidence of sand being transported out to sea in a rip current. The water may appear darker or lighter, depending on the color and composition of the sand.

2. Study currents at your favorite beach by plotting the movement of objects. Report your findings to the class. **NOTE:** Use objects that will not be affected by wind.
   a. Place objects in the path of advancing waves. Use objects of various

sizes, densities, and colors (seaweeds, plain or colored pebbles, or easily spotted debris). Record observations of how these objects are moved by the waves.

  b. On a day with little wind, release numbered coconuts, apples, or other nonglass floating objects from various locations. Observe how these move over an hour or more. Record their movements on a sheet of graph paper.

  c. Ask lifeguards and others familiar with the area to tell you what they know about currents there.

3. Study beach erosion problems in your community.
  a. Find out what methods are being used to protect property from wave damage.
  b. What determines where oceanfront houses may be built? Study designs for seawalls (revetments), jetties (bulkheads), and other features.
  c. Where did the old sand go? Where did the sand originally come from? Has additional sand been imported, and if so, where did it come from?

4. Investigate local issues related to the economic value of shoreline real estate and the increased popularity of ocean sports. Consider especially issues related to the construction of buildings or roadways along sand dune areas and the effects on vegetation and sand stability.

5. Simulate sand dune formation and erosion. Set up a beach simulation tank. Keep it dry. Put sand into the tank. Using a fan to simulate the wind, observe the process of sand dune formation. Simulate how dunes are eroded and how they migrate (move). Simulate ways to protect the dunes from erosion, including planting low vines, shrubs, and trees.

6. Study windward and leeward beaches of an island. Compare the two coastlines in terms of number and length of beaches. Estimate beach width and slope. Note the presence or absence of sand dunes and sandbars.

7. Using library references, learn about the stick-charts used by Micronesians to train navigators to sail the vast open regions of the tropical Pacfic Ocean. See Fig. 6–6. The navigators had to find remote islands by using waves, wave interactions, currents, and stars as guides.
  a. Learn what the parts of the Micronesian stick-charts represent.
  b. Make your own stick-chart.
  c. Compare stick-chart patterns with beach simulation tank patterns that you observed.

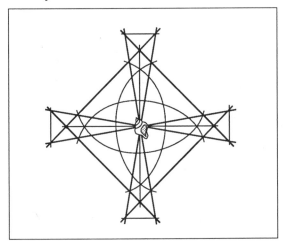

Fig. 6–6. Micronesian stick-chart showing the patterns of waves around an island

7. Tides

If you live near the ocean, you know about tides—the predictable daily rises and falls in sea level. But those gradual changes in sea level are waves whose periods are so long that hours go by between their crests and troughs. Fig. 7–1 shows the way the ideal wave of the tide wraps around the world with two crests and two troughs. High tides occur along a line connecting the centers of the earth and moon. This ideal tide wave exists only at certain times in the southern oceans. At other times and places tides are very complex.

We describe changes in the tide by stages. See Fig. 7–2. A **high tide** is the stage when the crest arrives at shore, rais-ing the sea level. A **low tide** is the stage when the trough arrives, lowering the sea level. The vertical distance between high tide and low tide is the **tide range**. An **ebb tide** is a falling or outgoing tide between **high water** (the crest) and **low water** (the trough). A **flood tide** is a rising or incoming tide between low water (the trough) and high water (the crest).

Do not confuse the daily tides with **tsunamis**, unpredictable and often destructive waves, caused by disturbances such as earthquakes, landslides, or volcanic activity. This confusion is common, and tsunamis are often inaccurately called tidal waves.

QUESTIONS

1. In Fig. 7–1 which way is the earth rotating? How many high tides will there be in a single day?

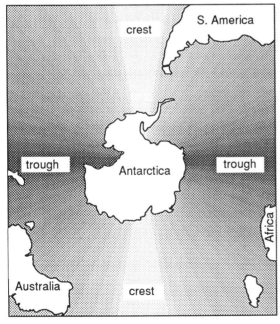

Fig. 7–1. The ideal global tide as seen in the southern oceans

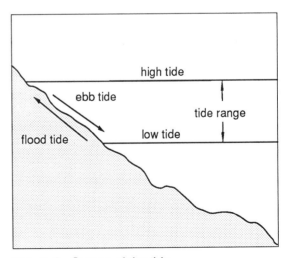

Fig. 7–2. Stages of the tide

2. How long does it take a tide to move latitudinally around the southern oceans?

3. Assume that you live on the shore of a bay that is 20 ft deep at high tide. The entrance to the bay is over a rocky ledge which is only 10 ft deep at high tide. The tide range is 4 ft.
   a. What would be the depth of the bay at low tide?
   b. What would be the depth over the rocky ledge at low tide?
   c. During what stage of the tide would water flow into the bay? Out of the bay?

Measuring Tide Height

Tide height is usually measured from the low-water mark as the **zero point**. This procedure is relatively simple in areas where the tide is constant. However, in areas where tides are continually changing, an average (mean) of the low tide levels called the **mean lower low-water level** is used. All tide heights at that location are measured from this zero point. When the low-water level is lower than the zero point, tide height is measured with a negative number and is called a **minus tide**. This procedure is somewhat like measuring temperature in degrees below zero.

Tide Tables

Tide tables are based on average tidal data obtained at a given location for many years. Daily tide tables are printed in newspapers of most coastal communities, usually near the weather report. An example is shown in Table 7–1. Tide table data may be plotted to make **tide graphs**.

ACTIVITY 1
Plot a tide graph from a tide table.

PROCEDURE
1. From the tide data in Table 7–1, make a tide graph showing high and low tides.

Table 7–1. Tide table for San Francisco Bay entrance (Golden Gate), December 1983   Ⓦ

Moon phases	Day	Date	High tide		Low tide		High tide		Low tide	
			Time	Ht (ft)	Time	Ht (ft)	Time	Ht (ft)	Time	Ht (ft)
Full	Tue	20	12:26am	4.8	4:37am	3.1	10:49am	6.8	5:40pm	−1.4
N. Eq.*	Wed	21	1:15am	4.9	5:24am	3.2	11:35am	6.8	6:26pm	−1.5
Perigee	Thu	22	2:03am	5.0	6:15am	3.2	12:20pm	6.6	7:12pm	−1.3
	Fri	23	2:51am	5.1	7:13am	3.2	1:13pm	6.2	8:03pm	−1.0
	Sat	24	3:38am	5.2	8:22am	3.0	2:11pm	5.7	8:54pm	−0.6
	Sun	25	4:27am	5.4	9:37am	2.7	3:18pm	5.1	9:51pm	0.0
3rd quar	Mon	26	5:15am	5.6	11:01am	2.2	4:40pm	4.5	10:45pm	0.5
Equa**	Tue	27	6:03am	5.8	12:15pm	1.5	6:13pm	4.1	11:45pm	1.2
	Wed	28	6:50am	6.1	1:19pm	0.8	7:44pm	4.1	- - - -	- - - -

* N. Eq. = North of the equator   ** Equa = At the equator

a. From Table 7–1 determine the time and tide height for the first high tide on Tuesday, December 20.

b. Plot this on the tide graph in Fig. 7–3.

c. Repeat steps (a) and (b) for the remaining high and low tides on December 20.

d. Complete the tide graph in Fig. 7–3 by entering tidal information for the rest of the week.

2. Connect the points on the graph with a line. Because the tide level changes gradually, draw a smooth, curved line between the data points.

QUESTIONS

4. On the tide graph find the day with the largest tide range.

a. On what day did it occur?

b. What was the range (in ft)?

5. Examine Table 7–1 and find the day with the smallest tide range.

a. On what day did it occur?

b. What was the range (in ft)?

6. On what days and times do you expect the

a. strongest flood tide?

b. weakest flood tide?

c. strongest ebb tide?

d. weakest ebb tide?

7. Imagine that you are in charge of planning a field trip to an **intertidal area** that is exposed only during minus tides. You have only 1 hour before and after the low tide to explore the tidepools. You must be back at school by 5 p.m. Which would be the best day for the field trip?

8. You have been invited to a party at a yacht club on December 23. The invitation reads "BYOB (bring your own boat); 6–10 p.m." Your boat draws (depth below the waterline) 3 m, and the entrance to the yacht club harbor is 3 m at 0 tide level. Could you attend the party? Why?

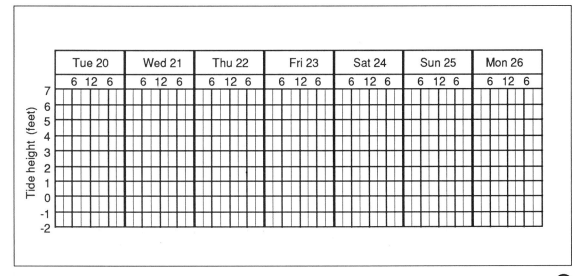

Fig. 7–3. Tide graph for San Francisco Bay entrance (Golden Gate), December 1983

Tide Formation

A combination of forces acts on the oceans to produce tides. These forces include

- the gravitational pull of the moon,
- the gravitational pull of the sun,
- the centrifugal force of the earth as it rotates,
- the relative positions of the moon and the sun, and
- the angle of the orbit of the moon around the earth.

Let's consider how each of these forces acts separately and then see how they work together to cause the daily variations in the tide.

Gravitational Pull of the Moon

Gravity is the force of attraction between two bodies. It is directly proportional to their masses and inversely proportional to the distance between them. Gravity draws the moon and the earth toward each other. If there were no resistance to this force, the moon and the earth would collide. However, as the moon and the earth revolve around a central point, a balancing **centrifugal force** is created that keeps them apart. You can see an example of centrifugal force when a large person and a child hold hands and spin around together. The centrifugal force tends to pull them apart.

Water on the earth in the region directly beneath the moon is pulled by gravitational force toward the moon. On the opposite side of the earth, centrifugal force pulls water away from the earth, opposing the gravitational force of the moon. Water in the ocean bulges as shown in Fig. 7–4. (The bulge is greatly exaggerated for illustration. The actual bulge is only a few meters high in most cases.)

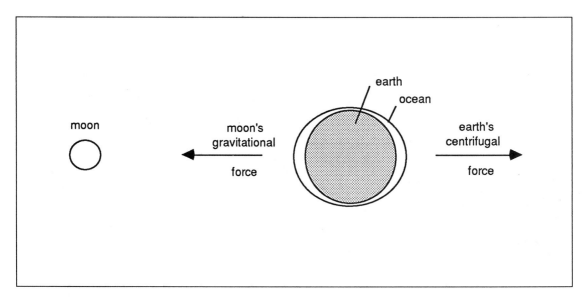

Fig. 7–4. Tides are caused by gravitational and centrifugal forces acting on the ocean.

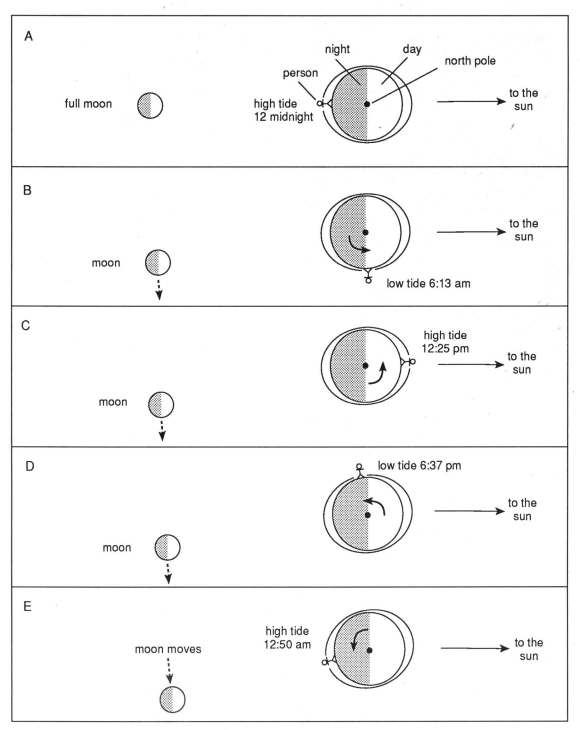

Fig. 7–5. Tides at various times of the day (north polar view)

Imagine yourself in a spaceship looking down at the north pole. See Fig. 7–5. Suppose you could see a person standing on the shore of the ocean near the equator.

At 12 midnight the person would see a high tide, caused by gravitational force of the moon. See (A) in Fig. 7–5. As the earth rotates during the day, the person would gradually move into a region of low tide at about 6:12 a.m. See (B) in Fig. 7–5. At 12:25 p.m. there would be another high tide, caused by centrifugal force. See (C) in Fig. 7–5. At about 6:37 p.m. there would be another low tide as in (D) in Fig. 7–5. Note also that the moon moves slightly (about 12°) in its orbit around the earth during the 24-hr period. Therefore the earth must rotate slightly longer (about 50 min more) before the moon would be again directly overhead of the person. This explains why the moon "rises" about 50 min later each night. The times of the tides are also 50 min later the next day. Although a **solar day** is 24 hr, a **lunar day** is 24 hr and 50 min.

QUESTIONS

9. What actually causes the tidal changes during a single day—the movement of the water, the movement of the moon, or the movement of the earth? Explain.

10. How much later would the high tide appear at the end of the second day? The end of the third day?

11. In Fig. 7–5, a high tide occurs at 12:25 p.m., not at 12 noon. Why? Why does a low tide occur at 6:13 a.m.? At what time would the evening low tide occur?

12. Select several days from Table 7–1. Calculate the time interval between a high tide and the next low tide each day. Are the time intervals exactly 6 hr and 12 min? Explain.

Gravitational Pull of the Sun

The sun exerts a second gravitational force on the earth, producing its own tide. Opposing the sun's tidal force is the centrifugal force of the earth, which produces a bulge of water on the side opposite the sun. As the earth rotates, the tide level changes due to the sun's gravitation from high to low and back again, just like the moon. But these changes occur during a solar day, or 24 hr. Although the sun's mass is much greater than the moon's, the sun is much farther from the earth, so its tidal force is about half that of the moon.

Interactions of the Moon and Sun

As we have seen, the moon moves a little farther each day (about 12°) in its orbital journey around the earth. Therefore the tides caused by the moon's gravity occur 50 min later than the tides caused by the sun's gravity. It takes the moon about 29.5 days to complete its orbit around the earth. This period is called a **lunar month**. The moon and the sun cause predictable, periodic changes in tidal range during a lunar month (29.5 days). Therefore a lunar month is also called a **tidal month**.

When the earth, moon, and sun are in a straight line, they exert maximum gravitational pull on the surface of the ocean. See Fig. 7–6. This is when the moon is a **new moon** or a **full moon**. Extra-high and extra-low tides occur at this time. They are called **spring tides** because they spring or jump up.

When the sun and moon are at a right angle (90°) to each other, the moon is in its **first quarter** or its **third quarter**. In this position the two tend to neutralize each other's tidal pull, and we get a reduced tide called a **neap tide**. See Fig. 7–7. There are two spring tides and two neap tides in a tidal month.

In Figs. 7–6 and 7–7 the ideal tide curves caused by the sun and the moon are shown as if they occur independently of each other. However, as you may remember from your study of waves, when two waves meet, they combine to form a single wave bigger than either of the two alone. This is also true of tide waves.

ACTIVITY 2

Graph the combined effect of tidal changes caused by the sun and the moon during a spring tide and during a neap tide.

PROCEDURE

1. Construct a tide graph showing the combined effect of the sun and the moon when they are in line with the earth.
   a. Determine the tide height at 12 midnight caused by the moon and by the sun. Use (B) in Fig. 7–6.
   b. Add the two tide heights together.
   c. Plot the combined tide height in (C) in Fig. 7–6.
   d. Repeat steps (a) to (c) for each hour during a full day (24 hours).
   e. Connect the data points to produce the tidal curve for this day.

2. Construct a tide graph showing the combined effects of the sun and the moon when they are at right angles to the earth. Repeat the steps in Procedure 1 but use the information given in the graphs in (B) in Fig. 7–7.

3. The drawing in (A) in Fig. 7–6 shows the tide at full moon. Make a similar drawing of the tide at new moon. What would such a tide look like?

4. The drawing in (A) in Fig. 7–7 shows the tide at the first quarter of the moon. Make a drawing of the tide when the moon is in its third quarter. What would such a tide look like?

QUESTIONS

13. Which of your graphs shows spring tides? Which shows neap tides?

14. Approximately how many days does the moon take to move from its position shown in (A) in Fig. 7–6 to its position shown in (A) in Fig. 7–7? Explain your reasoning.

15. Assume that the tide graph you drew in Procedure 1 occurred on March 1. On what date would the tides plotted in Procedure 2 occur? In Procedure 3? In Procedure 4?

16. Look at the combined tide curves in Fig. 7–6 and Fig. 7–7. At what time are the low tides?

17. Note that in Fig. 7–6 the high tides caused by the sun and the moon both occur at 12 midnight, but that in Fig. 7–7 the high tide caused by the moon occurs at 6 a.m. Explain why this is so.

18. Using the tide graphs you produced, how could you predict what the tides would be on any given day of the month? Try it by making a 1-month tide graph.

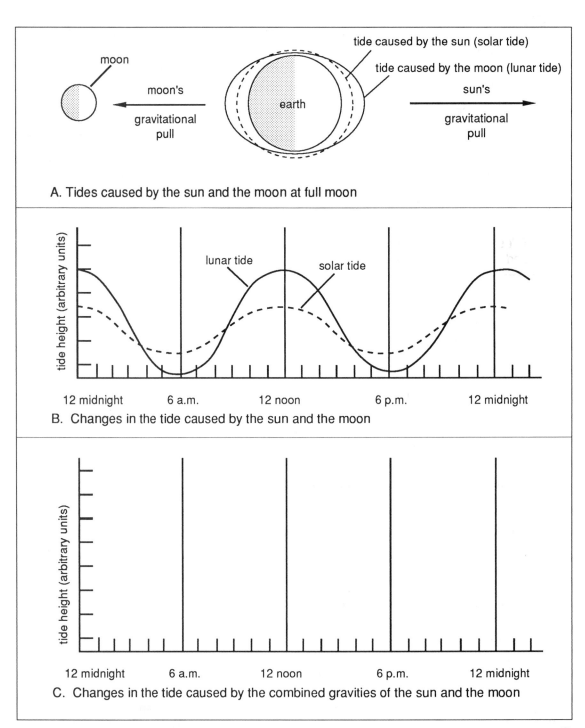

Fig. 7–6. Changes in tide levels when the sun and moon are in line with the earth

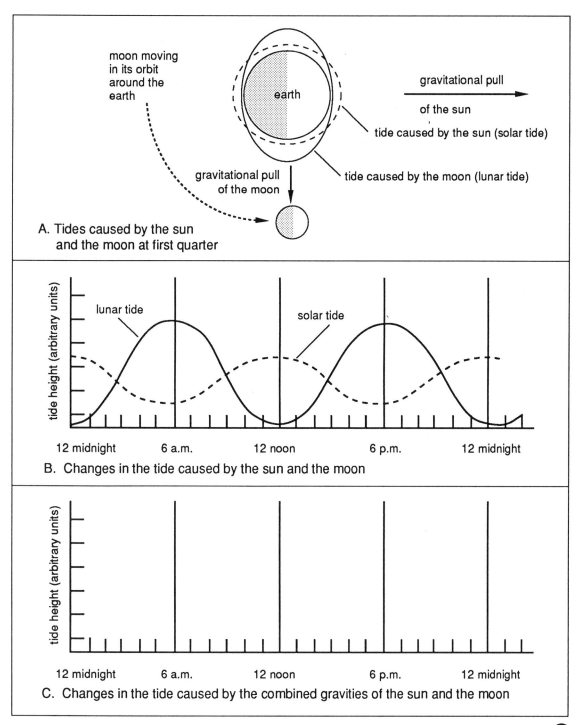

A. Tides caused by the sun and the moon at first quarter

B. Changes in the tide caused by the sun and the moon

C. Changes in the tide caused by the combined gravities of the sun and the moon

Fig. 7–7. Changes in tide levels when the sun and moon are at right angles to the earth

121

Angle of the Orbit of the Moon

The moon in its orbital path around the earth does not travel around the equator. Its orbit is tilted to about 28.5° from the equator. See Fig. 7–8. Thus during a lunar month the moon is north of the equator half the time and south of the equator half the time. On only two days in the lunar month is it directly above the equator. The moon's angular distance north or south of the equator is called its **declination**.

When the moon is north of the equator, the tidal bulge is also north of the equator. See (A) in Fig. 7–9. The location of this bulge causes daily changes in the tide. Imagine a person standing on a shoreline at 45° north of the equator. (Note that the view in Fig. 7–9 is from the equator, not from the north pole as in Fig. 7–5.) Twelve hours later the person will see a smaller high tide. The tidal curve would follow the pattern in (B) in Fig. 7–9.

To complicate things even further, the declination of the moon gradually changes over a period of 18.6 years from 28.5° to 18.5°, then back to 28.5°.

QUESTIONS

19. Refer to Fig. 7–9. What does the tide curve look like to a person standing at the equator? At 45° south latitude? Sketch these tide curves in (B) in Fig. 7–9.

20. Refer to Fig. 7–8. Note that as the moon moves in its orbit, it eventually (about 7 days later) arrives at a point directly over the equator. What would the tide curve look like at this time at 45° north latitude? At the equator? At 45° south latitude?

Ellipitical Orbits

The moon does not orbit the earth in a perfect circle. Instead, it follows an **ellipitical orbit**, coming closer to the earth and moving farther away. See Fig. 7–10. Its point nearest the earth is called **perigee**; its farthest point is its **apogee**. This is repeated every 27.5 days. (Note that this period is different from the lunar month, which is 29.5 days.) During perigee the moon's gravitational pull is greatest and the lunar tidal range is largest; during apogee its gravitational pull is least and the lunar tidal range is smallest.

The earth also follows an elliptical orbit around the sun. The earth is closest to the sun during the northern hemisphere winter months. This point is called **perihelion**. The gravity of the sun is greater, so the solar tides increase. During the northern hemisphere summer the earth is farthest away from the sun (**aphelion**), and the tidal range is less. The complete cycle occurs about every 365.25 days (a **solar year**).

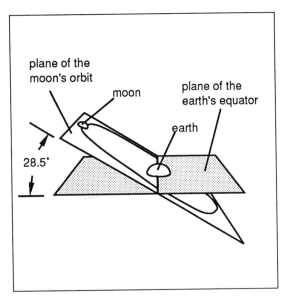

Fig. 7–8. Declination of the moon

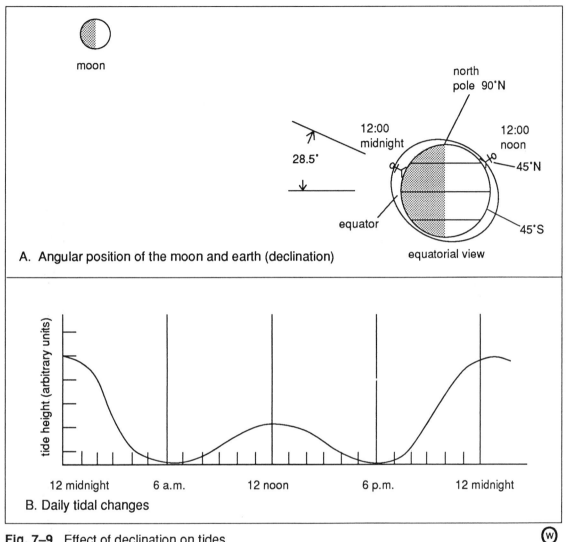

A. Angular position of the moon and earth (declination)

B. Daily tidal changes

Fig. 7–9. Effect of declination on tides

Cyclical Changes

Perigee, apogee, declination of the moon, perihelion, and aphelion are all cyclical changes in the relative position of the moon and sun with respect to the earth. These cycles differ from each other in length of time. The tide is therefore constantly changing. Only rarely do all these cycles coincide to cause exceptionally high and low tides. Maximum tidal range is produced when

- the earth is at perihelion,
- the moon is at perigee,
- the moon is either new or full, and
- both the sun and the moon have the same declination (directly over the equator).

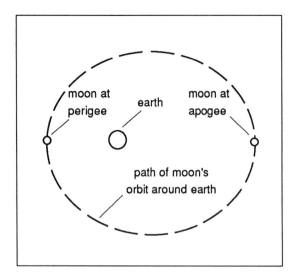

Fig. 7–10. Elliptical orbit of the moon around the earth

It has been calculated that this maximum range occurs only once every 1600 years. The last time was in A.D. 1700.

QUESTIONS

21. Under what conditions are the tides the lowest? Why?

22. How does the declination of the moon affect the tides at different locations during a lunar month?

23. How do the elliptical orbits of the sun and moon affect the tides?

24. How often do you expect new moon and perigee of the moon to occur on the same day? Explain your reasoning.

25. Which has the greater effect on tides during a single month, the elliptical orbit of the earth around the sun or the elliptical orbit of the moon around the earth? Why?

26. In what year will all cycles affecting the tides coincide again to cause maximum high and low tides?

Coastal Tides

Tides along coastlines vary greatly. We have already seen that tides are influenced by the interactions among the earth, the moon, and the sun. Another factor that influences the tides is the shape of seafloor features.

We learned in Unit 2, Topic 5, that as a wave approaches shore, it slows and changes shape, depending on the contours of the ocean floor near the shoreline. This is also true of the tide wave.

Tidal ranges vary considerably along different points of a coastline. In some places tides are exceptionally high. For example, in the Bay of Fundy in Nova Scotia, the tidal range may be 15 m (almost 50 ft), higher than the roof of a three-story house! Just imagine how important it is for people living there to know the tides if they want to fish from shore, go tidepooling, or go boating in coastal waters. By contrast, on many midocean islands the tidal range may be measured in centimeters.

Types of Tides

Tides occur in characteristic patterns along the coastlines of different regions of the earth. They may be classified into three common types.

The tide graph in (A) in Fig. 7–11 shows a **semidiurnal** tidal cycle. This type of tide is characterized by two high tides daily of about equal heights occurring about 12 hr

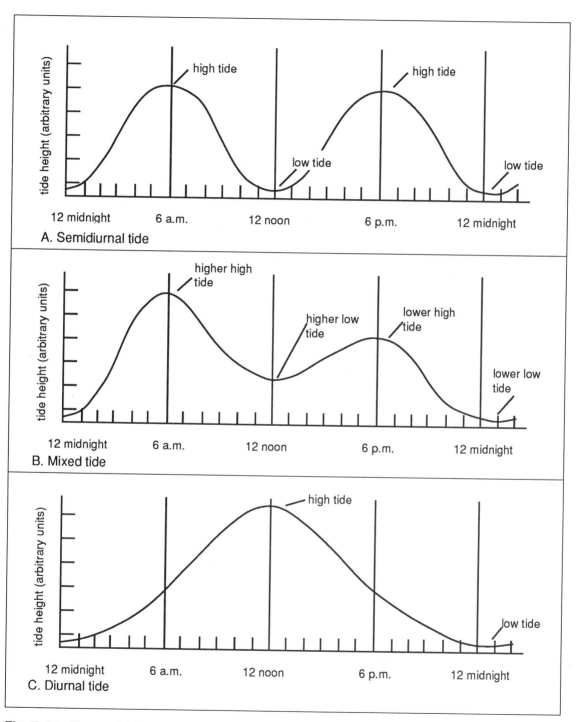

Fig. 7–11. Types of tides

125

and 25 min apart. The east coast of the United States usually experiences semidiurnal tides. See Fig. 7–12.

The tide graph in (B) in Fig. 7–11 shows a **mixed** tidal cycle in which the tides also occur twice daily, but the two high tides and two low tides are unequal in height. The inequality is due to the changing declination of the moon. Mixed tides occur on the West Coast of the continental United States as shown in Fig. 7–12, and in Alaska and Hawaii.

The tide graph in (C) in Fig. 7–11 shows a **diurnal** tidal cycle where one high tide occurs every 24 hr and 50 min. Diurnal tides typically occur in partially enclosed basins such as the Gulf of Mexico. See Fig. 7–12.

Many places in the world may have a variety of tides throughout the tidal month. For instance, the tide may be a typical semidiurnal type for a few days, gradually change to a mixed tide, and finally show signs of being a diurnal tide for a few days. See Fig. 7–13.

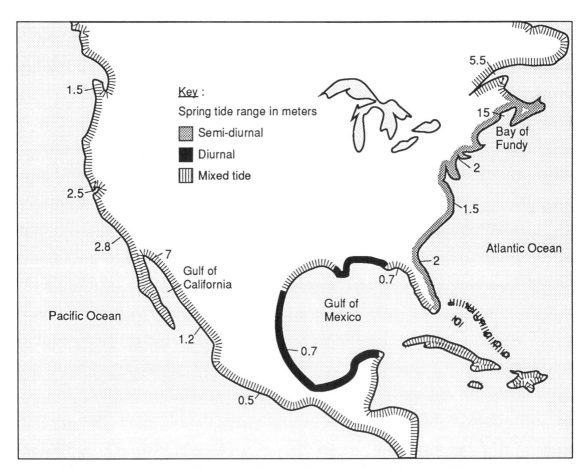

Fig. 7–12. Map of the United States showing locations of different types of tides

ACTIVITY 3
Compare tide records in two parts of the world.

PROCEDURE
1. Refer to Table 7–2. Identify the days when the declination of the moon is farthest north (28.8°N). Write the symbol (N) for this event on the two tide records under these two dates as shown in Fig. 7–13.

2. Transfer the remaining information on events affecting the tides from Table 7–2 onto the tide graphs in Fig. 7–13.

Table 7–2. Events affecting the tides   ⓦ

Event	Date of occurrence	Symbol
Declination of moon		
28.5° N	1, 28	N
0° (equator)	8, 22	Eq
28.5° S	16	S
Phase of moon		
new	8	●
1st quarter	16	◐
full	23	○
3rd quarter	29	◑
Orbit of moon		
apogee	9	A
perigee	23	P
Position of sun		
autumnal equinox	23	AE
(sun over equator)		

QUESTIONS
27. What type of tide occurred most commonly during September in New York? In Honolulu?

28. On a few days other types of tides occurred in both cities. What types were they? On what days did they occur?

29. What was the maximum tidal range during the month in each city? Give a possible explanation of why one was much greater than the other.

30. On what days did minus tides occur in each city?

31. When did spring tides occur? What event caused these tides?

32. When did neap tides occur? What event caused these tides?

33. What events occurred on September 22–23? How did they affect the tide?

Nearshore Tidal Currents
Tidal currents are produced by the general rising and falling of the sea's surface caused by the tides. As the tides change, large quantities of water move toward or away from shore. During a flood tide the tidal current flows toward shore. See Fig. 7–14. The greatest tidal current occurs midway during flood tide or ebb tide. At high and low tide the current ceases. Then, during ebb tide, the tidal current changes direction and increases again, flowing away from shore. Tidal currents can be very strong at the mouths of rivers and in the narrow inlets of bays and harbors. For example, all the water moving into and out of

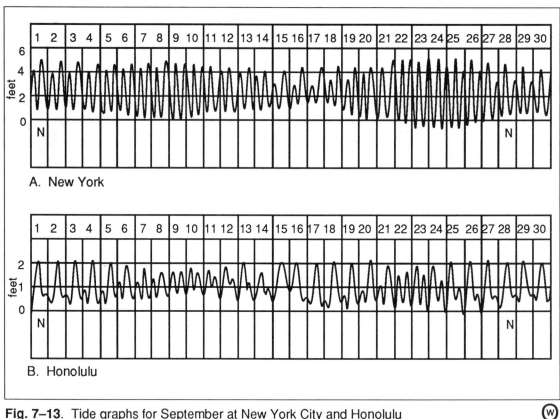

Fig. 7–13. Tide graphs for September at New York City and Honolulu

San Francisco Bay must pass through the inlet to the bay under the Golden Gate Bridge.

In places where an incoming high tide enters a harbor or river, the higher water level forms a wave called a **tidal bore**. To an observer on the bank, an approaching tidal bore looks like a turbulent wave of water that suddenly raises the water level.

Tidal currents are usually the strongest currents in a coastal region. Experienced coastal sailors know that they must be prepared for both tides and tidal currents when navigating sailboats and other craft into and out of coastal inlets. They must make sure the hulls of their crafts do not run aground

during low tide and that they have enough power to advance against these strong tidal currents.

QUESTIONS

34. Because tidal currents are related to the rise and fall of the tide, how many times each day does a tidal current change direction in coastal waters
    a. near Honolulu?
    b. near New York City?

35. During a mixed tide when do tidal currents occur? See (B) in Fig. 7–11. In what direction? Are all these currents equally strong? Why?

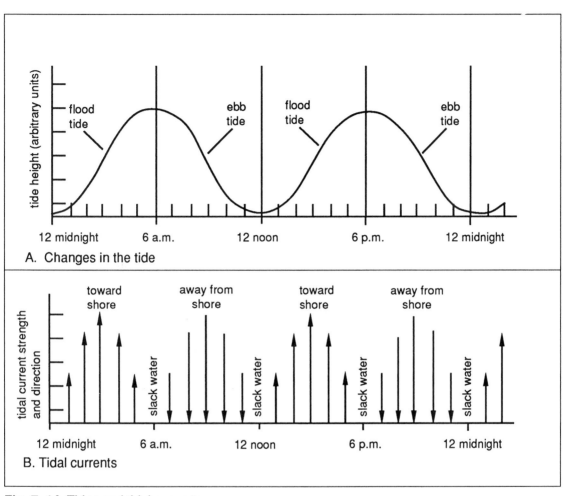

Fig. 7–14. Tides and tidal currents

36. When and in what direction do tidal currents occur during a diurnal tide? See (C) in Fig. 7–11.

37. If you were about to enter a harbor where the tides were similar to those in New York City, during which part of the tidal cycle would you choose to begin your entry? During which times would you not enter?

FURTHER INVESTIGATIONS

1. Practice estimating the ebb and flood of tides and their heights. Here are some suggestions:

a. On walls, piles, and piers, look for barnacles and oysters, which are usually covered only at high tide. The line of the highest oysters is a fair estimate of the high-tide level. Attached green algae are exposed only during low

129

tides; they often appear bleached white as a result of exposure during very low tides.

b. On rocks and rocky outcroppings, make the same type of observations as for vertical walls. Notice especially the horizontal zonation of the mollusks (seashells), which is determined by their preference for being wet by seawater. Littorines prefer not to get wet, so they are found above the high tide water level in the splash zone. Nerites are usually covered by water during high tides, and limpets are exposed only during the very lowest tides.

c. On sandy beaches, look for algae or the flotsam and jetsam left behind by waves that broke on shore during receding high tides. These mark the highest level reached by waves during a high tide. Look carefully for the wet sand level made by very recent waves.

2. Report on one or more of the following topics. If possible, make diagrams or find pictures to illustrate your topic. Here are some suggestions:
   a. how tides are measured with tide gauges

b. how loading docks, boat ramps, and bridges on navigable waters must be modified to allow for tidal changes

c. special cradles for holding sailboats and other craft during low tides

d. regions where the highest tides in the world occur

e. proposals that have been made for harnessing the energy from tides to produce electricity

3. Obtain a tide table for your area or for a region that you might visit on a vacation. What information other than tide levels is given in the tide tables? Using the tide table, make a tide graph for a 1-month period.

4. Obtain a nautical chart for the areas included in the tide table.
   a. Assuming that you have a sailboat with a 6-ft draft, which sections shown on the nautical chart could you sail in during high tide but not during low tide?
   b. What would be the probable direction of tidal currents during a flood tide? An ebb tide?

8. Destructive Waves

Ocean waves carry huge amounts of energy. The energy of a wave is its capacity to do work such as moving objects. Waves do work when they cut the faces of sea cliffs, build and carry away beaches, and grind great boulders into pebbles.

In this topic we will first look at how physical oceanographers describe and measure energy in waves. We will then consider wave energy in surf and storm waves, in hurricane waves, and in tsunamis (sometimes mistakenly called tidal waves).

Wave Energy

Many forms of energy are carried as waves: heat, electricity, light, sound, and water. All forms of energy can be transformed into work. Ocean waves break rock, carry sand away, and produce heat and sound when they slam into the shore. Furthermore, the energy in waves can be used to drive generators to produce electricity, which then can be transformed into light or power.

We can measure the amount of energy in joules (J) of work, kilocalories (kc) of heat, or kilowatt hours (kwh) of electricity, and each can be equated with the others. For our purposes we will use the joule (J). A **joule** is the amount of energy needed to lift about 1 kg of matter 1 m at sea level. The same amount of energy is produced if the matter falls back to the point from which it started.

The amount of energy in a wave depends on its height. The higher a wave, the more energy it releases when it falls back to sea level. A wave that is double the height of another wave has four times the energy per square meter of water surface. In other words, energy per square meter is proportional to the square of the height.

For comparative purposes, we can describe wave energy in terms of energy in a gallon of gasoline. One gallon of gasoline produces about 160 million J (1.6×10^8 J) of energy. This is equal to 44 kilowatt hours (kwh) of energy, the energy consumed by an average American home each day. That same 1.6×10^8 J is equal to the energy of a 2-m wave with a surface area of about 32,000 m^2 (a wave with a height of 2 m and a wavelength of 14 m breaking along 2 km of coastline). See Fig 8–1.

QUESTIONS

1. Explain what is meant by energy, work, and energy transformation.

2. What are some forms of energy?

3. How can wave energy be transformed into electricity?

4. What is a joule?

Storm Waves and High Surf

Each year periodic high surf pounds our shorelines, eroding and destroying property worth millions of dollars. High surf waves are generated by oceanic storms. Moving in trains, storm swells can travel thousands of miles across open ocean.

Storm waves begin as confused seas

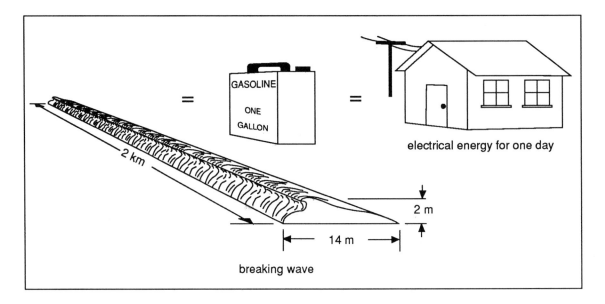

Fig. 8–1. Energy comparison

near a storm site but become swells as they move away from the storm center. As they travel, their wavelengths increase. Thus the closer a storm is to land, the shorter the wavelength of the resulting high waves that reach nearby coasts.

We saw in the previous topics that deep-water waves change into breaking shallow-water waves as they approach shore. The higher the wave, the more energy is spent when it breaks. Higher waves also thrust greater volumes of water on shore. High surf during high tide can be particularly destructive, causing localized shoreline flooding and damaging of shore-front property. If high surf is caused by localized storms, heavy rains may flood low-lying coastal areas.

In the United States few lives are lost to high surf because shoreline residents are given ample warning from the National Weather Service and civil defense agencies.

Hurricane Storm Surges

Hurricanes (called **typhoons** in the western Pacific Ocean and **tropical cyclones** over most of the South Pacific and the Indian Ocean) are storms with winds exceeding 64 knots. Hurricanes grow from tropical storms that develop in the oceans near the equator, typically from 5° to 20° north or south latitude.

Hurricanes form when heat energy stored in the surface water of equatorial oceans heats the air above it. The heated air rises, causing a low-pressure center to form. Winds blow inward over the ocean, heating, then rising and flowing outward at upper levels, creating the cloud formation shown in the cross-section in Fig. 8–2. In the center, cool air moves downward, forming the eye of the hurricane. In the northern hemisphere, winds flow in a counterclockwise direction; in the southern hemisphere, they flow in a clockwise direction.

As the storm grows, wind speeds in-

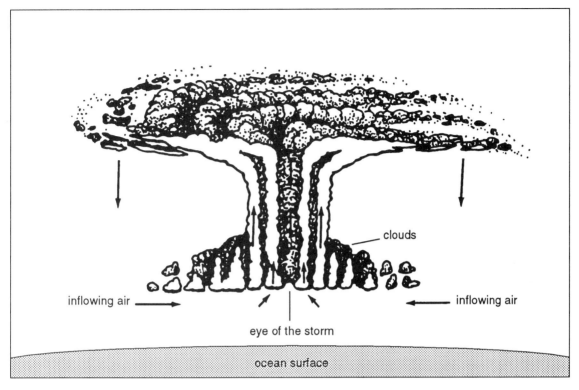

Fig. 8–2. Profile of a hurricane

crease to hurricane-force intensity. In a hurricane, winds of more than 120 km/hr blow over fetches greater than 300 km. Hurricane winds may persist for days as the storm moves to higher latitudes. Waves generated at sea grow to 15 m or more. These move out in wave sets, eventually crossing the ocean as deep-water swells.

A mature hurricane is characterized by very low atmospheric pressure. The water level of the ocean rises, pushed toward the low-pressure center by the high-pressure areas surrounding it. This extra-high water, called a **storm surge**, can cause extensive flooding when a hurricane crosses a coastline, particularly if it moves inland during a high tide. Hurricane-generated breaking waves pile even more water ashore, adding to the coastal destruction from the winds.

Each year hurricanes damage much property and take many lives because of their destructive waves and related shoreline flooding. In May 1985, for example, more than 5,000 people were drowned by hurricane waves and flooding in the flat deltas of Bangladesh bordering the Bay of Bengal. Worldwide, about 40 hurricanes occur each year, causing destruction wherever they move toward land. With the aid of modern weather forecasting, however, coastal residents in the United States usually have sufficient warning to take steps to minimize property damage and to move to safety.

QUESTIONS

5. Refer to Table 4–1. How high are the open-ocean waves formed by storms? By hurricanes?

6. What is a storm surge?

7. If a high surf warning is given, what precautions should coastal residents take?

8. If warnings are issued about an approaching hurricane,
   a. what precautions should coastal residents take?
   b. what precautions should boaters take?

Tsunamis

Tsunamis (pronounced "soo-nah'-meez") are sets of great sea waves produced by the sudden displacement of a large volume of water in the ocean. Tsunamis formed by earthquakes and massive landslides are also called **seismic sea waves**. Less frequently, a violent volcanic eruption (like the 1883 eruption of Krakatoa, in Indonesia) can set tsunamis in motion. See Fig. 8–3. The term *tsunami* is borrowed from Japanese and translates as "harbor wave."

The term "tidal wave," although popular, is misleading because tsunamis are not formed by the gravitational pull of the moon as true tides are. They may have been misnamed "tidal waves" because the troughs of these great waves cause coastal waters to recede between waves.

With a tsunami wave, the water level changes suddenly in 10 to 15 min. In a true tide, the water level changes gradually over 6-hr and 12-hr periods. Other important differences are that the water in

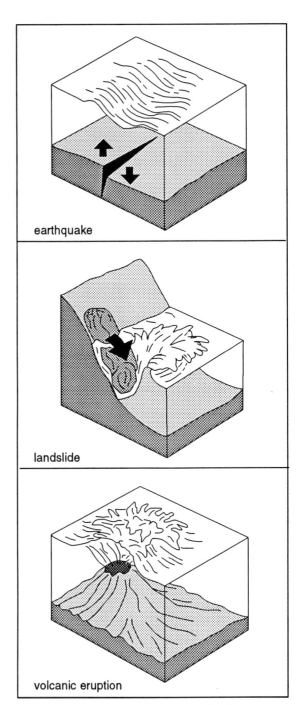

earthquake

landslide

volcanic eruption

Fig. 8–3. Causes of large water displacements in the ocean (Source: Adapted from W. Bascom, *Waves and Beaches*, 1964.)

tsunamis travels much faster than tides, and the incoming waves can become huge.

Tsunamis form wave sets that radiate from their point of origin. The waves are most destructive near their source. As they travel across the open ocean, tsunamis are usually no more than about 30 cm high, with wavelengths ranging from 120 to 720 km (75 to 450 mi). Ships cannot detect tsunamis passing beneath them. Because of their wavelength, the energy of tsunami waves extends thousands of feet down to the abyssal plain, the bottom floor of the ocean basins. Tsunamis may therefore be classified as shallow-water waves (D < 1/20 L).

When a tsunami approaches shore, it slows and grows in height. Like other waves, a tsunami striking shore has a height and shape determined by its direction and the shape of the bottom. As water in contact with the bottom slows, faster-moving water behind piles over the top, creating a wall of water. A tsunami trough, which may precede the first tsunami crest, looks like a very rapidly receding tide.

When tsunamis strike shore, they can form catastrophic breaking waves. In 1960, for example, tsunamis generated by an earthquake in Chile killed 4,000 people. In Laupahoehoe, Hawaii, one of these waves destroyed several classrooms in a school building on top of a 10-m cliff, killing 46 students and teachers. Geologists also have evidence of a monstrous 300-m tsunami that struck coastal areas thousands of years ago. They hypothesize that it was generated by a massive landslide.

Tsunami Warning System

Warnings of approaching tsunamis are given through the National Weather Service. The Pacific Tsunami Warning Center now monitors instruments around the clock for first signs of potential tsunami-generating earthquakes. When such an earthquake occurs, a **tsunami watch** is issued to all stations in the Pacific, telling where the earthquake occurred and warning of the possibility of tsunamis. The estimated time of arrival of the tsunamis is calculated and included in the message.

Because tsunami speed is determined by water depth, arrival times for tsunamis from distant locations can be calculated. Since the average depth of the ocean is 5 km and the maximum speed of tsunamis is about 720 km/hr (450 mph), the tsunami wave energy touches bottom. The tsunami wave set is slowed by friction.

Fig. 8–4 shows the reporting stations of the Pacific Tsunami Warning System and estimated tsunami travel time to Honolulu. For example, a tsunami generated by an earthquake near Crescent City, California, takes 5 hr to reach Honolulu. Even though they can predict the arrival time of a tsunami, oceanographers cannot yet predict the height of the waves that will strike shore. Furthermore, the height of a tsunami may vary considerably along a coastline. Some of the highest waves occur when the wave enters a funnel-shaped bay or strikes a cliff or headland. Typically, there are six to eight waves in a tsunami wave set.

Once there is evidence that a tsunami may have formed, a **tsunami warning** is issued. Agencies such as the Civil Defense Division alert the public. Coastal residents are evacuated and other emergency actions are taken. In Hawaii, residents are alerted by a steady 1-min blast of a siren.

Information broadcast over radio stations advises which coastal areas can expect incoming tsunamis and what action to take. Generally, danger areas for tsunamis of distant origin are those less than 15 m above sea level and within 1 km of the coast. For tsunamis of local origin, danger areas are those less than 30 m above sea level and within 1 km of the coast.

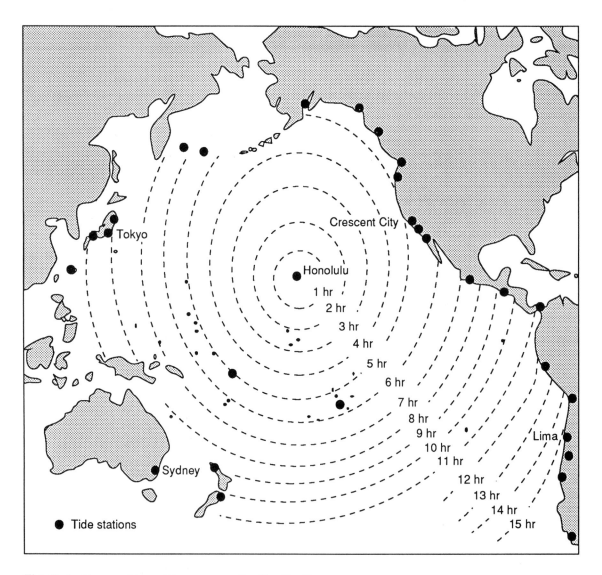

Fig. 8–4. Tsunami travel time across the Pacific Ocean

QUESTIONS

9. Do all earthquakes cause tsunamis?

10. Is a tsunami a single wave?

11. How might a tsunami wave be small at one beach but huge at another beach just a few miles away?

12. How many hours does it take for tsunami waves generated in the Aleutians to reach Hawaii?

13. Ocean trenches may be as deep as 11 km. Does a tsunami wave touch the bottom of a trench?

ACTIVITY

Simulate tsunamis and observe their properties.

MATERIALS

• plastic dishpan
• sand
• 2 sheets of construction paper
• transparent ripple tank
• overhead projector or lamp
• masking tape
• sponges
• large sheet of paper
• pencil
• map of Pacific Ocean (optional)

PROCEDURE

1. Using a plastic dishpan or other flexible container half-filled with water, find as many ways as you can to simulate tsunamis.

    a. Confirm that the waves you produce are shallow-water waves by placing sand grains at the bottom of the container and noting whether they move.

    b. Observe and sketch the waves. Make watermarked pictures.

2. Observe tsunami-like wave behavior in a transparent ripple tank with an overhead projector. See Fig. 8–5.
   CAUTION: Be sure that the projector plug is properly grounded and that the ripple tank does not leak or spill.

    a. Place a transparent ripple tank on an overhead projector. Be sure the tank is level. Line the inside edges of the tank with a porous dampening material such as sponges. Fill about one-third full with water. Or, if you do not have an overhead projector, put the transparent ripple tank between two tables. Shine a light down onto the water surface and place a large piece of white paper on the floor to view the shadows of the waves.

Fig. 8–5. Transparent ripple tank and overhead projector

b. Tape a large sheet of paper to the wall. Focus the overhead lens to project an image of waves on the paper.

c. Create small point-source waves by tapping the surface of the water once per second with your finger near one edge of the tank.

d. Note the pattern of the wave(s) produced. Draw the image of the wave pattern on the white paper.

e. Draw a series of small arrows perpendicular to the wave crest to represent the direction of energy movement at that point on the wave crest.

3. Simulate the movement of tsunami-like waves across the Pacific Ocean.
a. Generate tsunami-like waves.
b. Focus the image of these waves on a map of the Pacific Ocean basin. Compare the image with Fig. 8–4.

QUESTIONS

14. Describe the appearance and movement of simulated tsunamis using terms like **radiating** or **parallel waves**. Refer to Table 6–2 as needed.

15. How many waves are formed from a sudden simulated earthquake or landslide? What does the wave train look like?

16. As a wave crest moves from its point of origin outward, what happens to the energy within the wave? How does this alter the shape of the wave?

17. Where would a tsunami probably cause more damage, 100 km from the epicenter of an earthquake or 1,000 km away? Why do you think so?

18. Under what conditions might water displacement form not only a tsunami but also a destructive seiche?

FURTHER INVESTIGATIONS

1. Consult references to find reports of ocean engineering research on harnessing the energy in waves to produce electricity.

2. Consult references and report on how tsunamis caused by earthquakes are related to plate tectonics, the movement of enormous crustal plates that form the solid surface of our planet.

3. Use references to find out about tsunamis caused by earthquakes. (One notable example was the eruption and collapse of Krakatoa in 1883.)

4. Compare tsunamis and tides. Tides are the longest waves in the ocean. What makes tsunami waves more destructive?

5. Make a report describing major hurricanes and the destruction they cause on coasts.

6. Learn about careers in weather forecasting. Find out what roles are played by meteorologists, oceanographers, satellite experts, civil defense workers, and people in the news media.

9. Sand

Sand is a common substance, but few people take time to look at it. In this topic we will learn how sand is classified by particle size. We will also find out what sand is made of and how it differs from place to place.

Scientists who specialize in the study of sand are called **arenologists**. (You are probably familiar with a similar word, **arena**. Long ago in Greece sports arenas were covered with sand.) Sand is of interest to geologists and oceanographers who seek to learn more about the earth and its ocean basins.

What comes to mind when you think of sand? Close your eyes and imagine a beach. What does it look like? The chances are that you've imagined a sandy beach, probably white or light in color. However, once you actually start looking at beaches, you'll quickly see that they are made of particles of many sizes and colors.

Classification by Size

The Wentworth scale shown in Table 9–1 is one system used to classify sediments by particle size. Notice that the term **sand** is used for particles between 0.25 mm and 2 mm in diameter. Smaller particles are classified as **mud**, larger particles as **gravel**. Although granules are too large to be classified as sand, they are included in our study because they are common in sandy beaches. **Sediment** is a general term for all particles, including boulders, gravel, sand, and mud.

Table 9–1 also shows that the size of sediment particles is related to the slope of a beach. As a general rule, the steeper the beach, the larger the particle size.

Table 9–1. Wentworth grain-size scale

Class	Subclass	Diameter (mm)	Average beach slope
Boulder		256 or more	>25°
Gravel	Cobble	65–256	19°–25°
	Pebble	4–64	13°–19°
	Granule	2–4	11°
Sand	Very coarse sand	1–2	9°
	Coarse sand	0.5–1	7°
	Medium sand	0.25–0.5	5°
Mud	Fine sand	0.07–0.25	5°
	Silt	0.003–0.07	0°
	Clay	0.003 or less	0°

Particles can be separated into size groups by shaking them through a set of sieves. **Sieves** are containers with mesh bottoms. Graduated geology sieves usually stack, the one having the largest mesh openings on top and the one having the smallest mesh openings on the bottom.

Shape and Particle History

Shapes of particles are important too because they reveal information about their history. Rough, irregular particles are younger than rounded, smooth ones. Pure, distinctly shaped crystals are rarely found. Rough or sharp-edged particles become rounded and polished through **weathering**, changes caused by waves, wind, and rain. When wind or waves move particles, the particles rub against each other, wearing down rough edges and smoothing surfaces. Water from waves or rain also acts to change particles by dissolving out soluble ions. Mature, rounded sand particles are

more worn and smaller, containing fewer types of chemicals than less mature, angular particles do. Fig. 9–1 provides a visual classification of particles by shape.

ACTIVITY 1
Analyze the composition of beach sediments by size and shape.

MATERIALS
- sample of beach particles for each team
- set of graduated geology sieves
- balance
- six 10 X 10-cm weighing papers
- white glue
- hand lens or dissecting microscope
- 6 vials

PROCEDURE
1. Prepare a 100-g sand sample as follows:
   a. Obtain a sample of beach particles. Rinse particles with fresh water to re-

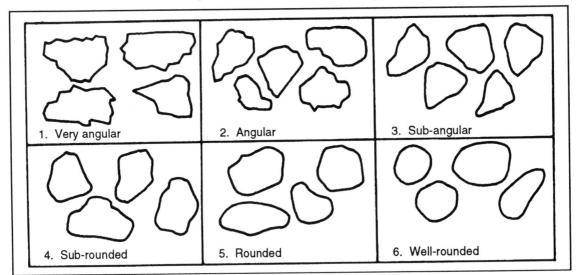

Fig. 9–1. Magnified sand particles showing classification of sand by shape (Source: Redrawn from F. P. Shepard and R. Young, "Distinguish Between Beach and Dune Sand," *Jou. Sed. Petrology*, 1961.)

1. Very angular
2. Angular
3. Sub-angular
4. Sub-rounded
5. Rounded
6. Well-rounded

move salt and mud. Dry thoroughly.

b. Remove the gravel, which includes the **cobbles**, **pebbles**, and **granules**. Either pick out the gravel-size particles or remove them by shaking the sample through the sieve with the largest mesh. The particles that fall through the sieve are sand particles.

c. Weigh out a 100-g sample of sand.

2. Sift the sand particles into very coarse sand, coarse sand, medium sand, and fine sand. See (A) in Fig. 9–2.

a. Stack the sieves by mesh size, with the coarsest one on top and the finest on the bottom. Put a container or a sheet of paper under the bottom sieve.

b. Shake the entire 100-g sample through the stacked sieves.

3. Determine the percentage composition of sand sorted by particle size. See (B) and (C) in Fig. 9–2.

a. For each sieve, use a square sheet of weighing paper about 10 X 10 cm. Label each sheet of paper with the sieve number. (Let the sieve with the largest mesh size be sieve 1.)

b. Empty the contents of each sieve onto a sheets of preweighed paper.

c. Weigh each sample and record its mass in Table 9–2.

d. Determine the percentage composition of the entire sand sample sorted by size. (Recall that the original sample was 100 g. Therefore 1 g = 1% of the total sample by mass.)

4. Make a bar graph showing the percentage composition of sand sorted by sizes. Glue samples of each particle size onto Fig. 9–3 in your workbook.

5. Using a hand lens or 10X dissecting microscope, examine the shapes of the par-

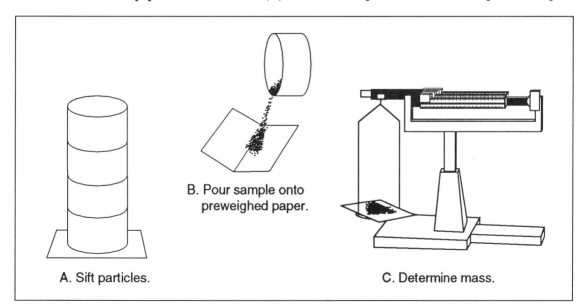

A. Sift particles.

B. Pour sample onto preweighed paper.

C. Determine mass.

Fig. 9–2. Sifting and weighing sand particles

Table 9–2. Composition of sand sorted by size

	Fine sand	Medium sand	Coarse sand	Very coarse sand	Gravel, granules, & pebbles	Total
Mass (g)						100 g
Percent composition						100 %
Shape						

100 g sand sample from _____ (name of beach)

Location _____ Date _____ 19____

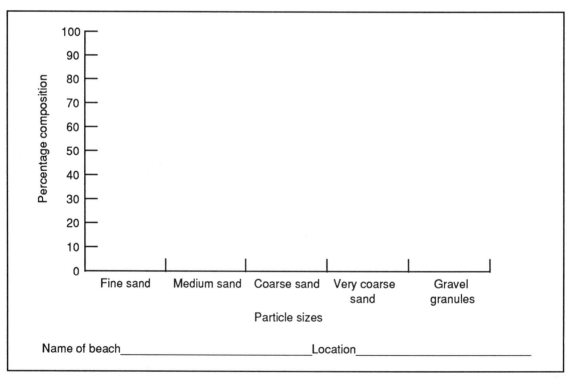

Fig. 9–3. Bar graph showing percentage composition of sand sorted by particle size

142

the shapes you find, using the terms from Fig. 9–1. Record data in Table 9–2.

6. Save the remainder of your samples for Activity 2. Gently tap each sieved sample into a vial. Label vials "sieved sand from (name of beach)" and record the sieve size.

QUESTIONS

1. Describe each of the sand samples you analyzed by particle size. Use the bar graph to show your findings.

2. How does particle size relate to the slope of a beach?

3. Compare sand samples analyzed in class. From this evidence, predict which beach has the steepest slope. Which beach is the flattest?

Components of Sand

By identifying the components of sand, we can tell what sand is made of and where it probably came from. Sands can be classified by their source into two types. The first type, called **abiogenic sand**, is made of eroded pieces of rocks. The second type, called **biogenic sand**, is made of the skeletal remains of plants and animals.

Abiogenic Sands

Abiogenic sands are inorganic mineral sands. Abiogenic sand particles are formed as rocks break down through weathering and erosion. **Weathering** is the slow breakdown of rocks caused by water, by chemicals in the air and from plants, and by temperature changes. **Erosion** refers to the work that water and wind do to level the land.

Abiogenic sands are formed from rocks in the continental crust or the oceanic crust of the earth. The continental crust includes most of the major dry continental landmasses of the world. Mountains in the continental crust are composed mostly of **granite**. Mineral sands formed by the breakdown of granite usually contain **quartz** and **feldspar.** Quartz and feldspar break down more slowly than **mica** or dark minerals like **magnetite**, which are also common in granite. Because they resist chemical and physical breakdown, quartz and feldspar are referred to as **resistant minerals**. The sands of most beaches along the coasts of the continental United States are called **quartz sands** because quartz is their most abundant resistant component. Where continental volcanoes form, **olivine** and **obsidian** (volcanic glass) may also be found. Fig. 9–4 shows some perfect crystal structures of components of abiogenic sand. Perfect crystals are rare in sand deposits. Over time these crystals are worn down, as was shown in Fig. 9–1.

The oceanic crust is another type of abiogenic sand. The oceanic crust is made up of volcanic material called **basalt**. Volcanic islands, lava from volcanic eruptions, and the bottom substrates of the ocean basins are all made of basalt. Basalt is denser than granite and darker (black, gray, or brown) because it is richer in minerals containing heavy metals such as iron and manganese. Basalt contains no quartz, but it does contain resistant minerals (olivine) and glassy basalt sands (obsidian). Smaller amounts of other less resistant inorganic minerals are also found in basalt sands. Components of abiogenic sand are listed in Table 9–3.

143

Table 9–3. Common components of abiogenic sand

Basalt. Black lava flows are basalt. As they erode, they may form dull black, gray, or brownish red grains of gravel and sand.

Feldspar. Feldspar is clear, yellow, or pink squarish crystals with smooth, glossy, or pearly luster.

Garnet. Garnets are usually amber or beer-bottle color, but some are light pink. Perfect crystals have 12 faces. (Perfect crystals are rare because the ocean waves round off the edges rapidly.) Garnet is often used in making sandpaper.

Granite. Grains are usually light-colored to pink, with a salt-and-pepper pattern of mineral crystals all about the same size.

Magnetic mineral grains. These may be grains of iron ore (magnetite) or other metals. **Magnetite** crystals resemble a double pyramid. These grains are dense and tend to accumulate at the botton of containers. They are attracted to a magnet.

Mica. Mica forms shiny, paper-thin, translucent flexible sheets. It is light-colored or white and may appear iridescent.

Olivine. Olivine is a shiny crystal that can be various shades of olive-green to almost brown. It may be transparent or translucent and often contains specks of other crystals. It is found in basalt.

Quartz. Quartz grains are clear or transparent, resembling small pieces of broken glass. Quartz comes from granite and sandstone erosion. It is the most abundant mineral found in continental sand.

Volcanic glass. Hot, black lava forms black, shiny, irregular but sharp-edged particles when rapidly cooled; continental volcanoes form obsidian.

Other. "Beach glass" is formed when broken shards of manufactured glass are rounded and frosted by wave action. Other manmade substances (especially plastics) may also be found on the beach.

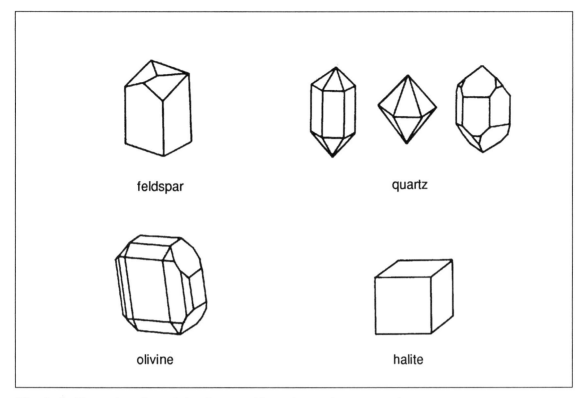

feldspar

quartz

olivine

halite

Fig. 9–4. Examples of crystals of some abiogenic sand components

Biogenic Sands

The skeletal remains of plants and animals are a second source of sands. **Biogenic sands** are also called **organic sands** or **biological sands**. They are sometimes called **calcium sands** (or limey sands) because the chemical composition of most skeletal remains is calcium carbonate ($CaCO_3$), the material our bones are made of.

A simple chemical test for distinguishing calcium (biogenic) sands from inorganic (abiogenic) sands is to drop vinegar or other acid onto a pinch of sand particles. If the sand contains calcium carbonate, the particles react with the acid to form bubbles of carbon dioxide.

Most biogenic sands are composed of fragments of corals, coralline algae, and mollusks. Usually biogenic sands are described by their most abundant component—for example, coral sand or coralline algae sand. Some of the components are the skeletal remains of entire organisms, such as the micromollusks or the single-celled foraminifera. Biogenic sands also include other resistant biological fragments, such as sea urchin spines and sponge spicules. Fossil remains such as tiny teeth and parts of jawbones are sometimes found in beach samples. Some biogenic sand components are listed in Table 9–4 and shown in Fig. 9–5.

145

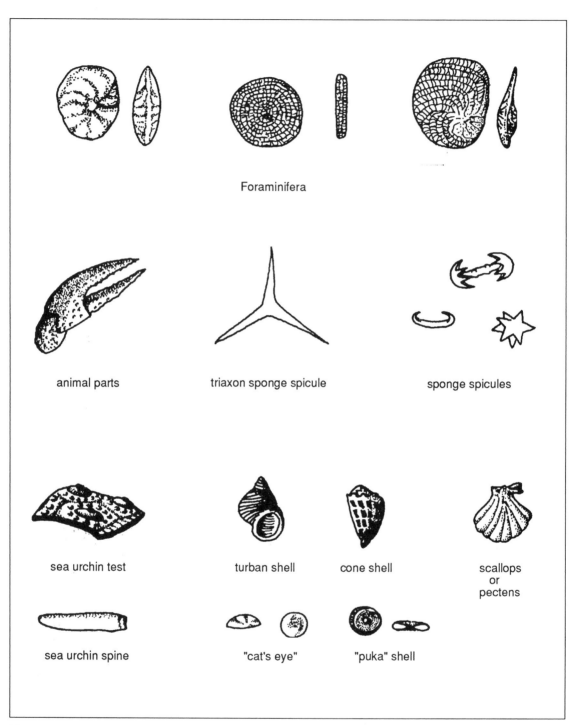

Foraminifera

animal parts   triaxon sponge spicule   sponge spicules

sea urchin test   turban shell   cone shell   scallops or pectens

sea urchin spine   "cat's eye"   "puka" shell

Fig. 9–5. Biogenic sand components

146

Table 9–4. Common components of biogenic sand

1. **Barnacle fragments.** Pieces of the calcareous plates that form the carapace (shell) of a barnacle, the only sessile group of crustaceans; may be white, yellow, pink, orange, lavender, or purple, occasionally with striped or notched pattern. (Earlier biologists mistakenly thought that barnacles were mollusks; hence the carapace was called a shell.)

2. **Bivalve mollusks.** Entire bivalve shells or pieces of clam, oyster, or mussel shells may appear white, gray, blue, or brown; usually not shiny; slow to dissolve in acid.

3. **Calcium-depositing algae.** **Calcareous algae** are those green or brown algae that secrete small amounts of calcium carbonate to form delicate or finely branched skeletons. An example is *Halimeda* with its short branches of articulated blades that when dried look like oatmeal. **Coralline algae** are marine algae that secrete large amounts of calcium carbonate to form stronger, more robust skeletons. Encrusting coralline algae appears rose or lavender when alive and white when dried. Solitary clumps of coralline algae are often mistaken for coral.

4. **Coral.** Fragments of dull-white coral rubble common in tropical sand. Larger, uneroded pieces from the outer layer of coral may be identified by their many small holes (cups) where individual coral polyps once lived.

5. **Foraminifera.** The skeletons of one-celled animals (protozoans). They may be white, dull or shiny, or be covered with tiny sand grains. They look like tiny shells except that their apertures are small and slitlike or porelike. "Forams" have a small hole where the living animal extended its false feet to trap food.

6. **Gastropod mollusks.** Entire snail-like shells or fragments, varying widely in color, shape, and pattern. Juvenile shells are more fragile than their adult forms and may differ in appearance. Eroded fragments may reveal internal spiral growth patterns. **"Cat's eyes,"** white disks, round on one side and flat on the other, are intact operculums from turban shells, trapdoor-like structures used to close the outer opening when the foot is withdrawn into the shell. **"Puka" shells** are the tops of eroded cone shells that appear as stout, light-colored disks with a hole in the center. Their slightly concave undersides sometimes show concentric rings. (*Puka* is Hawaiian for "hole.") A few years ago puka shells were collected, strung, and sold as necklaces all over the United States.

Table 9–4 (continued). Common components of biogenic sand

---

7. **Sea urchin fragments.** Spines may be white, purple, black, beige, or green. Viewed under a microscope, some have crystalline matrices that look like ornate corn-on-the-cob structures from the side or like concentric growth rings from the top. **Tests** are the inner skeletons of sea urchins. Test fragments have tiny holes and raised knoblike structures arranged in regular sequences; they appear dull white or lavender.

8. **Sponge spicules.** Spicules are usually clear and transparent or whitish; large triaxon sponge spicules may resemble the three-pointed logo of the Mercedes-Benz automobile. They make up the internal skeletal support structure of some sponges.

9. **Worm tubes.** Pieces of calcareous tubes secreted by worms. They are white or brownish and look ring-shaped when viewed from the top.

10. **Other.** Biogenic sand may contain other animal parts such as pieces of crabs or shrimps, or the colonial animals known as bryozoans.

ACTIVITY 2
Identify common components of sand with a stereo microscope.

MATERIALS
- sand samples
- teaspoon
- Petri dish
- stereo dissecting microscope
- toothpicks
- diluted white glue in small container
- 2 X 2-in square of poster board
- three 2 X 2-in 35-mm slide mounts
- 2 X 2-in square of heavy clear plastic or acetate sheeting
- fine felt-tip waterproof pen

PROCEDURE
1. Read the descriptions of sand components in Tables 9–3 and 9–4. Refer to this information as you carry out the procedures that follow.

2. Learn to identify the components commonly found in sand.
   a. Obtain samples of different kinds of sand. Rinse each sand sample with fresh water and air-dry before continuing. (You can use the vials of sieved sand from Activity 1.)
   b. Put 1/4 to 1/2 tsp of a sand sample into a clean, dry Petri dish. Clearly number and label the dish, telling

where the sand came from. Also record the sample number and the source in Table 9–5.

c. Using a stereo dissecting microscope, view the sand at lowest power. Be sure the sand is spread out in a thin layer in the Petri dish. With a toothpick move the sand particles, using a standard grid search. See Fig. 9–6.

d. Locate the components of sand. (For light-colored sands, use a dark background; for dark-colored sands, use a light background.) Look at the colors and shapes of the grains. Compare what you see with the descriptions in Tables 9–3 and 9–4.

e. Glue several grains of each sand component you find in the sample onto Table 9–5.

1) Place one small drop of diluted white glue in each appropriate square.

2) Transfer the sand particles from the Petri dish to Table 9–5 by touching them with the moistened end of a toothpick. The particles will cling to the toothpick. Use your fingers or another toothpick to brush the particles off the moistened toothpick into the glue. (Break the toothpick and discard it when you are done.)

3) Allow the glued samples to dry.

f. Repeat Procedures 2.a. to 2.e. using other sand samples. (By the time you are done, Table 9–5 should contain at least one specimen of each sand component.)

3. (Optional) Display samples of sands in well mounts. Refer to Figs. 9–7 and 9–8. Read Procedures a.–c. before you begin.

a. Decide what kind of sand display you want to make. Here are some options:

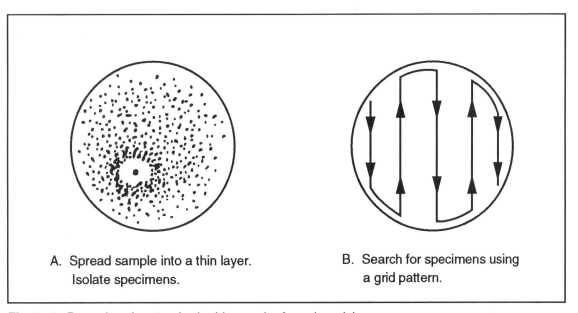

A. Spread sample into a thin layer. Isolate specimens.

B. Search for specimens using a grid pattern.

Fig. 9–6. Procedure for standard grid search of sand particles

149

Table 9–5. Microscopic identification of sand particles Ⓢ

Components of sand	Sand sample location			
A. Abiogenic components	1.	2.	3.	4.
1. Basalt				
2. Feldspar				
3. Garnet				
4. Granite				
5. Magnatite				
6. Mica				
7. Obsidian				
8. Olivine				
9. Quartz				
10. Other:				
B. Biogenic components				
1. Barnacle fragments				
2. Bivalve mollusks				
3. Calcium-depositing algae				
4. Coral				
5. Foraminifera				
6. Gastropod mollusks				
7. Sea urchin spines				
8. Sponge spicules				
9. Worm tubes				
10. Other:				

- a sample of sand from one beach containing mixed particle sizes.
- a sieved sand sample containing particles within one size range.
- picked specimens of each of the major components in a sand sample.
- a selected set of one component of sand. (An example is a picked set of micromollusks.)

b. Assemble the well mount as described below and shown in Fig. 9–7.

1) Obtain a 2 X 2-in square of heavy poster board for the base. Use white for dark-colored sands, black for light-colored sands. If desired, make a 0.5-cm grid in pencil on the base. See Fig. 9–8.

2) Glue two folded 35-mm cardboard photography slide mounts onto the base.

3) Ring the inside well with a thin coat of glue. This will seal the well and prevent sand particles from leaking through. Allow glue to dry thoroughly (24 hr).

4) Add sand samples using one of these options:

- glued sand: Coat the bottom of the well with glue. Sprinkle sand particles evenly over the glue; shake off excess.
- mounted sand specimens (for picked sand samples): In pencil, draw a 0.5-cm grid on the bottom poster board. Put a dot of glue in the center of each square. Transfer sand particles with a moist toothpick. Glue particles onto grid arranged as desired. (See example in Fig. 9–8.)
- loose sand: Put 1/4 to 1/2 tsp of sand particles into the well.

Leave room for the particles to roll around. Cover specimen with a 2 X 2-in piece of plastic. Glue it over the cardboard well with white glue.

5) If desired, frame the specimen by gluing two layers of a 35-mm slide mount (with no printed photography information) on top.

6) Label the specimen. Include its location (name of beach, where on beach, or at what water depth), treatment (intact, sieved, picked), component identification, collector's name, your name.

QUESTIONS

4. Describe each of the sand samples you analyzed in terms of its components. What components did you find that are not listed in the glossary in Table 9–3 and 9–4? (Use other reference books.)

5. What differences, if any, did you find between samples taken from a beach and samples taken from offshore? To answer this, compare the following samples:
   a. continental beach sand and offshore underwater continental shelf sand
   b. volcanic island sand and sand from nearby offshore underwater sites

6. Compare temperate zone sands and tropical zone sands in terms of biogenic components.
   a. Which zone seems to have more biogenic sand?
   b. Do both zones have the same kinds of biogenic components? If not, how do they differ?

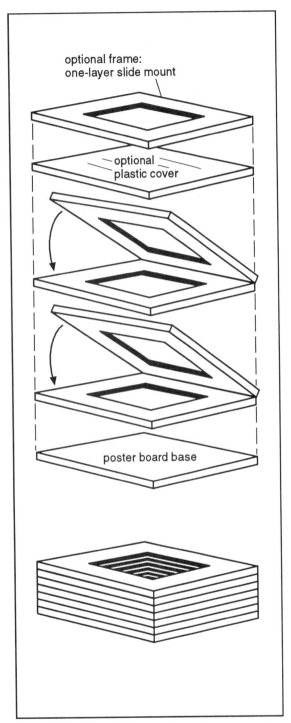

Fig. 9–7. Assembling cardboard well mount

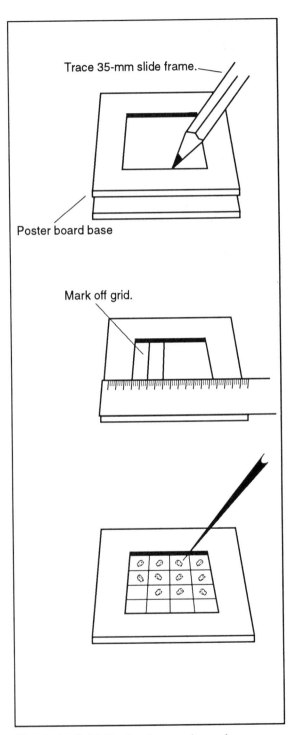

Fig. 9–8. Grid display for sand specimens

152

c. Which biogenic sand components were found only in tropical zone sand? Only in temperate zone sand?

FURTHER INVESTIGATIONS

1. Analyze and compare the volumes of sand samples. Place a 100-g sample of beach sand into a 100-mL graduated cylinder. Record its volume. Repeat this procedure with each type of beach sand you are studying. Then compare the volumes of the 100-g samples. Give explanations for any differences you observe.

2. Use references to find out the following:
   a. How do loose, unconsolidated sands and sediments become sedimentary rocks, including beach rock, mudstone, sandstone, and limestone? What fossils are often found in these rocks?
   b. How do weathering and erosion break down and transport rocks? How does sand get to the shorelines, and what happens to it after it gets there?

3. Make a descriptive study of your local beach. Include
   a. average size of sand particles on the beach.
   b. width and elevation of the berm.
   c. slope of the foreshore and inshore.
   d. the presence or absence of a sand bar, sand dunes, seacliff, or bluff.

4. Design a project to verify the relationship between particle size and beach slope. Measure slope angle and collect data on particle size.

5. Make a report on the economic importance of sand. Report on one or more of the following:
   a. The value of sandy beaches to people in real estate or in the recreational or tourist industry
   b. How sand is used in making products such as glass, crystal, cement, and abrasives
   c. How and where people are sieving sand today for minerals (such as gold) and for gems (such as diamonds)
   d. How the petroleum industry analyzes dredged or drilled sediment specimens for evidence of petroleum or other fossil fuels

6. Find out how oceanographers and geologists have used the analysis of the composition of sand and sediment samples to study
   a. movements of the earth's crust (plate tectonics).
   b. changes in the earth's climate.
   c. shifts in the earth's magnetic poles.

7. Find references describing the "painted desert" and acoustical sands that make sounds when walked on.

8. Compare sand samples from throughout the world. Include sand from seashores, lakes, rivers, and deserts. (Sand may be from a beach, dredged from beneath the water, or from ancient inland seas.)

UNIT 3
PHYSICAL OCEANOGRAPHY

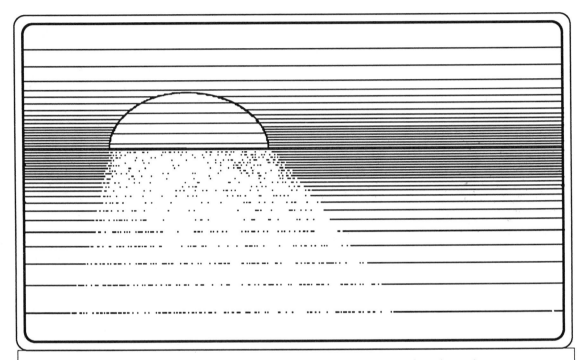

A whale swimming 1,200 meters beneath the ocean's surface is under a pressure of 120 kilograms of force on each square centimeter of its body. But when that whale breaches, it is under a pressure of a mere 1 kilogram of force per square centimeter. Why is there such a difference? How do things in the ocean's depth bear up under such pressure?

With a drop in temperature, water contracts, forcing more mass into each cubic centimeter it occupies. This more massive colder water sinks in warmer water. How does this phenomenon affect the temperatures of the ocean's surface and its depths? How does the ocean respond to this movement?

As the earth spins, it carries its fluids along. While water near the poles is traveling from west to east at a few kilometers an hour, water at the equator is racing in the same direction at more than two thousand kilometers an hour. What happens as these waters speed along in parallel paths? How do they interact?

These and other questions bring us to the study of the physical properties of water and the oceans.

1. Properties of Water and Other Liquids

Anyone looking at a drawing or a photo of the earth taken from outer space will see how much of the earth is covered with water. The earth is a watery planet. In the oceans, lakes, rivers, and streams, water is a liquid. Around the north and south poles, water exists in its solid forms, snow and ice. In the atmosphere, gaseous water vapor makes up the moisture in the air. Furthermore, all life on earth depends on water and contains water.

How much do we know about water? What are the properties of this substance that is so common to us, yet so unique to our planet? In a series of laboratory investigations we will observe and compare the properties of fresh water, salt water, and alcohol.

ACTIVITY
Observe water and describe its properties. Compare the properties of fresh water with the properties of salt water and alcohol.

PROCEDURE
1. Experiments to observe the properties of water are set up in a series of stations.

See Fig. 1–1. Go to your assigned station(s) and do the following:
 a. Follow the directions written on the procedure card.
 b. Record your observations in your notebook.

2. Form a hypothesis that explains what you observe.

3. When you are finished, put the station back in order. When instructed, go to the next station.

QUESTIONS
1. What is meant by the word "properties"? By the phrase "properties of water"?

2. For each station, what properties of water might account for your observations? Refer to Fig. 1–1 for a summary of the activities at each of the stations.

3. How do the properties of fresh water compare with the properties of salt water? Of alcohol?

4. Which of your observations can you not explain? Be specific.

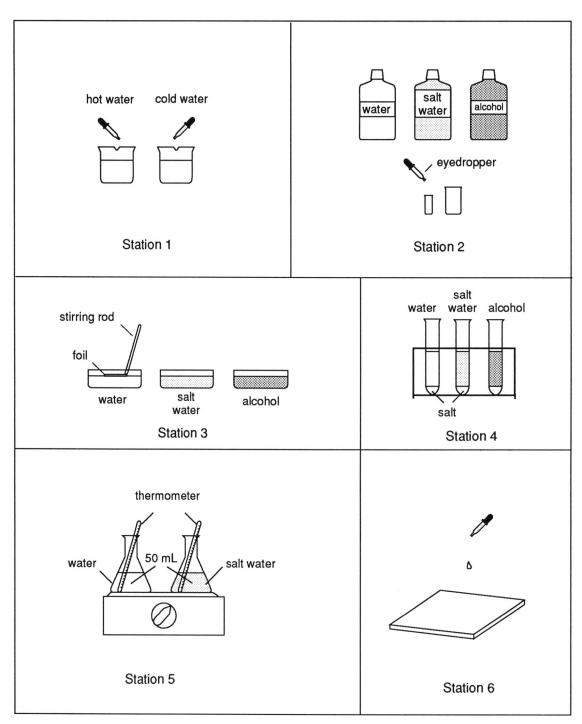

Fig. 1–1. Summary of station apparatus

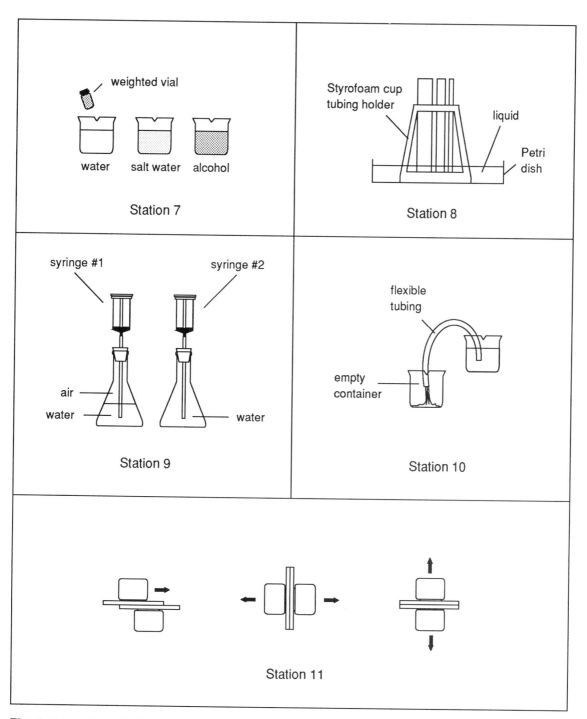

Fig. 1–1 (continued). Summary of station apparatus

157

2. Density, Temperature, and Salinity

If you have ever gone swimming or wading in water that was noticeably warmer at the surface and cooler at the bottom, you know that water can form layers. Oceanographers have found that seawater forms layers in the ocean. How do these layers form? Do the waters in these layers mix?

Whether a layer of water floats or sinks is determined by its density relative to the density of other layers. The **density** of a liquid is the amount of mass in a given volume of the liquid. When salt is dissolved in fresh water, the resulting solution is said to be **saline**, or salty.

In this activity we will put samples of different liquids into small plastic bags, seal the bags, and put the bags into beakers of liquids. The beaker of liquid simulates an ocean or lake; the bag of liquid simulates a layer of liquid. We will watch to see what happens when we change the salinity and the temperature of the liquids in the bags and in the beakers. See Fig. 2–1.

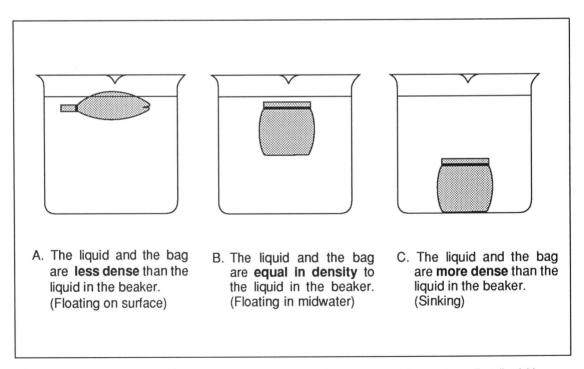

A. The liquid and the bag are **less dense** than the liquid in the beaker. (Floating on surface)

B. The liquid and the bag are **equal in density** to the liquid in the beaker. (Floating in midwater)

C. The liquid and the bag are **more dense** than the liquid in the beaker. (Sinking)

Fig. 2–1. Comparing the density of liquid in bags with the density of the surrounding liquid in beakers

ACTIVITY 1

Test the effects of temperature and salinity on the floating and sinking of liquid samples in bags.

MATERIALS

• four 2 X 3-in plastic bags with double-lock closures
• scissors
• heat source
• thermometer
• tongs or hot pad
• waterproof felt-tip pen
• cold fresh water (about 5°C)
• warm fresh water (about 50°C)
• cold salt water (about 5°C)
• warm salt water (about 50°C)
• food coloring (for liquids in bags)
• stirring rod
• two 1,000-mL beakers
• paper towels (for drying bags)

PROCEDURE

1. Watch as your teacher shows you how to fill the plastic bags and seal them so that they do not leak or have air bubbles inside.

2. Study the example in Fig. 2–1. We will determine the relative densities of the liquids by observing whether the bags sink or float. Note that food coloring is used only for the liquid in the bag to make it easier to observe.

3. Design experiments to test the effect of temperature (warm or cold) and salinity (fresh water or salt water) on the floating or sinking of the bags of liquid. Before you begin your tests, write out your experimental design as follows:
   a. Make a table or tables showing which combinations of liquids in bags and

Table 2–1. The density of cold liquid in bags compared with the density of cold liquid in beakers (example of one combination)

Liquid in beaker	Liquid in bag	
	Density of cold fresh water (5˚C)	Density of cold salt water (5˚C)
Cold fresh water (5˚C)	Predicted	Predicted
	Actual	Actual
Cold salt water (5˚C)	Predicted	Predicted
	Actual	Actual

liquids in beakers you plan to use. A sample for one combination of variables is shown in Table 2–1. Decide what table(s) you will need.

b. Make a list of the materials you will need.

c. Write each step of the procedure you will use in the experiment.

d. For each combination of liquids, predict whether the bag of liquid will sink or float. Record your predictions.

e. Check your design with your teacher before starting Procedure 4.

4. Carry out your experiment.

a. Use a waterproof pen to label the bags and the beaker.

b. Record your observations in your data table.

5. Present your experimental design and observations to the class. Compare results with other experiments conducted in the class.

6. (Optional) Allow a bag of liquid to remain in a beaker of liquid for 24 hours. Observe what happens.

QUESTIONS

1. Under what combination(s) of temperature and salinity does
   a. fresh water float?
   b. fresh water sink?
   c. salt water float?
   d. salt water sink?

2. How can the formation of layers in water be explained?

3. Using the term **density**, explain how a bag of salt water can sink in a beaker of salt water. Where might this occur in the oceans of the world?

4. If the temperature of the liquid in a bag and the liquid in a beaker were the same, under what conditions would the bag float? Where might this occur in nature?

5. Would fresh water flowing from a river into the ocean sink or float on top of seawater? Explain your reasoning.

6. How, if at all, do you think the food coloring affected the density of the liquids in the bags? How could you verify your answer?

7. What do you think might happen to the liquid in the bags if the bags were not sealed? How could you test this?

8. What do you think the density of the bag is? How does the density of the bag affect the results of your experiment?

9. If a bag of liquid remains in a beaker of liquid for 24 hours, what happens to
   a. the temperature of the two liquids?
   b. the salinity of the two liquids?
   c. the density of the two liquids?

Ocean Temperature Profiles

Temperatures in the ocean range from about –2°C to 30°C. The highest temperatures are found in the surface waters of seawater near the equator. The coldest temperatures (–2° to 2°C) are found in layers of seawater at the bottom of the deep ocean basins. Worldwide, the average surface temperature of the ocean is 17°C; the average temperature of the entire ocean from surface to seafloor is 3.5°C.

Seawater within the ocean is not uniform; it forms layers by temperatures. Data from temperature probes lowered into tropical oceans show that the warm surface layer ends abruptly. The zone where there is a sharp temperature change from warm to cool water is called the **thermocline**. Beneath the thermocline, seawater is cold.

ACTIVITY 2
Make graphs showing vertical temperature profiles of the Pacific Ocean.

PROCEDURE
1. Graph the vertical temperature profile of the Pacific Ocean at the equator (0°) as follows:
   a. Locate line (A) in Fig. 2–2. Line A is a vertical line drawn at the equator (0°) from the surface of the Pacific Ocean to the seafloor.
   b. Starting at the surface, determine the temperatures along line (A) for each 0.5 km of depth. Plot the temperatures on the grid in Fig. 2–3. Connect the points with a solid line. The graph you just made is called a **vertical temperature profile**.
   c. Examine the graph. Label the thermocline.

2. Make a second graph in Fig. 2–3, this time showing the vertical temperature profile at 40°S latitude. Obtain the temperature data from line (B) in Fig. 2–2. Connect these data points with a dashed line. Label the thermocline.

3. Make a third graph in Fig. 2–3, this time showing the vertical temperature profile at 70°S latitude, (C) in Fig. 2–2. Connect the data points with a dotted line.

QUESTIONS
10. Compare the three vertical temperature profiles. How are they similar? How are they different? Describe the thermocline in each profile.

11. Toward the south pole, the surface layer is colder than the layer just below the surface. How might this be explained? What probably happens to the density of the surface seawater?

12. Do the layers in the ocean appear stable, or do they appear to mix readily? What is your evidence?

FURTHER INVESTIGATIONS
1. Simulate the layers of water formed by differences in temperature and salinity.
   a. Prepare two 100 mL water samples, one of cold salt water (about 5°C), the other of warm salt or brackish water (about 40°C). Add a different food coloring to each.
   b. Put 100 mL of the cold water into a beaker. Slowly pour about 20 mL of the warm water down a stirring rod onto the cold water in the beaker to prevent mixing. See Fig. 2–4. Look for evidence of layering.

2. Prepare a demonstration that shows the class why surface seawater is so much warmer near the equator than near the north and south poles.

161

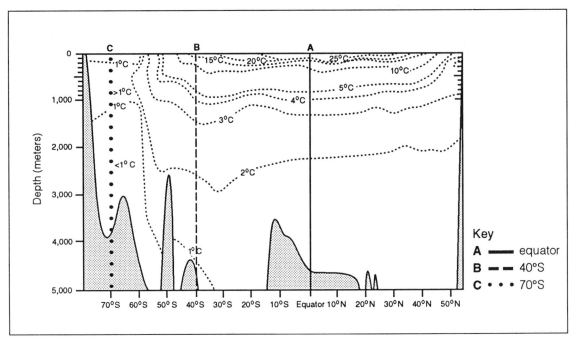

Fig. 2–2. Vertical temperature profile of the Pacific Ocean   (Shaded area indicates seafloor features.) Ⓦ

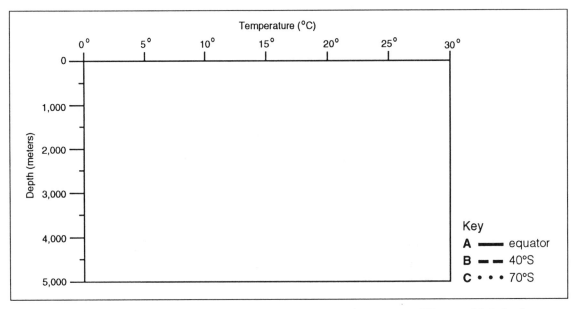

Fig. 2–3. Graph of the temperature of the Pacific Ocean at the equator (A), at 40˚S latitude (B), and at 70˚S latitude (C) Ⓦ

Pour water slowly down stirring rod.

Fig. 2–4. Simulation of a temperature-density gradient

3. Consult references to prepare a report explaining the technology for obtaining energy by using the difference in temperatures between layers of seawater
   a. in ocean thermal energy conversion (OTEC) technology.
   b. in salinity-gradient solar ponds.

4. Read library references, then devise a simulation to demonstrate
   a. how wind and wave action affect the temperature of the surface layer of the ocean, and
   b. how the temperature of the ocean affects the atmosphere and global climate.

5. Compare temperatures in the ocean with temperatures on land. What are the record high and low temperatures? What are the average temperatures? How do summer and winter affect the temperature?

6. Unusual natural ponds with warm salt water on the bottom and cool fresh water on the top are found near the ocean on some volcanic islands. Such ponds are called **anchialine** ("near the sea") **ponds**. Propose a hypothesis to explain how these ponds form.

3. Measuring Salinity

Salinity, the amount of dissolved mineral matter, is an important property of water. It is measured as the number of grams of minerals per kilogram of water (parts per thousand). The symbol for parts per thousand is ‰.

$$\text{Salinity ‰} = \frac{\text{grams of dissolved minerals}}{1{,}000 \text{ g water}}$$

The average salinity of seawater is about 35 g/kg, or 35‰ (35 parts per thousand parts of seawater). Seawater ranges from 33‰ to 38‰.

Water is not pure unless it has been distilled several times to remove dissolved matter. Freshwater lakes, rivers, and streams all contain some dissolved matter. Water that is a mixture of fresh water and seawater is described as **brackish**. Very salty seawater (like that sometimes found in tidepools) is described as **hypersaline** or **brine**.

Measuring Salinity

One of the most common methods for determining the salinity of a solution is to measure its density, then convert the density measurement to salinity. Density can be measured with a hydrometer. Fig. 3–1 shows a hydrometer calibrated for a range of densities from 1.000 to 1.060 g/mL.

Salinity can be determined from a graph if the density and temperature of a given water sample are known. See Fig. 3–2.

QUESTIONS

1. On the hydrometer in Fig. 3–1, what is the density range for normal seawater? Fresh water? Brackish water? Hypersaline water?

2. Why does fresh water show a range of densities? Is all fresh water the same? Explain.

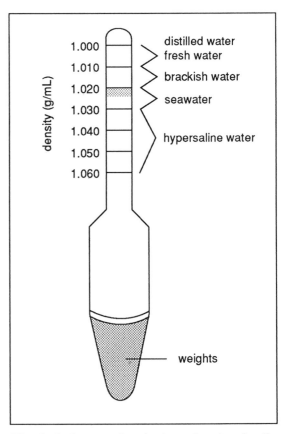

Fig. 3–1. An aquarium hydrometer showing the density range of water samples in g/mL

164

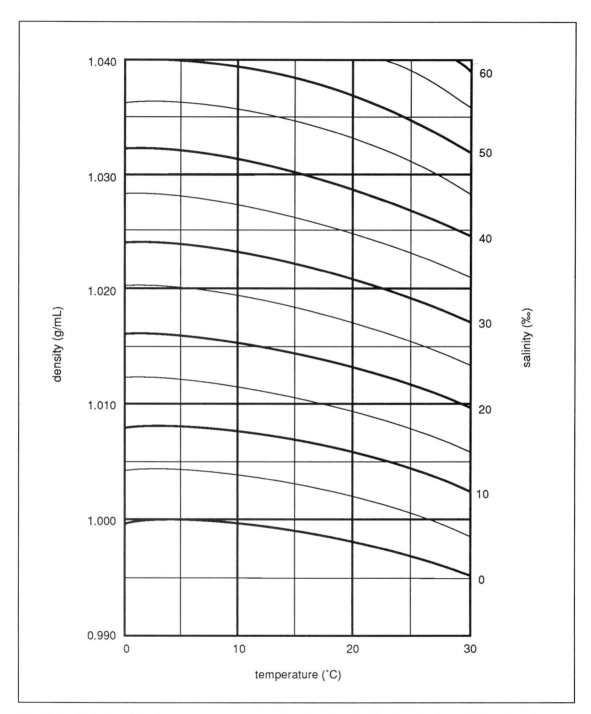

Fig. 3–2. Relationships between temperature (vertical lines), density (horizontal lines), and salinity (curved lines). Ⓦ

3. Study Fig. 3–2, then answer the following questions:
   a. As salinity increases, what happens to density?
   b. If density increases, what factors might be changing?
   c. At the salinity of average seawater, what happens to density as the temperature increases?

4. The left vertical scale in Fig. 3–2 gives density in g/mL. Label the scale to show fresh water, brackish water, seawater, and hypersaline water.

5. On Fig. 3–2 lightly shade in the average seawater salinity range between 33‰ and 38‰ in the temperature range for open-ocean seawater (use 0° to 30°C on this graph). What is its density range?

6. The shaded section on the hydrometer shown in Fig. 3–1 indicates the optimum density of saltwater aquaria at an average temperature of 20° to 25°C. How does this compare to the density range of open-ocean seawater?

7. If a hydrometer in an aquarium gives a density reading of 1.020 g/mL with the water temperature at 20°C,
   a. what is the salinity of the water?
   b. would the water be described as brackish water, average seawater, or hypersaline water?

8. Assume that you have a saltwater aquarium maintained at room temperature (25°C). A hydrometer reading shows that its density is 1.030 g/mL. To bring the aquarium back within the normal seawater range, select one course of action from each pair below.
   a. Would you add fresh water or salt water?
   b. Would you remove the excess salts from the sides or wash the evaporated salts back into the aquarium?

====================

ACTIVITY
Construct and standardize a hydrometer.

MATERIALS
- skewer
- centimeter ruler
- scalpel
- ballpoint pen
- 3-mL shell vial
- cork to fit vial
- quick-drying glue
- fast-drying varnish
- fine-grain sand
- solutions of known salinities in 1,000-mL beakers
- thermometer
- paper towels

PROCEDURE
1. Mark the hydrometer scale on a wooden skewer. See Fig. 3–3.
   a. Cut a skewer to 7.5 cm long. Sharpen one end with a scalpel.
   b. Starting at the unsharpened end, make marks 1 mm apart with a ball-point pen. Darken every fifth mark to identify 0.5 cm intervals. At every tenth mark, make a mark completely around the skewer.

2. Make the scale-and-cork assembly following the steps in Fig. 3–4.

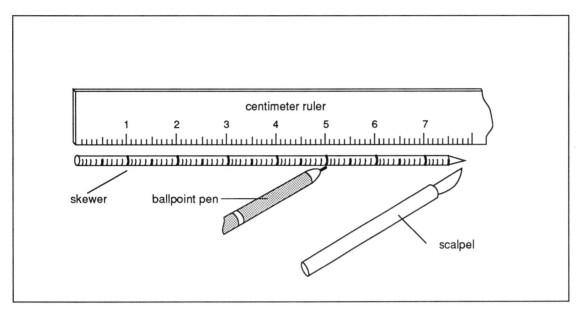

Fig. 3–3. Measuring and marking a skewer

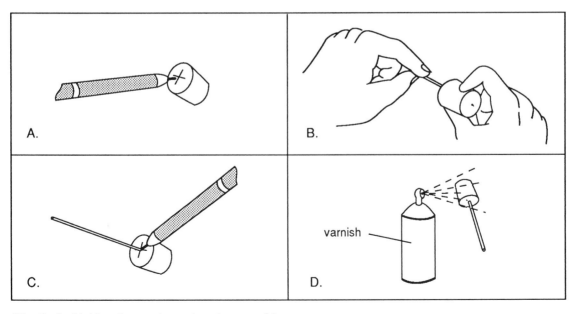

Fig. 3–4. Making the scale-and-cork assembly

a. Mark the centers of both ends of the cork. Write your initials on the side of the cork so that you will be able to identify your hydrometer.

b. Put glue on the sharpened end of the skewer and insert it into the cork until the tip of skewer sticks out the other end of the cork.

c. Darken the last mark so that if the skewer is pulled out, it can be reinserted to the same depth.

d. Seal the scale-and-cork assembly against water by spraying it with clear varnish.

3. Add weight to the vial and finish making the hydrometer.

a. Put sand in a small shell vial to a depth of about 1.5 cm. (The amount varies depending on the type of sand.) Tap the sand down so that it is deposited firmly on the bottom of the vial. Insert the scale-and-cork assembly into the vial. Push down on the cork.

b. Test the hydrometer in fresh water and in very saline water. Adjust it by adding or removing dry sand. Each time you adjust it, replace the cork to the mark on the skewer, then retest the hydrometer. When you are finished, the hydrometer should float as follows:

1) When placed in fresh water, it will not sink completely. About 1 cm of the scale will remain above the water.

2) When placed in very saline water, most of the skewer will be above water, but the cork will remain just under the surface.

c. Once the hydrometer is adjusted, dry the cork carefully without changing its position. Seal the cork into the vial by lightly covering it with spray varnish.

4. Standardize your hydrometer.

a. Record in Table 3–1 the salinity of the solutions provided by your teacher.

b. Measure the temperature (in °C) of the solutions. Record in Table 3–1.

c. Place your hydrometer in the distilled

Table 3–1. Standardizing the hydrometer ⓦ

Salinity of solution (‰)	Temperature (°C)	Hydrometer reading	Density
0 (distilled water)			

water sample. Twirl it gently to overcome surface tension. Determine how much of the skewer is out of the water. Read the scale in millimeters and record the measurement in Table 3–1. Dry the hydrometer.

d. Repeat steps (b) and (c) with the remaining standard solutions. Work from least to most saline, drying the hydrometer after each test to avoid contaminating the solutions.

5. Use Fig. 3–2 to determine the density of each solution at the measured temperature. For example, if the solution has a salinity of 10‰ at 25°C,

a. locate 25°C on the horizontal axis on the graph in Fig. 3–2.

b. move vertically along this line until it intersects the 10‰ salinity curve.

c. move left horizontally to the density scale.

d. record the density in Table 3–1.

6. Make a graph in Fig. 3–5 of the standardization data recorded in Table 3–1.

a. Record the temperatures of the test solutions in the space provided.

b. For each solution tested, mark the data point on the graph where the density and hydrometer readings meet.

c. Draw the line that best fits the plotted data points.

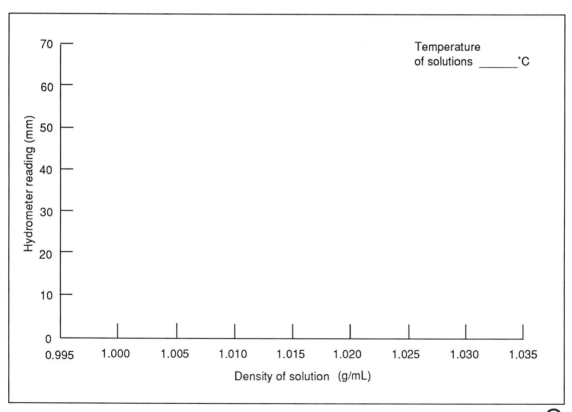

Fig. 3–5. Graph of standardization data

7. Obtain one or more unknown solutions from your teacher. Use your hydrometer to determine the density of each liquid. Record your procedure and your results.

QUESTIONS

9. What are the highest and lowest readings (in mm) that you can make with your hydrometer? How could you determine the salinity and density of each?

10. Explain why the small diameter of the skewer increases the sensitivity of the hydrometer. Why not use a thicker skewer?

11. Explain what happens if the hydrometer is not twirled in Procedure 5.b.

12. Explain how differences in the densities of the liquids affect the rising and sinking of the hydrometer.

13. What would the density of a liquid be if the hydrometer reading were 23 mm? 47 mm? 16 mm? Use your graph in Fig. 3–5.

14. How could you use the hydrometer and its standardization graph (Fig. 3–5) to determine the densities of solutions at different temperatures? Explain.

15. Explain how you could restandardize your hydrometer for other kinds of liquid solutions.

FURTHER INVESTIGATIONS

1. Other methods for determining salinity of a water sample are described below. Read references to obtain more information about these methods or try the methods yourself. Report your findings to the class.

a. Recover the salts by evaporating all the water from a 1,000-g sample of seawater; then weigh the solids that remain. Salinity can then be calculated using the formula given at the beginning of this topic.

b. Measure the electric current that flows between two electrodes immersed in a solution. The conductivity of a salt solution is directly related to the salinity.

c. Measure the angle at which light is refracted or bent by a solution. Light is refracted more by solutions of greater salinity. The device used for this method is called a **salinity refractometer**.

2. Using the procedure in the activity, construct hydrometer/density graphs to be used for solutions at other temperatures. For example, cool the solutions to 10°C and repeat the procedures.

3. Using your hydrometer, determine the salinity of samples of water — tap water, rainwater, and water from a stream or lake, an estuary, the seashore, the open ocean, and freshwater and seawater aquaria.

4. Formation of Currents

In Topic 2 we learned that water forms layers in the ocean because of differences in density, temperature, and salinity. What causes these layers to mix and distribute oxygen, nutrients, and salts throughout the oceans? How can we account for the observation that temperature of deep-ocean water is the same at the equator and near the poles?

In the next three topics we will investigate **ocean currents,** the movements of masses of water in the ocean. A **current** is a moving mass of a fluid—either a gas or a liquid. Hence winds and moving waters are called currents. The oceans can be thought of as collections of many currents moving in different directions at different levels. Total movement of all ocean currents is called **ocean circulation**.

Movement occurs when unequal forces meet. Movement is always in the direction of the stronger force. A **force** is a push or a pull. The forces that move water to produce ocean currents are caused by gravity, the rotation of the earth, and winds.

Gravitational Currents

Vertical (up-and-down) movement in the ocean can be explained in terms of two forces, the **gravitational force** (G) that pulls down and the **buoyant force** (B) that pushes up. Movements caused by interaction between these two forces are sinking, rising, and floating.

Sinking is a downward vertical movement that occurs when the gravitational force on a body of water is greater than the buoyant force supporting it (gravitational force > buoyant force). See (A) in Fig. 4–1. A sinking mass of water that moves toward the ocean floor is an example of a **gravitational current**; its movement is called **gravitational flow**.

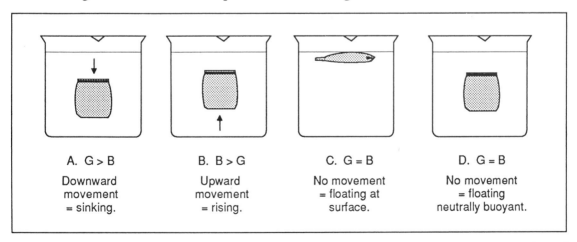

A. G > B	B. B > G	C. G = B	D. G = B
Downward movement = sinking.	Upward movement = rising.	No movement = floating at surface.	No movement = floating neutrally buoyant.

Fig. 4–1. Sinking, rising, and floating result from interactions between the forces of gravity (G) and buoyancy (B).

Rising is upward vertical movement that occurs when the buoyant force is greater than the gravitational force (buoyant force > gravitational force). See (B) in Fig. 4–1. Thus a mass of water rises toward the surface when its buoyant force is greater than the gravitational force of the earth.

Floating occurs when a mass of water neither rises nor sinks but stays in place, whether at the surface or below it. No vertical movement occurs because the buoyant force of the ocean equals the gravitational force (buoyant force = gravitational force). See (C) and (D) in Fig. 4–1. When an object floats under water, it is sometimes described as **neutrally buoyant.**

Unbalanced forces in water cause currents to form. Throughout the oceans conditions arise that cause layers of different densities to come together. For example, freshwater runoff from melted snow can flow into warm seawater.

In this activity we will prepare two-liquid systems and look for evidence of vertical gravitational flow.

ACTIVITY 1
Determine what conditions cause gravity currents to form in liquids.

MATERIALS
Per team
- lab aprons
- 2 narrow-necked 100-mL bottles
- 2 food colorings or other water-soluble dyes in dropper bottles
- 3 X 3-in plastic card
- tray or newspaper

Per class
- fresh water
- stock solutions of brackish water, seawater, and hypersaline water
- heat source
- ice cubes

PROCEDURE
1. Watch as your teacher demonstrates the procedure for setting up a two-liquid system as shown in Fig. 4–2.

2. In Topic 2 we observed whether bags of liquids sank or floated in beakers of liquids. Refer to your data from Topic 2 as needed to carry out Procedure 3.

3. Two examples of a two-liquid system are shown in Table 4–1. Think of three more examples and record the two liquids in each system in Table 4–1.
   a. For each example you describe, predict the movement or lack of movement of the liquids. Record your predictions.
   b. Test each two-liquid system using the procedure demonstrated by your teacher. Record your observations in Table 4–1. Use sketches if desired.

4. For each two-liquid system that you test, name a location where such conditions might occur. Look at the example in Table 4–1.

5. Share your results with the class.

QUESTIONS
1. Write a description of the interaction between the gravitational force and the buoyant force in Example 1 in Table 4–1.

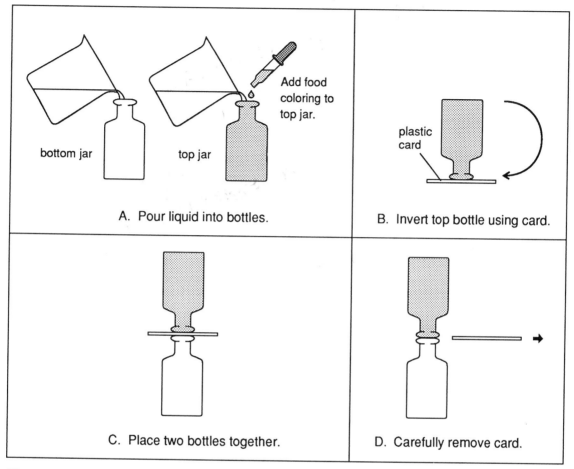

Fig. 4–2. Steps in manipulating bottles of liquids to observe gravitational flow between two liquids

2. Explain sinking, rising, and floating in two-liquid systems in terms of
   a. the densities of the two liquids.
   b. the forces of gravity and buoyancy

3. Examine your data in Table 4–1. How well did your observations agree with your predictions? How might any differences be explained?

4. How could you test your predictions about possible locations where your two-liquid systems might occur?

Thermohaline Circulation

Thermohaline circulation is water movement caused by differences in temperature and salinity. As we have seen, differences in temperature and salinity affect density.

Knowing what causes differences in salinity in the ocean helps us understand how thermohaline circulation patterns develop. Two processes decrease salinity: **precipitation** and **freshwater runoff**. Precipitation is rain and snow. When precipitation falls on the ocean surface, it adds fresh

Table 4–1. Gravitational flow in a two-liquid system (W)

Two-liquid system	Possible location where two-liquid system occurs	Predicted flow	Observed flow
Example: Top layer: fresh water, room temperature Bottom layer: seawater, cold	Summer rains fall into cold seawater in a bay in Maine.	No flow of liquids; fresh water floats.	
System 1 Top layer: seawater, warm Bottom layer: seawater, cold			
System 2 Top layer: Bottom layer:			
System 3 Top layer: Bottom layer:			
System 4 Top layer: Bottom layer:			

water to the ocean. Near the equator during the rainy season, for example, rainfall dilutes surface seawater. Runoff from rivers, streams, or estuaries emptying into the ocean also adds fresh water, thereby diluting surface seawater. Freshwater runoffs from melting snow and heavy monsoon rains are seasonal. The surface ocean water, diluted with fresh water, is less salty and therefore less dense than the water below it. Water that is partly salty is called brackish water.

Two other processes increase salinity: **evaporation** and **freezing**. Most of us can understand how evaporation, by removing fresh water, makes seawater saltier. But freezing also removes fresh water by locking up water molecules in the form of ice. When ice sheets form in the ocean, fresh water is removed, leaving the surface water saltier than average seawater. This saltier surface seawater is denser. Very salty seawater is called brine.

Thermohaline circulation occurs in the waters surrounding the Antarctic continent, where a large mass of very cold, very dense water forms. During winters in the Antarctic, large ice sheets and massive icebergs develop, removing fresh water. Cold brine forms at the surface, then sinks. This Antarctic bottom water slowly flows just above the seafloor northward into the Pacific, Atlantic, and Indian ocean basins. As it spreads, it slowly mixes with other layers of water. Mixing takes 500 to 800 years in the Atlantic and Indian oceans but about twice that long in the deeper Pacific Ocean. Eventually the water warms, mixes with other layers, and returns to the surface. At the surface the water may again be diluted, evaporated, or frozen, perpetuating the thermohaline cycle. Thus within the ocean basins, large-scale circulation cycles are set up. Thermohaline circulation accounts for deep, slow currents in the major ocean basins that circulate and mix seawater all over the globe. Currents also have a powerful effect on global climate.

QUESTIONS

5. What conditions increase the density of seawater? What conditions decrease the density?

6. Arrange the following list from most dense to least dense:
    a. seawater at the surface in a tropical rainstorm
    b. seawater at the surface around Antarctica during winter
    c. seawater at the surface in tropical sun
    d. seawater at the surface in the tropics at night
    e. seawater directly beneath a mass of polar ice

ACTIVITY 2

Simulate the convection currents formed between hot equatorial water masses and cold polar water masses.

MATERIALS
- 2 transparent plastic cups
- nail or pencil
- four 1 X 2-in pieces of masking tape
- transparent plastic shoe box
- fresh water
- 2 sheets of white paper
- two 250-mL beakers
- red food coloring
- heat source
- thermometer
- tongs or hot pads
- blue food coloring
- ice cubes
- 30 pennies (for weights)
- salt
- balance
- centimeter ruler

PROCEDURE

1. Study the apparatus shown in Fig. 4–3. Make sketches to show the predicted direction of the currents that will be set in motion. The pattern they form is called a **convection current**.

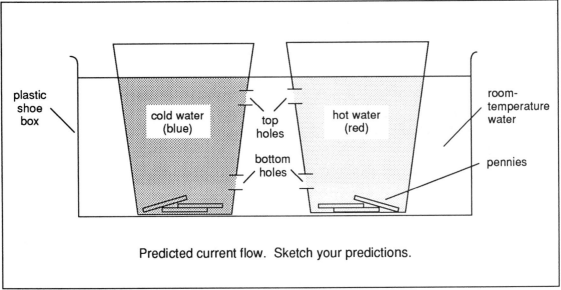

Predicted current flow. Sketch your predictions.

Fig 4–3. Simulating convection current(s) between hot equatorial water and cold polar water Ⓦ

2. Test the system as follows:
   a. Obtain two transparent plastic cups. Make two holes in each cup as shown in Fig. 4–3. You can make the holes either by firmly twisting a pencil point into the plastic or by melting holes in the plastic with a hot nail.
   b. Cover each hole with a small piece of masking tape. Make a tab or keep one end loose so that the tape can be removed easily.
   c. Put the cups next to the shoe box. Fill the shoe box with clear room-temperature water to a level above the two holes on each cup but at least 2 cm lower than the rim of the cups.
   d. Put white paper behind and under the plastic shoe box.
   e. Put red-colored tap water into a 250-mL beaker and heat it to 50°– 70°C. Handle the beaker with a hot pad or tongs.
   e. Put blue-colored tap water into a 250-mL beaker. Add ice to cool it to about 5°C.
   f. Put the plastic cups in the water in the shoebox. Have your lab partner hold the cups down.
   g. Fill one of the plastic cups with the heated red water up to the shoebox waterline. Fill the other plastic cup with the chilled blue water up to the shoebox waterline.
   h. If weights are needed to keep the cups stable, add pennies one at a time. If desired, preheat the pennies for the hot water cup and chill the ones for the cold water cup.

3. Make sure the holes in the two cups are facing each other. Peel off the masking tape, disturbing the water as little as possible.

4. Observe the movement of the water from the side of the shoebox and from the top. Make a series of sketches to record the pattern of flow
   a. as soon as the tapes are removed.
   b. after 1 min.
   c. after 5 min.
   d. after 10 min.

5. (Optional) To test the effect of salinity, repeat Procedures 1–4 using saltwater solutions. If they are not already available, prepare saltwater solutions approximating seawater (3.5 g salt/L), brine (more than 3.5 g salt/L), and brackish water (less than 3.5 g salt/L). Color the brine blue and the brackish water red.

6. If time permits, test the combined effects of temperature and salinity. Chill the brine and heat the brackish water.

QUESTIONS
7. Describe what happens in a convection current
   a. to cold polar water after it sinks and flows toward the equator.
   b. to warm equatorial water after it flows toward the poles.

8. Explain how differences in salinity can cause
   a. vertical (up-and-down) movement in water.
   b. horizontal (sideways) movement in water.

9. Explain how differences in temperature can cause
   a. vertical (up-and-down) movement in water.
   b. horizontal (sideways) movement in water.

10. Thermohaline circulation is a type of convection current mixing cold polar seawater with warm equatorial seawater. How do you think these currents affect
    a. the distribution of heat on our planet?
    b. the distribution of oxygen and nutrients throughout the ocean?

Marginal Seas
Thermohaline circulation also occurs in shallow, marginal seas. One pattern is found in marginal seas near arid regions where evaporation is greater than precipitation. One such place is the Mediterranean Sea. See Fig. 4–4. During the summer the Mediterranean region is constantly swept by hot, dry winds. Large volumes of water evaporate, making the surface water warmer and saltier. During the winter the surface water cools, sinks, and pours through the Straits of Gibraltar into the Atlantic Ocean. At the same time, less-dense water from the Atlantic Ocean flows into the Mediterranean, replacing the outflowing denser water. Notice in Fig. 4–4 that the denser water flows over a partial underwater rock barrier called a **sill**. A similar thermohaline circulation pattern occurs in the Red Sea, the Persian Gulf, and some lagoons.

The opposite pattern occurs where precipitation or runoff is greater than evaporation. In the Black and Baltic seas, for ex-

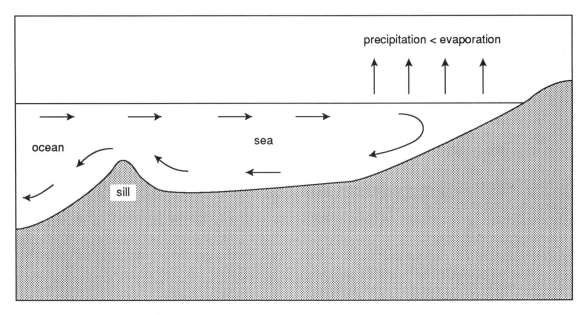

Fig. 4–4. Thermohaline circulation in the Mediterranean Sea where less-dense water flows in and denser water flows out

ample, dilute, less-dense water (brackish water) remains at the surface and flows out while saltier, denser water flows in along the bottom. See Fig. 4–5. This circulation pattern is also found on a smaller scale in **fjords**—deep, narrow inlets cut between steep cliffs by glaciers. Fjords are common in Norway, Greenland, and on the high-latitude coasts of North America.

Estuaries

A third pattern of thermohaline circulation occurs in **estuaries**—relatively shallow, partially enclosed bodies of water that connect to the open sea. In this pattern, a freshwater outflow from the land mixes with a tidal inflow of seawater from the ocean. See Fig. 4–6. Salinity is highest at the **mouth** of the estuary, which opens to the sea. Fresh water from rivers and streams flows into the **head** of the estuary. In the waters between the mouth and the head, current patterns may be complex because of the size, shape, and depth of the estuary. In general, the circulation pattern at high tide is wedge-shaped, with denser inflowing seawater meeting less-dense outflowing freshwater. See Fig. 4–6. Mixing patterns between the layers vary widely, depending on the tides, the season, and the length of the estuary. Estuaries in hot, dry regions flow in patterns similar to those in the Mediterranean Sea.

Bays, like estuaries, are partially enclosed bodies of water. They differ from estuaries in that they have a constant salinity throughout, largely because less fresh water flows into bays than into estuaries and because the waters in bays are well mixed by ocean winds and waves.

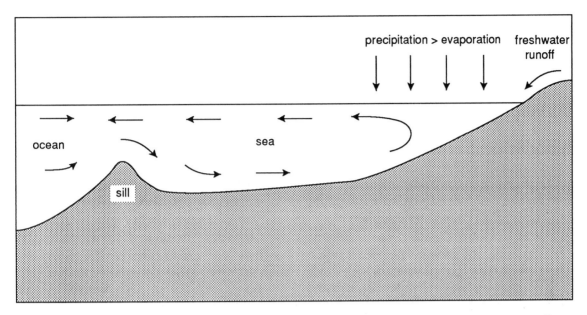

Fig. 4–5. Circulation pattern in marginal seas, such as the Black Sea, where less-dense water flows out and denser water flows in

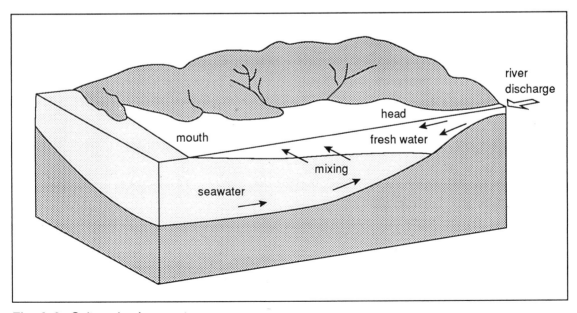

Fig. 4–6. Salt wedge in an estuary

QUESTIONS

11. During World War II, submarines passed in and out of the Mediterranean Sea through the Straits of Gibraltar without using their engines. How could they do this? See Fig. 4–4.

12. In the middle of the Atlantic Ocean and in parts of the Pacific and Indian oceans, there are hot spots at the margins of continental plates. How might these affect deepwater circulation?

13. Throughout all the ocean basins, even at the equator, deep water is very cold. Where does the cold water come from?

14. Contrast the thermohaline circulation patterns in the Mediterranean Sea with those in the Black Sea. In your own words, explain how each circulation pattern forms.

15. Explain how differences in temperature and salinity can cause
    a. movement of water.
    b. formation of a current.
    c. formation of a water mass with its own properties.

FURTHER INVESTIGATIONS

1. Locate and read reference materials on different types of partially enclosed bodies of water. Report to the class on your findings. Include the origins or methods of geological formation and types of current patterns that are characteristic in each of the following:
   a. marginal seas such as the Mediterranean Sea
   b. marginal seas such as the Black Sea
   c. coastal plain estuaries such as Chesapeake Bay
   d. fjords
   e. lagoons with a bar or barrier beach
   f. lagoons inside coral reefs
   g. estuaries such as San Francisco Bay formed by the tectonic movement of crustal plates

2. Organisms that live in estuaries experience changes in salinity during daily tidal cycles. The water in their environment may vary from salt to fresh, depending on their location in the estuary. Research and report on how plants and animals are adapted to live in such variable water conditions.

3. Simulate the different types of thermohaline circulation patterns. Adapt ideas from Activity 2, or design your own simulations.

4. Density is the amount of mass in a given volume. In Activity 1 we used two bottles with the same volume. What could be predicted about the masses of two liquids in a system with gravitational flow? What could be predicted where no water movement was observed? How could you test these predictions?

5. Read reference materials on the role of thermohaline currents in the global distribution of heat. Look for recent studies on Atlantic bottom water and on polynyas, vast gaps in the ice around Antarctica. How might thermohaline currents be related to global climate and to predictions about global heating of the earth, called the **greenhouse effect**?

5. Effect of a Rotating Earth

The earth constantly rotates or spins on its axis. Because the earth is a sphere, the velocity (speed) of rotation at its surface is greatest at the equator and least at the poles. Fig. 5–1 illustrates the differences in rotational velocity between a point located near the equator (moving at a rate of 462 m/sec or 1,040 mi/hr) and a point located about 50 km from the north pole (moving at a rate of 7.46 m/sec or 16.8 mi/hr).

If ocean water near the equator moves faster than ocean water near the poles, what happens to global ocean currents as the earth rotates?

In this investigation we will use a drop of a liquid to simulate a current of water flowing from the north polar region across the equator to the south polar region. We will observe what happens to the direction of the water flow as it moves southward on a spinning globe.

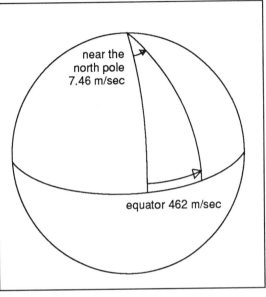

Fig. 5–1. As our spherical earth rotates, points on the equator move at a greater rotational velocity than points near the north or south pole.

ACTIVITY
Observe the demonstration and determine the effect of global rotation on currents.

MATERIALS
- lab apron
- safety goggles
- 500-mL round-bottomed flask
- two 15-cm lengths of wire
- string
- rubber band
- phenolphthalein solution (in a bowl or pan)
- pencil
- dilute sodium hydroxide solution (in dropping bottle with dropper)
- pen or crayon
- 2 ringstands

PROCEDURE
1. **CAUTION:** Be sure that the person who does the demonstration wears a lab apron and safety goggles.

2. Assemble equipment as shown in Fig. 5–2. Coat the round bottom portion of the flask with phenolphthalein solution.

181

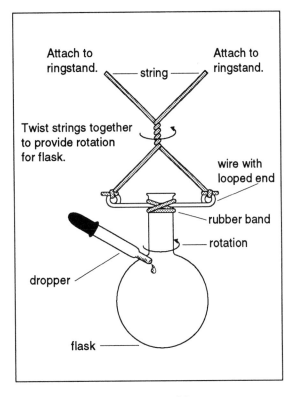

Fig. 5-2. Equipment assembly

Allow it to dry. When dry, the flask will have a cloudy white coating on its surface.

3. Predict the path of a drop of liquid as it flows down the flask as shown in Fig. 5-2. With a pencil, draw the predicted paths on Fig. 5-3 when
   a. the flask is not moving.
   b. the flask is spinning clockwise.
   c. the flask is spinning counterclockwise.

4. Test the path of flow of a drop of sodium hydroxide solution when it is placed on a nonspinning flask.
   a. Release one drop of sodium hydroxide solution just below the neck of the flask.
   b. Observe its path of flow. With a pen or crayon, record your observation in (A) in Fig. 5-3.

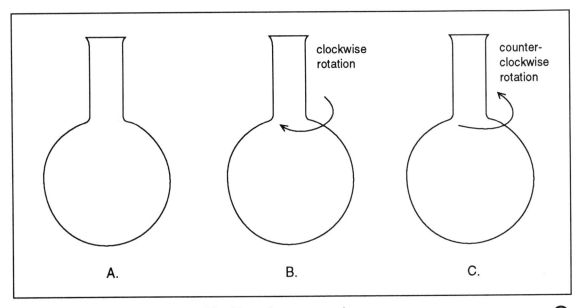

Fig. 5-3. Path of flow of a drop of liquid moving over a sphere

5. Rinse the flask with water and wipe it dry. Recoat the round bottom portion with phenolphthalein solution. Let it air-dry.

6. Test the path of a drop of sodium hydroxide solution placed on the flask while it is spinnng clockwise.
   a. Wind the apparatus, then release it to start the flask spinning.
   b. Just when the flask starts spinning, put a drop of sodium hydroxide solution on the flask.
   c. When the flask stops spinning, observe the drop's path of flow. With a pen or crayon, sketch your observation in (B) in Fig. 5–3.

7. Repeat Procedure 5, this time spinning the flask counterclockwise. Record your observation in (C) in Fig. 5–3.

QUESTIONS
1. How does the path of flow of the drop of sodium hydroxide solution on a non-moving flask compare with the path of flow of a drop on a spinning flask?

2. How does the direction of rotation affect the path of the drop? Suggest an explanation.

3. What forces acted on the drop of liquid as it flowed over the surface of the flask
   a. when it was not rotating?
   b. when it was rotating?

4. From a vantage point in outer space at the north pole, would the earth appear to move clockwise or counterclockwise? Cite evidence and make a diagram or demonstration to explain your answer.

5. The earth's rotational velocity is greater at points on the equator than at points near the poles. Explain or demonstrate why this is so.

FURTHER INVESTIGATIONS
1. Using references, find the meaning of each of these terms:
   a. the Coriolis effect
   b. centrifugal force
   c. centripetal force

2. Using references, read about the Ekman spiral, then make a diagram showing how a wind-driven current changes in direction and speed with increased depth.

6. Wind and Surface Currents

Thus far in our study of ocean currents we have investigated gravity currents, thermohaline circulation, and the effects of the earth's rotation. Now we look at wind, how it forms in the atmosphere, and how it produces both surface waves and surface currents.

Winds are currents of air. Winds develop whenever two adjacent bodies of air have different densities. Denser air sinks, pushing less-dense air upward. This movement produces a convection current. See Fig. 6–1.

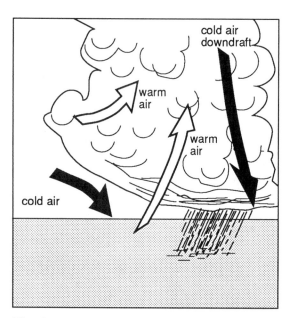

Fig. 6–1. A convection current forms when a dense, high-pressure air mass sinks and pushes up a less-dense, low-pressure air mass.

Two things affect the density and air pressure: temperature and water vapor. Warm air is less dense; cold air is more dense. Water vapor in an air mass decreases its density because vapor is only about half as dense as air. Rain, snow, and dew formation remove vapor from an air mass, leaving behind dryer, denser air.

Air is pulled toward the surface of the earth by gravity. The force of the air mass on the earth is called **air pressure**. Air pressure varies with the density of the air mass. At the same temperature, dry air exerts a greater force than moist air. Dry, dense air masses therefore produce high-pressure areas; moist, less-dense air masses produce low-pressure areas.

QUESTIONS

1. What is wind? How does wind develop?

2. How is a convection current produced in the air?

3. How can air become more dense? Less dense?

4. What kind of weather is associated with low pressure? With high pressure?

5. Look at a weather map in your local newspaper or on the evening TV news program. Where are the air masses more and less dense? What kind of weather would be associated with these air masses?

Global Winds

Sunlight is the earth's primary heat source. The energy from sunlight heats the oceans, atmosphere, lands, and forests, but the energy is not evenly distributed over the earth's surface. About 60 times more sunlight falls on equatorial areas than on polar areas. See Fig. 6–2. Consequently, hot equatorial air masses, which are often humid, are less dense than cold polar air masses, which are often dry.

At the poles, cold, dense air sinks, then flows toward the equator. Polar air becomes warmer as it moves away from the poles. Air masses at the equator move in the opposite manner. At the equator, hot, moist, and less-dense air rises and moves toward the poles. Equatorial air gradually cools as it moves away from the equator. The sinking of polar air and rising of equatorial air forms large-scale circulation patterns.

Earth's Rotation and Its Effect on Wind

When the earth rotates, it turns from west to east. However, because the earth is spherical, the surface at the equator moves much faster than at the poles. See Fig. 6–3. The atmosphere surrounding the earth also rotates at the same speed as the land and the ocean surface beneath it.

When we simulated the rotation of the earth in Topic 5, we saw that a fluid is deflected as it flows from the pole toward the equator. This deflection also occurs when an air mass moves toward the equator. See Fig. 6–3. In the northern hemisphere, as cold polar air travels southward, its rotational speed is slower than the rotational speed of the land and water beneath it. The cold air mass cannot keep up with the rotating earth. Therefore, air flowing from the north pole lags behind, producing cold, surface-level

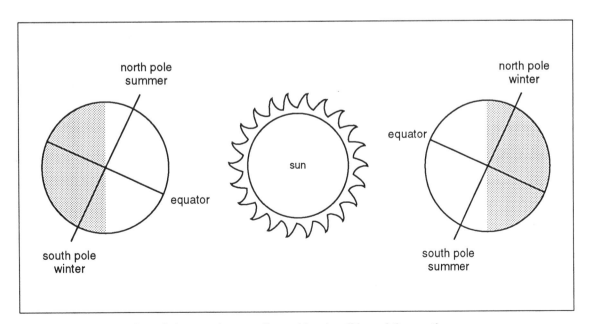

Fig. 6–2. Amount of sunlight at poles as affected by the tilting of the earth

185

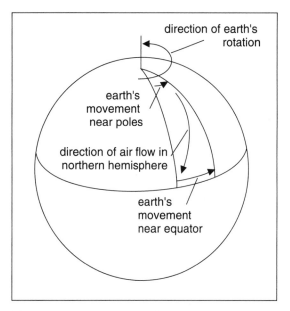

Fig. 6–3. An air mass flowing from the north pole toward the equator is deflected by the rotation of the earth.

winds that blow from the northeast. See Fig. 6–4. These winds are called the **polar easterlies.** Winds are named by the direction *from* which they blow.

As the polar easterlies move toward the equator, they become warmer and less dense. At about 60°N the air mass rises and moves northward at high altitude. This path of air circulation forms a closed loop called a **circulation cell**. See Fig. 6–4.

At the equator hot, humid air rises, cools, and loses moisture, producing rain. The cool dry air moves toward the north pole at a high altitude. The air gradually becomes cold, dry, and more dense. It begins to sink at about 30° N. The air then moves along the earth's surface back toward the equator, forming another circulation cell. See Fig. 6–4. These surface winds blowing from the northeast are called **tradewinds**. In the days when sailing ships carried goods from Eu-

rope to North America and from North America to the orient, they relied on these strong prevailing winds to make the journey as fast as possible.

A third circulation cell forms between 30° and 60° N. Here the surface winds blow from the southwest and are called the **prevailing westerlies**. The prevailing westerlies are the dominant winds blowing across most of the United States.

Similar circulation cells form in the southern hemisphere, producing characteristic surface wind patterns.

Two other areas were named because of the lack of steady prevailing winds. At the equator the air rises, producing a belt of weak, light, shifting winds called the **doldrums**. Because of the lack of winds, sailing vessels had a difficult time crossing the equator and were sometimes becalmed for

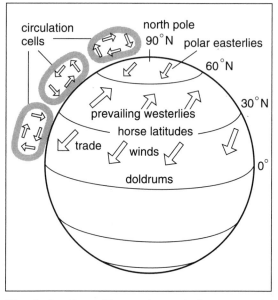

Fig. 6–4. Prevailing surface winds on a model of the earth, showing major circulation cells

186

long periods. Thus a long, monotonous period is sometimes called the doldrums.

At 30°N the air descends, also producing a region of light, variable winds. This region is called the **horse latitudes**. Supposedly, the horse latitudes got their name when sailing ships could not make headway and horses penned up in the hold died from lack of food and water and were thrown overboard.

QUESTIONS

6. Explain the reason that more sunlight falls on the equator than on the poles.

7. Show what the circulation cells look like in the southern hemisphere. Draw them on the edge of the globe as shown in Fig. 6–4. Show the vertical and horizontal direction of the wind in each cell.

8. Label either high or low pressure for the air masses
   a. at 30°N, 60°N, and 90°N.
   b. at 30°S, 60°S, and 90°S.

9. Using Fig. 6–4 as a model, draw arrows to show the circulation cells and direction of the surface winds as the air circulates in the southern hemisphere. Label the winds.

10. Compare the directions of the major currents of air in the northern and southern hemispheres. How are they similar and different?

11. Show where the doldrums and horse latitudes are located.

12. Winds at 40°S and 50°S are called the "roaring forties" and "furious fifties."

In which direction do they blow? Why do they blow so strongly?

Winds and Surface Currents

Winds can produce currents if they blow from the same direction for long periods. When wind pushes constantly on the ocean's surface, water particles at the surface begin to move, but not in the direction of the wind. Largely because of the rotational effect of the earth, surface water flows at a 20°– 45° angle to the right of the wind in the northern hemisphere and 20°– 45° to the left of the wind in the southern hemisphere.

Because water molecules tend to stick to each other, surface water movement sets deeper layers of water into motion. The speed of each successive layer decreases, and the angle of deflection increases with depth. Eventually some water particles flow in the direction opposite to the surface current. This current pattern is called the **Ekman spiral**. See Fig. 6–5.

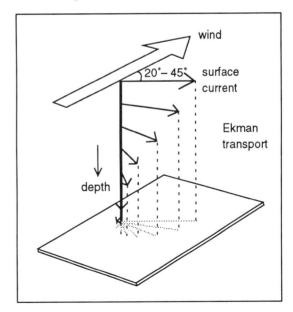

Fig. 6–5. The Ekman spiral

As a result of the Ekman spiral, water in a wind-driven current moves on the average about 90° to the right of the wind in the northern hemisphere and 90° to the left of the wind in the southern hemisphere. See Fig. 6–6. Water movement in surface currents is called **Ekman transport**. Note that winds are described by the direction *from* which they blow, whereas water currents are described by the direction *toward* which they flow.

QUESTIONS

13. Explain the similarities between water movement in wind-driven waves and water movement in currents.

14. On a sheet of paper draw arrows to represent the winds blowing from the west, the north, and the east. Then, using another colored pencil or a dashed line, show the average direction of the current produced by each wind.

Major Currents on the Ocean Surface

Continents affect both surface winds and currents. Fig. 6–7 is a simplified map showing some of the global surface winds that blow over the oceans. In the activity that follows, we will use information from Fig. 6–7 to account for the formation of currents. Circulation systems formed by currents are called gyres. A **gyre** is a circular current formed by a combination of the prevailing winds, the rotation of the earth, and land masses that interfere with the movement of water currents.

Gyres form in both hemispheres. To understand how a gyre forms, we will examine gyres in the northern hemisphere. Near the equator, tradewinds drive currents westward, forming the **north equatorial current**, which moves at about 100 cm per sec. At the western boundary of the ocean, the water turns and flows towards the north pole, forming the **western-ocean boundary currents**, the strongest in the gyre. Two ex-

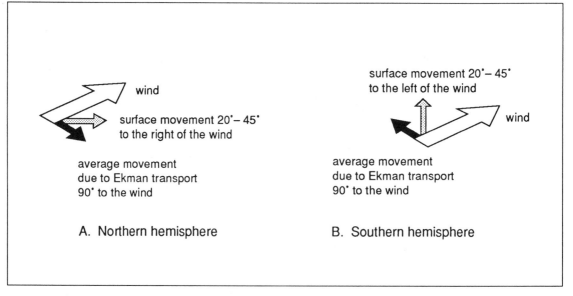

Fig. 6–6. The average deflection of water in wind-driven currents is 90°.

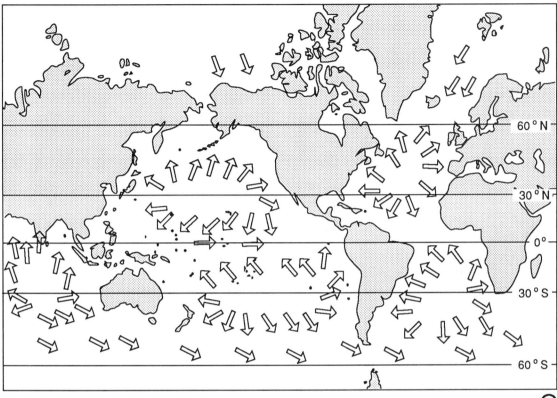

Fig 6–7. Simplified global wind patterns　ⓦ

amples are the **Gulf Stream** that runs in the Atlantic Ocean and the **Kuroshio Current** in the Pacific Ocean. They are narrower but deeper and swifter than the other currents in the gyre. Speeds of 200 cm/sec, for example, have been measured in the Gulf Stream. These currents, as deep as 1 km, generally remain in deeper water beyond the continental shelf. Western-ocean boundary currents carry warm water.

Eventually the currents fall under the influence of the westerly winds and begin flowing to the east. When they approach the eastern-ocean boundaries of continents, they turn and flow south, forming the **eastern-ocean boundary currents**. Eastern-ocean boundary currents are shallower and slower than western-ocean boundary currents. They flow over the continental shelves, carrying colder waters close to shore. Two examples are the **California Current** in the Pacific Ocean and the **Canary Current** in the Atlantic Ocean.

One major global current, the **equatorial countercurrent**, appears to be an exception to the circulation pattern set up by the gyres. This countercurrent forms just north of the equator in the region between the north equatorial current and the south equatorial current and flows in the opposite direction.

ACTIVITY 1

Relate major ocean surface currents to wind circulation patterns and the rotational effect of the earth.

MATERIALS

• blue and red pencils
• atlas (optional)

PROCEDURE

1. On Fig. 6–7, for each arrow indicating wind, draw another arrow with a blue pencil to show the average direction of the current set in motion by that wind.

2. Look for gyres, circulation patterns formed by the wind-driven currents. With a red pencil, lightly connect the currents that form each gyre.

3. Compare the simplified map of the currents you drew in Fig. 6–7 with the map showing the major surface ocean currents in Fig. 6–8. Describe the differences.

4. Using Fig. 6–7 as a guide, add arrows to the current lines in the North Pacific and North Atlantic oceans in Fig. 6–8.

5. Label the major ocean currents in Fig. 6–8. Refer to Table 6–1 for the names of the currents.

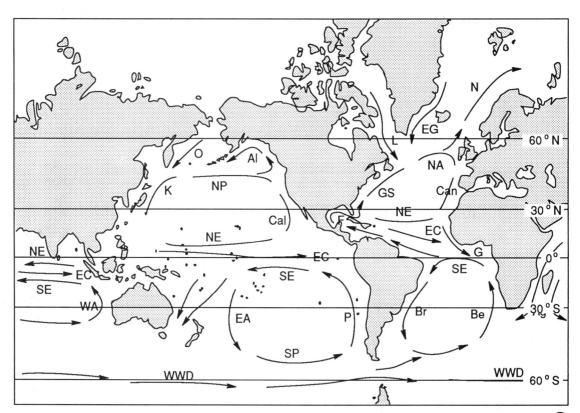

Fig. 6–8. Major surface currents of the earth's oceans

QUESTIONS

15. Look at the gyre formed in the North Pacific Ocean. Which of the prevailing winds drives
    a. the currents in the northernmost part of the gyre?
    b. the currents in the southernmost part of the gyre?

16. Describe the directions of the currents that flow offshore of the east coast and the west coast of the United States. How do these currents probably affect the climates along these two coasts?

17. Benjamin Franklin predicted the discovery of the Gulf Stream from his records of how long ships took to carry mail between the United States and England. Which way took longer?

18. In your own words, describe how each of the following affects current formation:
    a. prevailing wind
    b. the rotation of the earth
    c. the boundaries of the continents
    d. other currents or gyres

Water at Uneven Levels

We have all observed that water runs down hills. But what happens when one body of water is higher than the other and the two meet? This could occur when winds pile water up over the ocean, when the surface of the ocean rises in a low pressure area, or when two currents meet and one is stronger than the other, carrying more water.

Table 6–1. Key to the major surface currents shown in Fig. 6–8 ⓦ

Letter	Name of current	Letter	Name of current
Ag	Aguihas Current	K	Kuroshio Current
Al	Alaska Current	L	Labrador Current
Be	Benguela Current	N	Norwegian Current
Br	Brazil Current	NA	North Atlantic Current
Cal	California Current	NE	North Equatorial Current
Can	Canary Current	NP	North Pacific Current
EA	East Australia Current	O	Oyashio Current
EC	Equatorial Countercurrent	P	Peru Current (Humboldt)
EG	East Greenland Current	SE	South Equatorial Current
F	Florida Current	SP	South Pacific Current
G	Guinea Current	WA	West Australia Current
GS	Gulf Stream	WWD	West Wind Drift (Antarctic Circumpolar Current)

ACTIVITY 2
Simulate the interaction of bodies of water at different heights.

MATERIALS
- transparent plastic cup
- nail or pencil
- two 1 X 2-in. pieces of masking tape
- transparent plastic shoe box
- fresh water
- centimeter ruler
- waterproof pen
- blue food coloring
- coins for weights

PROCEDURE
1. Study the apparatus shown in Fig. 6–9. Notice the location of the hole in each cup.

2. Predict the direction of the gravity current that will form at each hole. Draw an arrow on each figure to show your prediction.

3. Test the system by carrying out the following steps:
   a. Obtain a transparent plastic cup and make a hole in the cup as shown in Fig. 6–9, either by firmly twisting a pencil point into the plastic or by melting a hole into the plastic with a hot nail.
   b. Cover the hole with a small piece of masking tape. Keep one end loose so that you can remove the tape easily.
   c. Fill the shoe box two-thirds full with room-temperature tap water.
   d. Fill the cup with blue-colored room-temperature water to a level about 1 cm above the water line on the shoe box. See (A) in Fig. 6–9. Add weights so that the cup will rest on the bottom of the shoe box.
   f. Gently place the cup in the liquid in the

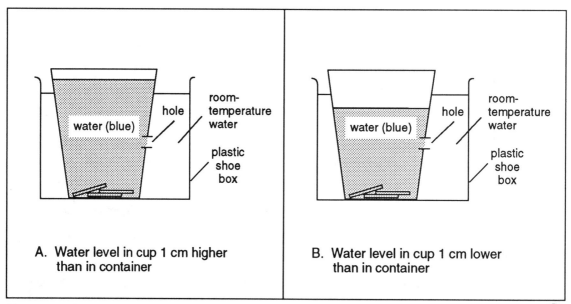

A. Water level in cup 1 cm higher than in container

B. Water level in cup 1 cm lower than in container

Fig. 6–9. Movement between water samples at different heights

shoebox. Then pull off the masking tape.

3. Observe the force and direction of the flow from the cup. Make a sketch to record your observations
   a. as soon as the tapes are removed.
   b. after 1 min.
   c. after 3 min.

4. Repeat Procedures 1–3, this time filling the cup to about 1 cm below the water level in the shoe box. See (B) in Fig. 6–9. Record your prediction and observations.

QUESTIONS

19. Wind blowing parallel to shore can create a current that moves out to sea, producing a valley in nearshore waters as shown in (A) in Fig. 6–10. A current of water, called an **upwelling**, moves from colder deep waters toward shore, filling the valley.
    a. Sketch arrows in (A) in Fig. 6–10 to show the water movement you predict in this example of an upwelling.
    b. Using the terms in this topic, explain this phenomenon.

20. Wind can pile up water, producing "hills" of seawater as shown in (B) in Fig. 6–10 Predict the current pattern that would result. Sketch arrows in (B) in Fig. 6–10 to show the water movement you predict in this example.

21. In the two examples in Fig. 6–10, which occurs in the southern hemisphere? In the northern hemisphere? How can you tell?

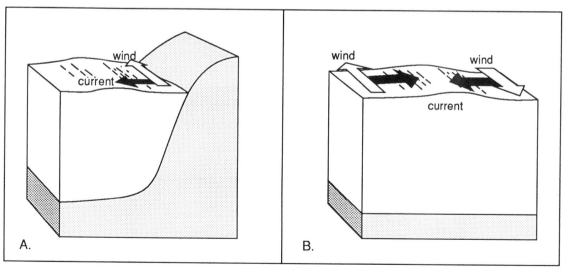

Fig. 6–10 . Situations in which water levels are uneven in the ocean   (W)

FURTHER INVESTIGATIONS

1. Save the weather maps from your local newspaper for about two weeks. Assemble them in order. Using what you know about changes in air mass density, atmospheric pressure, and prevailing winds, describe the pattern of weather changes during this period.

2. Invite an oceanographer or a meteorologist to class to talk about one of the following:
   a. global ocean currents and how they affect global and regional climate
   b. satellite studies of the ocean that reveal smaller-scale currents in coastal waters
   c. the relationship between currents and the richness of fishing grounds

3. Use references to learn more about upwellings. Where and when do they occur? What is the role of upwelling in supporting marine life? Report your findings to the class.

4. Read about the periodic phenomenon called El Niño. How is it related to uneven water levels? How and why does it form? Explain what it is and what effects it has on the ocean, on local and world climate, and on economies of nations.

5. Use information from atlases
   a. to show how shipping routes are related to currents and gyres.
   b. to compare the routes of great ocean explorers with maps of currents and gyres.

6. As a gyre forms, the water piles up in the center. Explain how higher water levels at the center of a gyre act in the opposite direction of the Ekman transport. Account for the westward movement of the equatorial currents.

7. Pressure

If you have ever held your breath and dived to the bottom of a swimming pool, you may have felt pressure on your ears. This **hydrostatic pressure** is due to the weight of water pressing on submerged objects. (**Hydro** means "water"; **static** means "at rest.") In this topic we will investigate how hydrostatic pressure changes with depth. We will also investigate whether hydrostatic pressure is the same in all directions. See Fig. 7–1.

Pressure is related to **force**. The difference between force and pressure is illustrated in Fig. 7–2. If you hold your hand palm-up and place a heavy book on it, you feel no pain. You support the book easily—

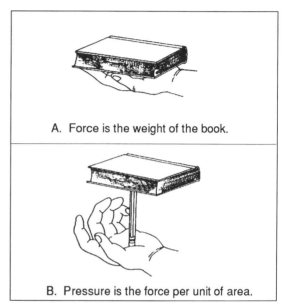

A. Force is the weight of the book.

B. Pressure is the force per unit of area.

Fig. 7–2. The difference between force and pressure

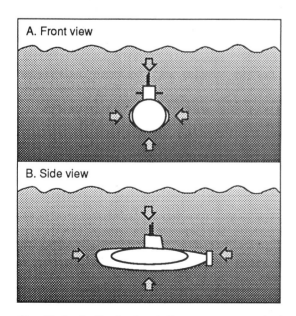

A. Front view

B. Side view

Fig. 7–1. Is the hydrostatic pressure exerted on a submarine the same in all directions?

unless it is a large unabridged dictionary. However, if you put a pencil on your palm with the eraser end down and put the book on top of the pencil, you are uncomfortable. Imagine what would happen if you turned the pencil end for end, rested the point on your palm, and put the book on the eraser end! Even the thought is painful.

In each case the same amount of **force** (the weight of the book) pushes down on your palm. When the book rests on your palm, the **pressure** is distributed over the entire surface of your palm. But when the book rests on the pencil, its force is applied to an eraser-sized area of your palm, increasing pressure on that area about 200 times. If you had rested the point of your pencil against your palm with the book on top of it, the pressure could have been as much as 4,000 times as great as the pressure of the book alone.

Pressure is calculated by dividing the amount of force by the surface area on which it rests.

Pressure = force/surface area

Manometer

A **manometer** is a device for measuring pressure. See Fig. 7–3. The one we will use consists of a J-shaped glass tube. Water is put in the tube so that the water level is the same in both the short and the long arms of the tube as shown in (A) in Fig. 7–4. We will measure pressure differences as the height to which the liquid rises in the long

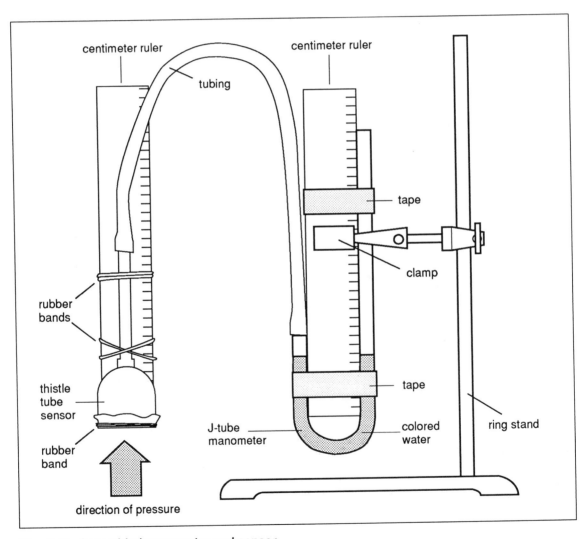

Fig. 7–3. Assembled manometer and sensor

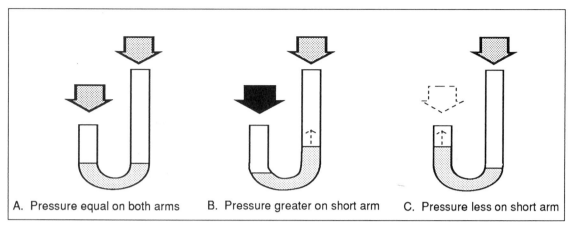

A. Pressure equal on both arms   B. Pressure greater on short arm   C. Pressure less on short arm

Fig. 7–4. Effects of pressure differences on liquid in a J-tube

arm of the J-tube. If pressure increases on the short arm of the tube, the water level rises in the long arm as shown in (B) in Fig. 7–4. Conversely, if pressure decreases in the short arm, the water level in the long arm falls. See (C) in Fig. 7–4.

In this activity we will connect a pressure-sensing device, called a **sensor**, to the short arm of a manometer. Even a slight change in pressure on the sensor will cause the water level in the long arm of the J-tube to rise or fall.

ACTIVITY
Investigate the nature of pressure in water.

MATERIALS
- glass J-tube
- 2 centimeter rulers
- masking tape
- ringstand and clamp
- colored water with 1 drop detergent
- balloon
- scissors
- thistle tube
- 3 rubber bands
- waterproof marking pen
- 100-cm length of tubing
- bucket, about 5-L capacity
- fresh water
- thermometer
- salt water

PROCEDURE
1. Set up the manometer. See Fig. 7–3.
   a. Attach the glass J-tube to a centimeter ruler with masking tape. Position the long arm of the tube next to the gradations on the ruler.
   b. Clamp the manometer to a ringstand so that the J-tube stands vertically as shown in Fig. 7–3.
   c. Fill the J-tube half-full of colored water.
   d. Gently tap both arms of the J-tube to prevent the water from sticking to the inside of the tube. There should now be equal amounts of water in both arms of the tube.

2. Assemble a sensor as shown in Fig. 7–3.
   a. Cut a piece of rubber out of a balloon

197

to fit over the end of the thistle tube. Attach the piece of balloon loosely with a rubber band.

b. Using a waterproof marking pen, make a dot in the center of the sensor.

c. Connect one end of the 45-cm tubing to the stem of the thistle tube.

d. Attach the sensor to the centimeter ruler with rubber bands.

3. Connect the tubing from the sensor to the manometer.

a. Be sure the tubing connections are airtight. Test by pressing on the sensor. The water level should rise in the longer arm of the J-tube. When you release the pressure on the sensor, the water levels in both arms of the J-tube should be at the same height.

b. If the water appears to stick to the inside of the tube, gently tap both arms of the J-tube.

4. Test the upward pressure exerted by fresh water.

a. Fill a bucket with fresh water.

b. Measure the temperature of the water. Record in Table 7–1.

c. Hold the sensor just above the water surface. Read the height of the water level in the long arm of the J-tube. The water may form a **meniscus**, a curved surface on the inside of the glass tube. Read the water level at the

Table 7–1. Water pressure by depth and direction

Water temperature °C: fresh water_____ salt water_____						
Depth of sensor (cm)	Height of water in long arm of J – tube					
	Upward pressure (cm)		Downward pressure (cm)		Horizontal pressure (cm)	
	fresh water	salt water	fresh water	salt water	fresh water	salt water
0						
1						
2						
3						
4						
5						
6						
7						
8						
9						
10						
11						
12						
13						
14						
15						
16						
17						
18						
19						

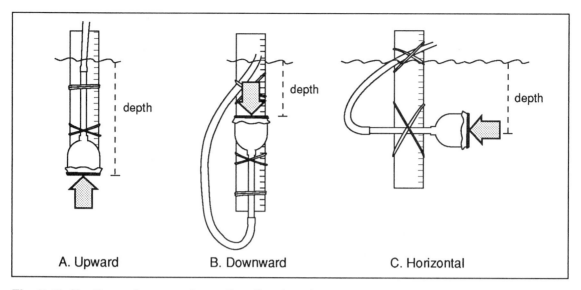

A. Upward   B. Downward   C. Horizontal

Fig. 7–5. Positions of sensors for testing direction of water pressure

bottom of the meniscus. Record this as the starting height in Table 7–1.

d. Push the sensor straight down 1 cm into the water. Read the height of the water in the long arm of the J-tube. Record your observations.

e. Repeat step (d), inserting the sensor deeper into the bucket. Measure hydrostatic pressure at depths to 20 cm, or as deep as you can go in the bucket.

5. Determine the downward pressure exerted by fresh water.
   a. Reposition the sensor as shown in (B) in Fig. 7–5.
   b. Repeat Procedures 4.c. through 4.e., this time measuring the depth of the sensor as the distance from the water surface to the stretched rubber surface of the sensor.

6. Determine the horizontal pressure exerted by fresh water.

a. Reposition the sensor so that it is fixed sideways on the centimeter ruler. See (C) in Fig. 7–5.

b. Start with the dot in the center of the sensor at the water surface. Repeat Procedures 4.c. through 4.e., this time measuring the depth of the sensor as the distance from the water surface to the dot.

7. Replace the fresh water in the bucket with salt water at the same temperature; then repeat Procedures 4 to 6. Record the data for salt water in Table 7–1.

8. Plot the pressure readings for both fresh water and salt water from Table 7–1. Use the grid in Fig. 7–6. Make separate graphs for the data from upward, downward, and horizontal pressure measurements. On each graph, display fresh water as a solid line and salt water as a dashed line.

199

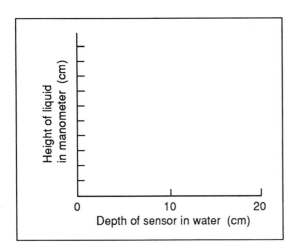

Fig. 7–6. Pressure variations of fresh water and salt water by depth ⓦ

QUESTIONS

1. Examine the three graphs you plotted on Fig. 7–6. What happens to the hydrostatic pressure
   a. as the depth increases?
   b. as the sensor is pointed in different directions?

2. Compare the three graphs. What differences, if any, are there between fresh water and salt water? How might this be explained?

3. From your data, what generalization can you make about the pressure on all sides
   a. of a very small sphere at 10 cm below the surface?
   b. of a submarine like the one shown in Fig. 7–1?

4. Analyze the experimental procedure.
   a. How accurate is the manometer-sensor device for measuring pressure? How can you tell?
   b. How reliable is the manometer-sensor device? What is your evidence?
   c. What problems occurred that could be sources of experimental error? How could the device or the procedure be improved?
   d. Predict what would happen if the rubber balloon were stretched tightly over the end of the thistle tube. If time permits, test your prediction.

5. Does temperature affect water pressure? Explain your answer.

Atmospheric Pressure

As we have just seen, water exerts pressure that changes with depth. The air we live in also exerts pressure, even though we are seldom aware of its presence. A familiar example is drinking through a straw. As the pressure inside your mouth is reduced, air pressure on the liquid forces it up the straw. See Fig. 7–7.

Fig. 7–7. Atmospheric pressure makes it possible to drink through a straw.

We live at the bottom of a layer of air more than 550 km thick that surrounds the earth. Gravity pulls the air toward the earth. Density within the layer gradually increases from least dense at the outer edge to most dense at the earth's surface. The average pressure at the earth's surface, measured at sea level, is defined as one **atmosphere** (atm).

1 atm = average pressure of
atmospheric layer (at sea level)

As we move toward the outer edges of the atmosphere, pressure decreases. Below sea level—in an air-filled mine for example—atmospheric pressure increases to more than 1 atm. Our bodies, adapted to living at 1 atm, are sensitive to pressure changes. For example, our ears feel pressure changes when we drive up and down a mountain road or when we go up and down in an elevator in a tall building.

Seawater is about 800 times denser than air. A column of seawater 10 m high exerts the same pressure as the entire 550 km layer of air above it. Hydrostatic pressure of seawater can also be measured in atmospheric units as follows:

1 atm = pressure exerted by 10 m seawater

Using the atmosphere as a unit of pressure, we can account for the total pressure exerted on a submerged object. See Table 7–2. A fish 10 m under the surface of the sea is under 2 atm of pressure—1 atm from the water above it and 1 atm from the air above the water. If the fish swims down to 20 m, perhaps to escape a predator, it is under 3 atm of pressure.

Because of pressure, living in the ocean differs from living on land. Air pressure

Table 7–2. Relationship between water depth and pressure

Depth in meters (m)	Pressure in atmospheres (atm)
0 = sea level	1
10	2
20	3
100	11

changes very little with modest vertical movement; water pressure changes rapidly. If we walk down the stairs in a building from the third floor to ground level, a vertical distance of about 10 m, the atmospheric pressure exerted on us essentially does not change. But if we dive from the surface of the ocean to a depth of 10 m, the atmospheric pressure exerted on us doubles from 1 to 2 atm. If we dive to 20 m, the pressure triples.

Marine mammals are like humans in many ways. They breathe air at the surface and hold their breath when they dive into the ocean. Their bodies have adapted for breath-holding and diving. Some can dive to great depths and remain there for long periods. Fig. 7–8 shows some records for depths and times for several species.

QUESTIONS

6. At sea level the density of fresh water at 4°C is 1.000 g/cm³, and the density of seawater at 4°C is 1.028 g/cm³. What is the water pressure at the bottom of a column of ten 1-cm cubes of fresh water? Of seawater?

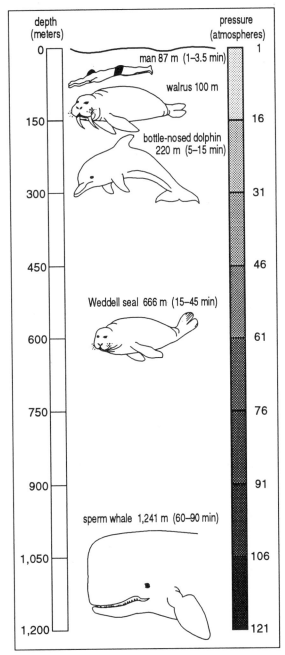

depth
(meters)

pressure
(atmospheres)

0 — 1

man 87 m (1–3.5 min)

walrus 100 m

150 — 16

bottle-nosed dolphin
220 m (5–15 min)

300 — 31

450 — 46

Weddell seal 666 m (15–45 min)

600 — 61

750 — 76

900 — 91

sperm whale 1,241 m (60–90 min)

1,050 — 106

1,200 — 121

Fig. 7–8. Diving depth and duration records (Source: Adapted from J. Cousteau, *The Ocean World*, 1979.)

7. How many atmospheres of pressure is each of the mammals shown in Fig. 7–8 experiencing when it is diving to its maximum depth?

8. Another unit used by engineers to measure pressure is **pounds per square inch (psi)** where

1 atm = 14.7 psi, and

1 psi = 0.06804 atm

Using the depths shown in Fig. 7–8, calculate the pounds per square inch for each mammal.

9. Aquaria vary greatly in size, shape, and purpose. Calculate the pressures at the bottom of
   a. a 10-L saltwater display aquarium filled to a depth of 1 m high.
   b. a 10-L saltwater breeding tank filled to 20 cm high.
   c. the Monterey Bay Aquarium's main display tank, which is 9.5 m (31 ft) high with a water depth of 8.5 to 8.6 m (28 ft) and contains 1,326,500 L (350,000 gal) of seawater.

FURTHER INVESTIGATION
Find out how pressure is measured and what units are used
   a. by meteorologists who give us daily weather reports.
   b. by airplane pilots.
   c. by physicists.
   d. by plumbers.
   e. by nurses and doctors who measure blood pressure.

8. Effects of Pressure

How well adapted are humans for diving and working under water? How does hydrostatic pressure affect the human body?

Let's consider what happens to a free diver (also known as a skin diver). At the surface, an adult male free diver can inhale and hold about 5 L of air in his lungs. The inhaled air is at a pressure of 1 atm. If he dives to a depth of 10 m, he is under 2 atm of pressure. See Fig. 8–1. What does the increased pressure do to the volume of air in his lungs? How does this increase affect his blood, tissues, and skeletal structure?

We will simulate the effects of pressure on a free diver's body by using the syringe system shown in Fig. 8–2. The syringe barrels simulate the diver's rigid skeletal structure. Air and water in the syringes simulate the gases and liquids in the diver's body. By pressing the plungers of the syringes, we can test whether increased pressure causes the air and the water to **compress**, that is, to decrease in volume. By pulling the plungers, we can test whether decreased pressure causes the air and the water to **expand**, that is, to increase in volume.

ACTIVITY
Investigate the effects of pressure changes on the volume of air and water.

MATERIALS
• two 50-mL graduated syringes
• 5-cm length of tubing
• water

PROCEDURE
1. Investigate the effect of increased pressure on air volume. See (A) in Fig. 8–2.
   a. Predict what will happen to the volume of the air in the syringes when pressure is increased. Record your predictions in Table 8–1.
   b. Assemble the equipment as shown in (A) in Fig. 8–2. Fill each syringe with

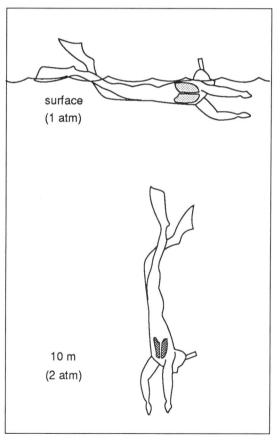

Fig. 8–1. How does increased water pressure affect a free diver?

surface
(1 atm)

10 m
(2 atm)

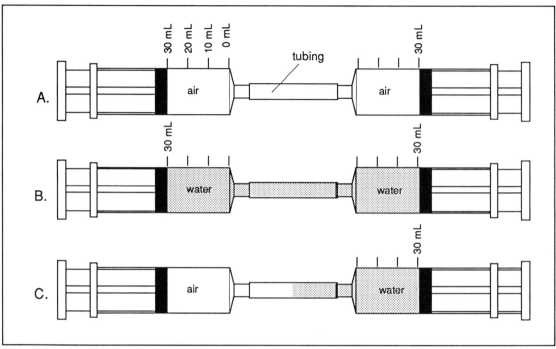

Fig. 8–2. Testing how pressure changes affect the volume of air, water, and an air-water system

30 mL of air. Connect the syringes with tubing.

c. Test the effect of increased pressure on gas volume by pushing in on the plungers of both syringes. Observe the volume of the air when it is under increased pressure. Record your data in Table 8–1.

d. Release the pressure on the plungers. Observe and record what happens to the volume of air in each syringe.

e. Disconnect the tubing before continuing to Procedure 2.

2. Investigate the effect of decreased pressure on air volume. See (A) in Fig. 8–2.

a. Predict what will happen to the volume of the air in the syringes when pressure is decreased. Record your predictions in Table 8–1.

b. Reassemble the equipment so that each syringe is filled with 30 mL of air. Record the starting volume of the air.

c. Test the effect of decreased pressure on air volume by slowly and steadily pulling both plungers. Observe what happens to the volume of the air. Record your data in Table 8-1.

d. Release the plungers. Observe what happens. Record your data.

e. Disconnect the tubing before going on to the next procedure.

3. Investigate the effects of changing pres-

Table 8–1. Effects of pressure on air and water volume

	Increased pressure			Decreased pressure		
	Starting volume (mL)	Volume when plungers pushed in (mL)	Volume after plungers released (mL)	Starting volume (mL)	Volume when plungers pulled out (mL)	Volume after plungers released (mL)

Air
  Predicted
  Observed						

Water
  Predicted
  Observed						

Air and water
  Predicted
  Observed						

sure on water. See (B) in Fig. 8–2. Repeat Procedures 1 and 2, this time using water in the syringes. Be sure the tubing contains water too. Record your observations in Table 8–1.

4. Investigate the effects of changing pressure on a mixed air-water system. See (C) in Fig. 8–2. Repeat Procedures 1 and 2, this time filling one syringe to 30 mL with water and the other to 30 mL with air. Connect the two syringes with tubing that is half-filled with water.

QUESTIONS

1. How did you measure the volume of the air and the water in the syringe system?

2. When pressure increased, what happened to the volume of the air? Of the water?

3. When pressure decreased, which showed the greater increase in volume, air or water?

4. How did an increase in pressure affect the air-water system? How did a decrease in pressure affect it?

5. Analyze the procedure.
   a. Did any air or water leak from the system while you moved the plungers? Did any enter the system? How could you demonstrate your answer?
   b. Did the mass of the air or water change? How do you know?

6. Apply what you have learned from the syringe system to the effects of pressure on the human body.
   a. Which is more affected by changes in water pressure, the air in the lungs or the liquids in the blood and body tissues? Explain.
   b. What happens to the volume of a free diver's body when descending? What happens to the lungs, the blood, other tissues, and the skeletal structure?
   c. What happens when the diver ascends?

7. If you had to transport supplies in a submarine or a spaceship—vessels with limited space—how would you transport air? Water?

Pressure and Gas Volume

A general statement describing the effect of pressure on gas volume is **Boyle's Law**:

> If the temperature of a gas does not change, its volume decreases as the pressure increases; conversely, as pressure decreases, its volume increases.

Let's apply Boyle's Law to a tube opened at one end and filled at the surface with 1 L of air. See Table 8–2. When the tube is lowered into water with its opening down, air is trapped inside by the upward pressure of the surrounding water. At a depth of 10 m, the water pressure is 2 atm, double the surface pressure. The hydrostatic pressure at 10 m compresses the air inside the tube to 0.5 L, half its original volume. Air compresses inside the tube until the air pressure inside the tube equals the water pressure. Thus at 10 m the air pressure inside the tube is 2 atm.

QUESTIONS

8. Complete Table 8–2.
   a. At each depth, air pressure inside the tube equals the hydrostatic pressure. Record the air pressure in the second column.
   b. Calculate the volume of the air in the tube. Tell how you made the calculations.
   c. Complete the sketches showing the volume of air in the tube.

9. Make a graph in Fig. 8–3 showing how air volume changes with depth. Plot the data from Table 8–2. At which of these intervals does the greatest change in air volume take place?
   a. from surface to 10 m
   b. 10 m to 20 m
   c. 20 m to 30 m
   d. 30 m to 40 m

10. We began this topic by asking what effect pressure has on a free diver. At the surface his lungs are filled with 5 L of air.
    a. What is the volume of air in his lungs at 10 m? Describe what happens to the air as he descends.
    b. To what depth would a person have to descend to reduce lung volume from its normal volume at sea level to one-third that volume?

11. The expansion of air as it rises to the surface can be used to lift heavy objects off the seafloor. For example, while under water a diver may attach a sturdy nylon or canvas lift-bag to a boat anchor, then put some air into the bag. The air inside the bag expands and helps raise the anchor.

206

Table 8–2. Changes in air due to changes in water pressure in a tube open at one end ⓦ

Depth (m)	Water pressure (atm)	Pressure of air in tube (atm)	Volume of air in tube (L)	Sketch of air in tube
0 (surface)	1	1	1.0	
10	2			
20		3		?
30			0.25	?
40				?

a. If a lift-bag is filled with 2 L of air at 40 m under water and allowed to rise, what is the bag's volume when it is at 15 m? When it reaches the surface?

b. How does the expansion of air make it easier to raise the anchor with a lift bag than without one? Explain in terms of density and buoyancy.

12. Some fish have a **swim bladder**—a gas-filled space that controls buoyancy. If these fish swim into a net at a depth of 40 m and a trawler quickly hauls them to the surface, what might happen to them? What could be done to minimize harm to these fish?

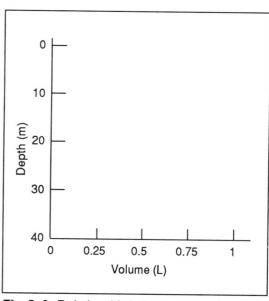

Fig. 8–3. Relationship between water depth and gas volume ⓦ

13. Crabs and lobsters do not have swim bladders. How would hauling them up from a depth of 30 m affect them?

Pressure and the Human Diver

Greater pressures under water affect the lungs and other air-filled spaces that connect to the outside of the body. These spaces include the middle ear, which is connected by the Eustachian tube to the throat, and the nasal sinuses, which are connected to the nasal passage. See Fig. 8–4.

As divers descend, they quickly feel the effects of increasing pressure as it compresses air in the body spaces. Pressure effects on delicate membranes in the ears and sinuses can cause senations that divers call "squeezes."

The eardrum between the middle ear and the outer ear is particularly sensitive to pressure changes. To avoid pain and damage to their eardrums, divers must equalize the water pressure outside and the air pressure inside their throat and ears. To do this they yawn, swallow forcefully, wiggle the jaw, or pinch the nose closed and blow gently. This opens the Eustachian tube and lets air from the throat enter the middle ear. The sensation divers feel when "clearing the ears" is like the popping you feel when you travel up a mountain or take off in a plane.

Injuries caused by pressure differences are called **barotrauma** (**baro** refers to pressure, **trauma** to injury). If the pressure is not equalized and the Eustachian tube remains closed, a diver may suffer pain, bleeding in the middle ear, or even a rupture of the eardrum— injuries that can lead to infection or even permanent hearing loss. Pressure imbalances can also affect nasal sinuses blocked by congestion.

QUESTIONS

14. Explain how water pressure affects a diver's eardrums. Make a sketch.

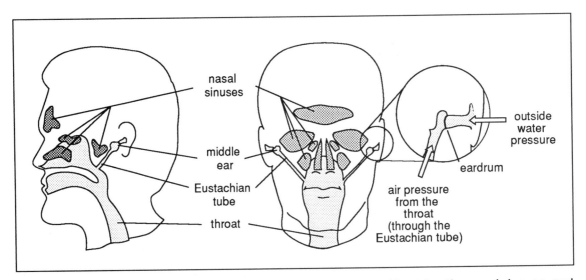

Fig. 8–4. Air spaces in the head include the middle ear, the Eustachian tube, the nasal sinuses, and the throat.

15. When a diver says she had to "clear her ears" while descending on a dive, what does she mean? What did she do?

16. Because faces differ in shape and size, divers must try on masks for proper fit, just as they try on shoes. Fig. 8–5 shows a diver fitting a mask over her eyes and nose without putting on the head strap.
    a. She inhales air through her nose. If the mask fits properly, it forms an airtight seal. As long as she holds her breath, the mask stays in place without the strap and without being held against her face. How is this possible?
    b. If the mask is airtight, will it be watertight under water? Explain your reasoning.

17. Occasionally during descent, air compresses inside a diving mask, causing an uncomfortable pulling sensation on a diver's eyes. What causes this and what could the diver do?

18. Explain how pressure changes affect our ears
    a. when we drive up a mountain.
    b. when we drive down a mountain.

19. Years ago airplane passengers were given chewing gum before the flight took off. Why? Why have airlines discontinued this practice?

20. What could happen to a diver if the opening to the nasal sinuses were blocked on the way back to the surface?

FURTHER INVESTIGATIONS

1. Use references to learn more about gases, including
   a. Dalton's law.
   b. Boyle's law.
   c. Charles's law.
   d. Henry's law.
   e. the general gas law.

2. What happens to a diver's vision under water? What colors does a diver see? How do things appear under water? Interview divers or use library references to find out.

3. Find out what happens to human hearing under water. How well does sound travel under water? How does being in water affect a diver's ability to hear?

Fig. 8–5. Trying on a mask for fit

9. Underwater Diving Technologies

People have known for centuries that they could carry air under water. **Diving bells** were first used in Europe in the 1600s for salvaging cannons, metals, and other precious materials from shallow bays and lakes. Such bells were made from wooden barrels, metal kettles, and other air containers.

In 1690 Edmund Halley, the English scientist who discovered Halley's Comet, designed a diving bell. His design was used for nearly 100 years. See Fig. 9–1. The Halley diving bell had two lead-weighted barrels—a large working barrel and a smaller air-refill barrel. Both barrels had openings on the bottom that allowed air and water to enter. Leather hoses attached to the barrels allowed air to flow to a person working inside the bell and to a diver working outside.

By the late 1700s inventors had devised ways to pump air continuously into diving bells, eliminating the need for a refill barrel. More advanced diving bells are still used today.

QUESTIONS

1. If the diving bell shown in Fig. 9–1 were moved to a deeper level, what would happen to the volume of air inside it?

2. How would this system provide air for the diver working outside the bell?

3. What would happen to the airflow if the smaller refill barrel were moved above the larger barrel?

Compressed Air

Recall from Topic 4 that movement is always in the direction of the stronger of two forces. Because pressure increases quickly with depth, air cannot flow down from the surface without additional force.

Air can be forced under water if it is compressed. Compression pushes the air particles closer together, increasing the pressure. This provides the force to move air to divers under water.

Hard-hat divers breathe compressed air that is continuously supplied from pumps on the surface. Conventional hard-hat divers wear suits, usually made from canvas, and heavy metal helmets. See Fig. 9–2.

Fig. 9–1. An air-filled wooden container permitted divers to work under water.

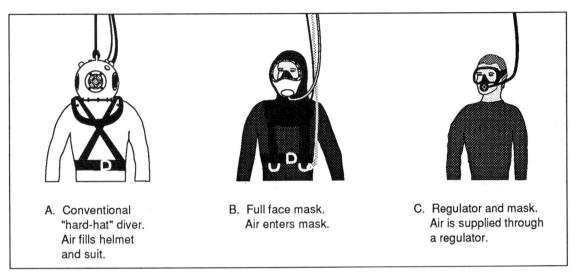

A. Conventional "hard-hat" diver. Air fills helmet and suit.

B. Full face mask. Air enters mask.

C. Regulator and mask. Air is supplied through a regulator.

Fig. 9–2. Common surface-supported commercial diving systems

Despite its awkwardness, this technology is widely used in underwater construction and repair, in the offshore oil industry, and for salvage or recovery operations. Newer diving gear uses rubber suits and lighter, smaller helmets or face masks.

A commercial hard-hat diver needs training to learn how to move about safely and to use tools under water. Hard-hat divers can remain under water for long periods, but their movement and vision are restricted.

Scuba Diving

The dream of being able to move about freely under water became a reality in 1943 when Jacques Cousteau and Emil Gagnan perfected the **demand regulator**, better known as **scuba**, which stands for **s**elf-**c**ontained **u**nderwater **b**reathing **a**pparatus. This device allows a diver to breathe safely and easily from a tank of compressed air. See Fig. 9–3.

In Topic 8 we discovered that compression forces a given mass of gas into a smaller volume, making it denser than atmospheric

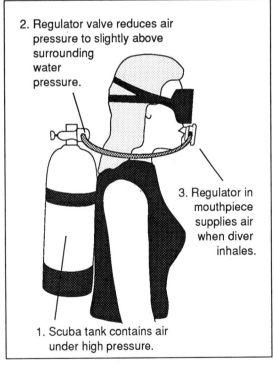

2. Regulator valve reduces air pressure to slightly above surrounding water pressure.

3. Regulator in mouthpiece supplies air when diver inhales.

1. Scuba tank contains air under high pressure.

Fig. 9–3. A scuba regulator adjusts the pressure of air inhaled by a diver so that it is about equal to the pressure of the surrounding water.

211

air. As the diver descends, the regulator adjusts airflow so that the air is at the same pressure as the water and the diver's lungs remain at their normal size.

QUESTIONS

4. At sea level, air density is about 0.0013 g/mL. Using the formula given below, find the mass of a liter of air at sea level.

$$\text{Density} = \frac{\text{mass}}{\text{volume}} = \frac{g}{mL}$$

5. What would be the mass of 1 L of air taken under water to 10 m? Explain how you arrived at your answer. Pressure increases gradually at the rate of 1 atm per 10 m. One atmosphere is about 1 kgf/cm.

6. Complete Table 9–1 and Fig. 9–4. In Fig. 9–4, sketch the size of the lung in the box below each diver. Put in dots to represent the density of air in each lung. The examples show divers at sea level. Explain the similarities and differences you find in the volume, density, and mass of the air in the lungs of the two divers.

Problems with Compressed Air

Scuba gear allows divers to descend more comfortably, stay under longer, and go deeper than they can as breath-holding free divers. However, problems related to pressure differences are more serious for divers using compressed air than for free divers.

Scuba divers must breathe in and out continuously. Holding their breath while

Table 9–1. Volume, density, and mass of the air in the lungs of a of a scuba diver and the lungs of a free diver at different depths ⓦ

Depth (m)	Pressure (atm)	Volume of lungs (L)		Density of air in lungs (g/L)		Mass of air in lungs (g)	
		Free diver	Scuba diver	Free diver	Scuba diver	Free diver	Scuba diver
0		5	5	1.3	1.3	6.5	6.5
10							13.0
20		1.66					
30				5.2			

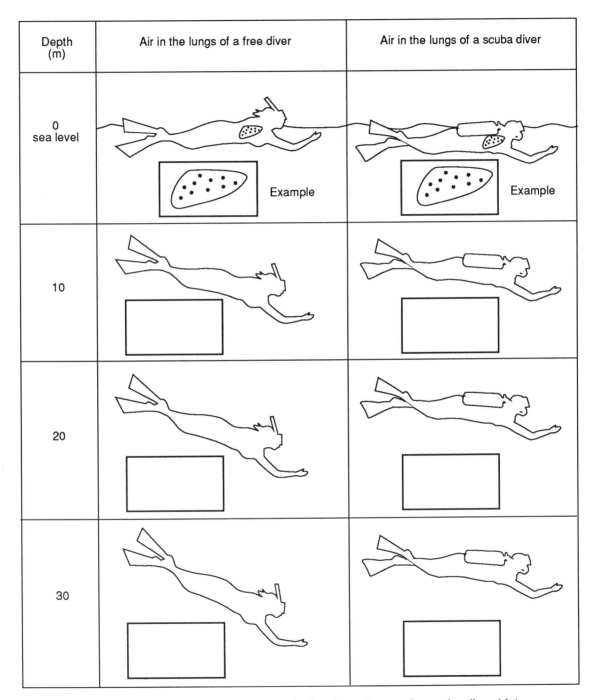

Depth (m)	Air in the lungs of a free diver	Air in the lungs of a scuba diver
0 sea level	Example	Example
10		
20		
30		

Fig. 9–4. Comparing lung volume and air density in a free diver and a scuba diver (dots represent "units" of air)

they ascend is very dangerous because trapped air expands when a scuba diver ascends. For example, the breath held in ascending from 30 m expands the lungs four times—enough to rupture them. Bubbles of air can also escape from the ruptured lungs into the circulatory system, blocking the flow of blood to vital parts of the body.

Scuba diving is an exciting sport, but no one should attempt it without instruction by a professional instructor. Scuba divers must learn how pressure affects gases, how to use specialized equipment, and how to plan for safe dives. For safety, dive shops require that customers be certified before they can rent equipment or have their tanks refilled with compressed air. Certification requires careful training, passing a written test, and demonstrating practical skills.

Pressure and Dissolved Gases

Another risk from scuba diving comes from the effect of pressure on gases that are dissolved in the blood. A familiar example of a gas dissolved under pressure greater than 1 atm is a bottle of carbonated soda. As long as the bottle remains closed and the pressure inside stays high, the gas (carbon dioxide) remains in solution. See (A) in Fig. 9–5. When the cap is removed, the pressure is released and the gas that was dissolved in the water begins to come out of solution, forming bubbles. See (B) Fig. 9–5.

The body of a scuba diver under water is much like soda bottled under pressure. The diver's lungs are filled with air at a pressure equal to the surrounding water, called **ambient** pressure. Air from the lungs dissolves in the blood and circulates throughout the body. High pressures force greater amounts of gas to dissolve in the blood and tissues than the body is accustomed to at sea level

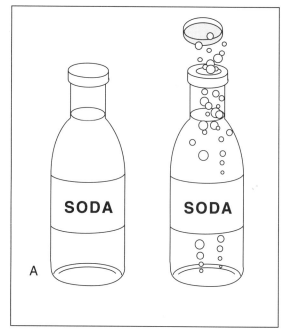

Fig. 9–5. Gas dissolved in a bottle of soda forms bubbles when the pressure is decreased.

(1 atm).

As Table 9–2 shows, air is a mixture of gases, mostly nitrogen and oxygen. Our bodies use oxygen rapidly in respiration. However, we do not use nitrogen gas, so under normal 1-atm conditions we exhale it. During scuba diving, however, excess nitrogen gas is forced under pressure into the tissues, where it accumulates in increasing amounts with depth and time under water until the tissues are fully **saturated**.

At a depth of 25 m or deeper, dissolved nitrogen gas can cause **nitrogen narcosis**, sometimes called "rapture of the deep." Divers affected by nitrogen narcosis feel an intoxication similar to the effect of alcohol. Their reaction times are slowed, and their judgment and reasoning are impaired. Disoriented divers are in peril if they become unsure of the direction to the surface. No

Table 9–2. Percentage composition of gases in air by volume

Nitrogen	78.1%
Oxygen	20.9%
Argon	0.9%
Carbon dioxide	0.03%
Water vapor	variable
Others Neon Helium Methane Krypton Hydrogen Nitrous oxide Xenon	0.07%

diver is immune to the effects of nitrogen narcosis, but susceptibility and the depth at which the symptoms occur vary. The symptoms may be relieved, with no lasting ill effects, by ascending to a shallower level.

Decompression sickness is a much more serious problem. **Decompression** is the reduction in pressure during ascent from deeper water. In decompression, excess nitrogen in the blood comes out of solution and forms bubbles the way an open bottle of carbonated soda does. If the nitrogen bubbles are tiny enough to travel through the circulatory system, they are not immediately dangerous. However, if the bubbles are larger, they may block tiny blood vessels, causing mild symptoms such as a tingling "pins and needles" sensation. If the bubbles are too large to get through the circulatory system, they can kill a diver by blocking the flow of blood to vital organs such as the brain, spinal cord, or heart. They can lodge in the joints, causing a painful condition called the "bends," or they can seriously damage nerves. See Fig. 9–6.

Divers can get decompression sickness if they
• stay down too long.
• dive too deep.
• come up too fast.
• make too many dives in too short a time.
• exercise heavily during the dive.
• travel to altitudes above 2,500 m too soon after diving.
Being in poor physical condition also increases a diver's risk of decompression sickness.

Avoiding Decompression Problems

Standard **dive tables**, based on those developed for U.S. Navy divers, show the

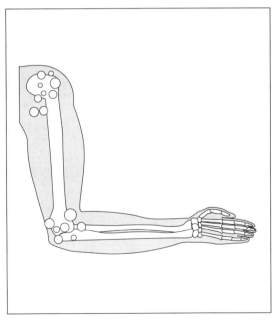

Fig. 9–6. Bubbles of nitrogen gas may form around the joints when pressure decreases.

215

maximum times scuba divers may remain safely at specific depths. Divers use these tables to plan dives that avoid decompression problems. They must be very cautious not to exceed the safe time and depth limits. They also must ascend at slow, safe rates varying from 0.3 to 1 m per second, about the rate that a small bubble of air floats to the surface.

If severe symptoms such as numbness, pain, or unconsciousness occur, a stricken diver must be rushed immediately to a recompression chamber and attended by a physician. See Fig. 9–7. A diver with decompression sickness is placed inside the recompression chamber, which is then tightly sealed. Pressure inside the chamber is increased so that the nitrogen bubbles lodged in the victim's body redissolve. Then the pressure inside the chamber is gradually decreased to 1 atm as the diver breathes off excess nitrogen gas.

Recreational scuba divers rarely stay at a fixed depth, so dive tables are not practical for them. Decompression computers have been developed for scuba diving at variable depths. These computers even account for the rates at which different kinds of body tissues absorb and release nitrogen. "Fast" tissues accumulate and release nitrogen more rapidly than "slow" tissues. Blood, muscle, and nervous tissues are fast tissues; bone, connective, and adipose (fatty) tissues are slow tissues.

Other factors that affect the rate of nitrogen accumulation and release include water

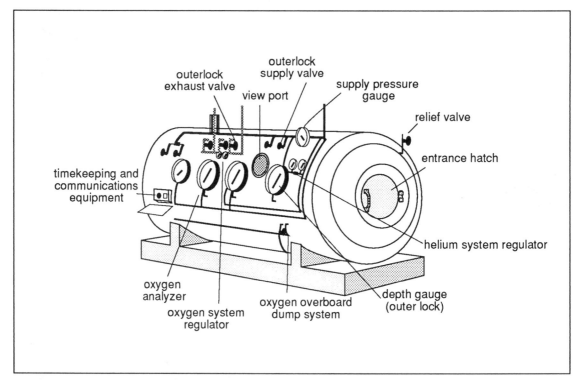

Fig. 9–7. Recompression chamber

temperature, amount of exertion, and the diver's age, sex, quantity of body fat, and state of health.

Gas Mixtures

Commercial scuba divers often need to work at depths that exceed the safety limits set for recreational divers. They use special gas mixtures that replace nitrogen with helium. Helium is expensive, but it is absorbed more slowly than nitrogen. For example, divers using compressed air may work to depths just under 65 m; with helium-oxygen mixtures they can work at depths down to 130 m. Because helium is less dense than nitrogen, the vocal cords vibrate faster, producing a high, squeaky voice. Special "unscramblers" had to be devised to make those voices understandable.

Ironically, oxygen, the gas vital for life, is also a limiting factor in scuba diving with compressed gases. At about 7 atm of pressure a condition called **oxygen toxicity** can cause convulsions or unconsciousness. Special gas mixtures with less oxygen are prepared for commercial diving that exceeds the safe limit.

QUESTIONS

7. Compare the advantages and disadvantages of conventional hard-hat diving with those of scuba diving.

8. Compare pressure-related problems for free divers and scuba divers.
   a. What problems occur on descent?
   b. What problems occur on ascent?

9. Most scuba divers are trained at sea level and in salt water. How might diving in high-altitude freshwater lakes differ from diving at sea level?

10. What is the difference between compressed air and compressed gas mixtures? Under what conditions is a compressed-gas mixture better for divers to use than compressed air?

Saturation Diving

With growing interest in offshore resources, a new type of diving technology called **saturation diving** was developed. This technology allows divers to go very deep or stay under water for such a long time that their body tissues absorb all the nitrogen (or helium) they can hold.

Saturation diving has disadvantages. It requires very slow, careful decompression. No matter how deep a saturated diver goes or how long the diver stays under water, the decompression time and procedure remain the same: 24 hours of decompression for every 30 m of depth. Saturation diving is also expensive because it requires costly gas mixtures, underwater life-support shelters, and highly trained surface-support teams with extensive equipment.

Underwater habitats provide divers, called **aquanauts**, with food, water, a supply of oxygen-containing gas, and a place to sleep and work. See Fig. 9–8. These habitats are designed to let aquanauts make scientific observations, conduct underwater experiments, and use computers, scientific instruments, and communication devices.

Because the entire habitat is filled with gas at a pressure equal to the pressure of the surrounding water, the aquanauts can leave and reenter the habitat to carry out their work. They are usually tethered to the habitat to keep them from getting lost. Some habitats are designed so that aquanauts working outside breathe gases from a hose connected to the habitat's supply; other

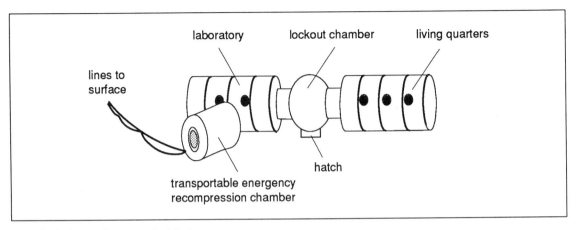

Fig. 9–8. An underwater habitat

habitats require aquanauts to use scuba gear for outside work. If divers run short of air, they must return to the habitat, not to the surface. They cannot make emergency swims upward without risking severe decompression problems because their bodies are saturated with dissolved gas.

Several techniques may be used to return aquanauts safely to 1-atm environments. In some cases, the aquanauts are sealed inside the habitat at high pressure, and the entire habitat is brought to the surface and set on a ship or on land. The aquanauts remain inside while the pressure is gradually reduced back to 1 atm. In other cases, the habitat remains on the seafloor, but the aquanauts are transported to the surface in special transport capsules for slow decompression. See Fig. 9–9.

QUESTIONS

11. What are the differences between an underwater habitat and a diving bell?

12. How does saturation diving differ from
    a. recreational scuba diving?
    b. commercial hard-hat diving?

13. Suggest some practical applications for saturation-diving technologies.

One-Atmosphere Diving

Using an entirely different kind of technology, called **one-atmosphere diving systems**, scientists have been able to dive to the deepest parts of the seafloor. These systems encapsulate divers in an environment maintained at 1 atm, no matter how deep they dive. The air-filled life-support chamber is

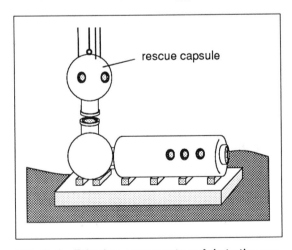

Fig. 9–9. Bringing aquanauts safely to the surface

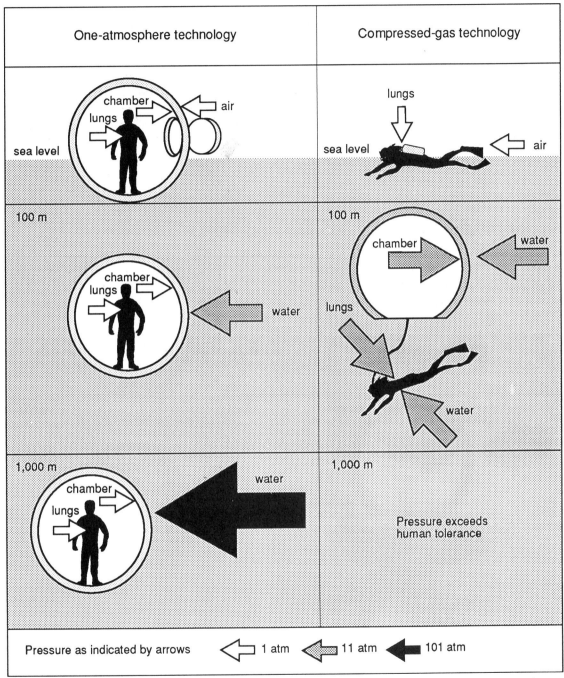

Fig. 9–10. Comparison of pressures in one-atmosphere diving technology and compressed-gas diving technology

219

enclosed within a hull strong enough to withstand tremendous outside water pressure. Fig. 9–10 compares the pressures in one-atmosphere systems and in ambient-pressure systems.

One of the earliest one-atmosphere hulls was the **bathysphere** shown in Fig. 9–11. In 1934 naturalist William Beebe and his engineer associate, Otis Barton, descended to 923 m (3,018 ft) in a steel bathysphere only 1.37 m (54 in) in diameter. Beebe was the first to observe and photograph deep-sea organisms. Unlike modern one-atmosphere systems, the bathysphere had no propellers. It merely hung in the water on a heavy steel cable. A second cable carried electricity for a light and a telephone connection with the surface-support ship. Compressed-air cylinders inside the sphere released air to the divers. Beebe's pioneering explorations generated such great public interest that he became as familiar an undersea explorer in the 1930s and 1940s as Jacques Cousteau became three decades later.

In 1960 Jacques Picard and Lt. Don Walsh descended to 11,933 m (35,800 ft) in

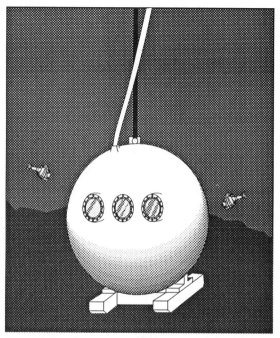

Fig. 9–11. The bathysphere is an example of a self-contained one-atmosphere system.

the Marianas Trench, the deepest known place in the ocean. They used a **bathyscaph**, called *Trieste I*, establishing a depth record that still stands today. See Fig. 9–12.

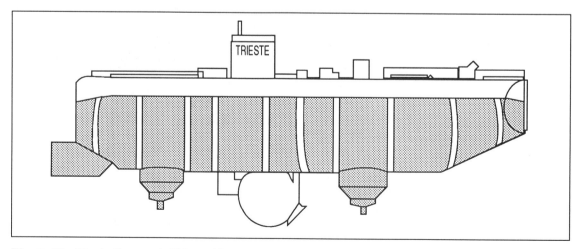

Fig. 9–12. The bathyscaph *Trieste I* in 1960 set a depth record for a one-atmosphere submersible.

Submarines are designed to remain under water for long periods. They have air-recirculation devices that filter the air to prevent the buildup of carbon dioxide and moisture. **Submersibles** are much smaller than submarines but like submarines are self-propelled, so they can move about freely under water. See Fig. 9–13. Submersibles are usually equipped with lights, manipulator arms, sampling devices, and other equipment for conducting underwater research, retrieving objects from the seafloor, and carrying out search-and-rescue missions.

Tourist submarines equipped with viewing ports in their hulls are now making it possible for non-divers to venture into the underwater world. Small tourist submarines

dive as deep as 300 m. Bus-sized ones that can carry about 50 people to a depth of 40 m are now operating in the Caribbean and in Hawaii. See Fig. 9–14.

Fixed-bottom stations are large underwater life-support structures that maintain a 1-atm environment inside. These stations are moored or fixed to the seafloor in 5-m to 20-m water; they are used as research stations or as restaurants or hotels.

Personal atmospheric diving suits look strikingly like suits worn by astronauts. See Fig. 9–15. They are made of sturdy but bulky metal with flexible joints that let the diver bend arms and legs. The diver's hands are completely encased in the diving suit, so the diver must manipulate clawlike mechanical hands. The record depth for per-

Fig. 9–13. Submersible with lights, equipment, and power supply

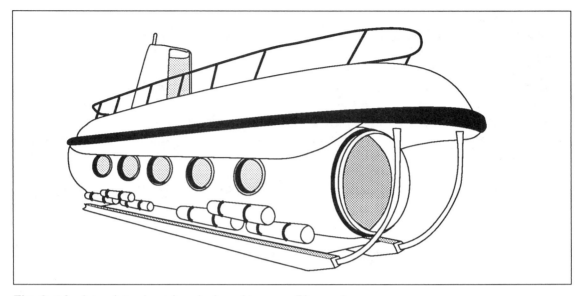

Fig. 9–14. A tourist submarine designed to carry 50 people

sonal atmospheric diving was set in 1979 by Dr. Sylvia Earle, who walked unaided at a depth of 1,000 m.

Compressed-gas and one-atmosphere technologies may be used in combination. For example, **lock-out submersibles** are designed with an air lock that allows a diver to enter and exit the chamber under water without resurfacing. These mobile submersibles are capable of transporting divers under water. A submersible designed for submarine rescue operations can transport people from a stranded submarine to the surface. Special chambers in some lock-out submersibles can also serve as recompression chambers.

Underwater Technologies

Today many types of underwater technologies permit diving and working under water for long periods and at great depths. Fig. 9–16 shows the average depth reached by some kinds of underwater technologies.

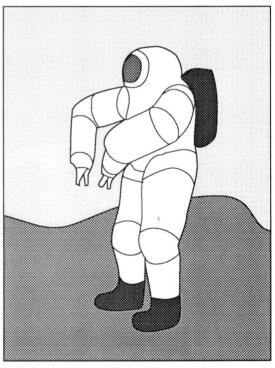

Fig. 9–15. Personal one-atmosphere diving suit

222

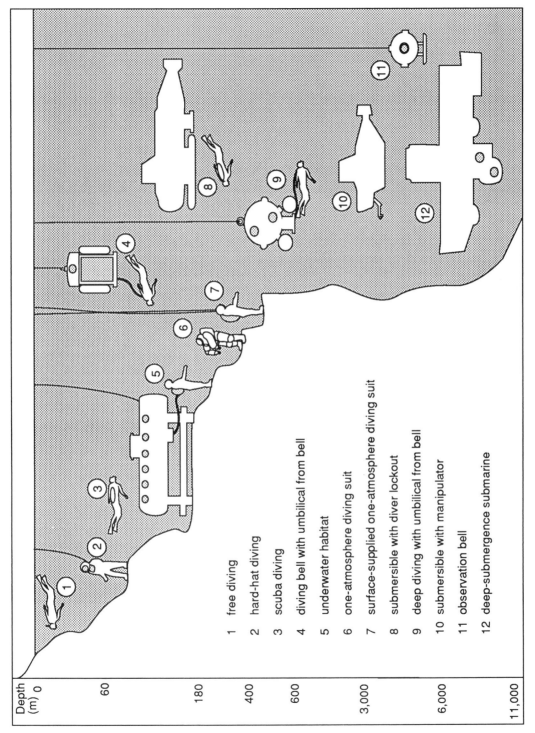

Fig. 9–16. Technologies developed for humans diving and working under water (Source: Adapted from G. Haux, *Subsea Manned Engineering*, 1982.)

Depth (m)	
0	
60	
180	
400	
600	
3,000	
6,000	
11,000	

1 free diving
2 hard-hat diving
3 scuba diving
4 diving bell with umbilical from bell
5 underwater habitat
6 one-atmosphere diving suit
7 surface-supplied one-atmosphere diving suit
8 submersible with diver lockout
9 deep diving with umbilical from bell
10 submersible with manipulator
11 observation bell
12 deep-submergence submarine

223

QUESTIONS

14. How does water pressure affect a submarine at 10 m? At 100 m?

15. Suggest some of the design features necessary to support life in a one-atmosphere diving system.

16. Compare hull designs among compressed-air scuba tanks, submarines, and habitats. How do pressure concerns differ?

17. Describe each of the types of technologies shown in Fig. 9–16, telling
    a. whether it represents free diving, self-contained diving, or surface-support diving.
    b. whether it uses one-atmosphere or greater than one-atmosphere diving.
    c. whether it uses compressed gas and, if so, whether air or a mixed gas should be used.

18. Compare Fig. 9–16 with Fig. 7–8. How do the depths reached by humans using diving technologies compare with the depths reached by animals adapted to the ocean?

FURTHER INVESTIGATIONS

1. Do research and report on one or more of the following topics:
   a. The history of submarines and submersibles. Put dates on the technologies shown in Fig. 9–15.
   b. The best shapes, designs, and materials for submarines. Consider depth, speed, weight, displacement, and life-support capabilities in relation to their mission.
   c. The best shape and design for a pressure hull (the life-support capsule) in a submersible.

2. The United States has a national program for testing new technologies and conducting research on undersea biology, geology, and ecology. The program, administered by the NOAA Office of Undersea Research, supports five regional facilities collectively called the National Undersea Research Program. Learn about the program nearest you. Find out what kind of research is being done and what technologies are being used or developed to support the research. If possible, visit a hyperbaric research facility or invite a speaker to the class.

3. Read and report to the class on the biological adaptations that make it possible for marine mammals to dive to the great depths shown in Fig. 7–8.

4. Learn about careers related to designing, developing, and testing underwater technologies to support diving, exploring, and working in the ocean.
   a. Use library references and career information systems to make a list of related occupations. Find out what kinds of abilities and interests people should have to work in these fields. What educational training and experience are required? What is the employment outlook?
   b. Contact people who work in these fields. Invite speakers to talk to the class about what they do and what they like about their work. Alternatively, plan and conduct interviews.
   c. If a particular career interests you, ask your school counselor to help you ar-

range to visit someone in that field at the workplace.

5. More than 60 types of underwater habitats have been tested over the past 20 years, including *Sealab*, *Tektite*, *Conshelf*, *Hydrolab*, and *Aquarius*. Read about one or more of these. Find out
   a. why undersea habitats are being designed and tested.
   b. what research and engineering questions were being tested.
   c. how the aquanauts fared living under water.
   d. what methods were used to recompress the aquanauts.

6. Using library references, find out about other deep-sea diving technologies that have been developed to allow people to work on the seafloor. Include deep-sea suits, modern diving bells, and deep-sea submersibles. If possible, obtain sketches that explain how each technology works. Report to the class.

7. Fig. 9–17 shows two types of technologies for launching submersibles. Use references to learn more about them. What are the advantages and disadvantages of each?

8. Some futurists (people who predict new developments) have proposed that people live on or in the ocean, conserving land for agriculture. Read articles on "cities in the sea." Report to the class.

9. Learn more about dissolved oxygen in seawater, including
   a. how plants and animals extract dissolved oxygen from water.
   b. how photosynthesis and respiration affect the supply of dissolved oxygen. Set up experiments to demonstrate these processes in water environments.
   c. how plants and animals living deep beneath the photosynthetic layer of the ocean obtain their oxygen.

Fig. 9–17. Two types of technologies for launching submersibles

10. Read about the development of the **hemosponge**, the technology being developed that enables submerged laboratory animals to extract dissolved oxygen directly from water much as fish do with their gills. What is the outlook for developing technological "lungs" for humans?

11. Find out how temperature affects human divers and diving technology.

a. What must be done to protect a human diver in cold water? A diver who dives under ice?
b. How do cold water temperatures affect pressure and gas volume?
c. What is the difference between a "wet suit" and a "dry suit" and a "hot water suit"?

12. How can divers communicate under water? What technologies have been developed to aid underwater communication?

UNIT 4
CHEMICAL OCEANOGRAPHY

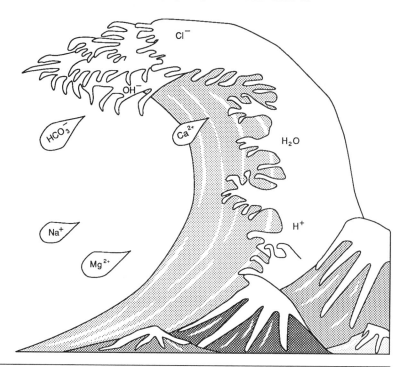

Millions of tons of oil gush from the ruptured side of a tanker. For months a sticky mass lies on the ocean's surface, moving with tides and currents, suffocating sea animals, coating beaches, never mixing, always spreading.

On a wintry morning, gulps of chilled air pierce our lungs and puffs of condensing vapor trail from our noses and mouths, making us aware of our own respiration as we breathe in oxygen and breathe out water and carbon dioxide.

Sulfurous smoke belches from the stack of a midwestern power plant. Two days later and 400 miles to the east, acid rain falls on a mountain lake, killing the embryos of trout.

A Hindu family carries seawater to a shallow clay basin, where the sun evaporates the water, leaving clear crystal cubes of rock salt.

Floating, spreading, suffocating, respiring, poisoning, crystallizing—all these are processes made understandable by knowing how atoms and molecules interact. So next we turn to the infinitesimal world of molecular matter, a world in which water plays a special role.

1. Seawater

Seawater covers 70% of our planet. But what is seawater composed of? How does its composition affect life in the sea? How does it affect human life? To seek answers, we turn to the concepts and methods of chemistry.

Water

Water, the most abundant substance on the earth's surface, is the principal component of seawater. Water exists in three states: as a liquid, as a gas (vapor), and as a solid (ice). It is a compound of the two **elements**, hydrogen and oxygen. See Table 1–1 and Fig. 1–1 for definitions of new terms.

Composition of Water

Because water is a **compound**, it can be broken down into its two elements, hydrogen and oxygen. But water is an extraordinarily stable compound that does not decompose easily. If we heat water with a Bunsen burner, a physical change takes place as liquid water evaporates into water vapor, but the compound water is not broken apart. Even the heat of a volcanic eruption does not create enough energy to decompose water. But electricity can be used to decompose water.

Passing an electrical current through a compound to break its chemical bonds is called **electrolysis**. An electrical current is a flow of electrons, which are negatively charged particles. In electrolysis, electrons are moved by a battery. The wire connected to the positive (+) pole of the battery is called

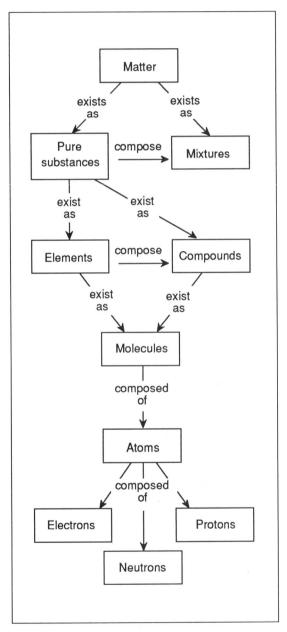

Fig. 1–1. Diagram of basic chemical terms

228

Table 1–1. Basic chemical terms

Matter is anything that takes up space and has mass or can be weighed. In chemistry we substitute the term **substance** for the term **matter**. Matter exists in three states:
•As a **solid** it has a definite shape and volume.
•As a **liquid** it has a definite volume; it takes the shape of its container.
•As a **gas** it has no definite shape or volume; it takes the shape and volume of its container.

A *pure substance* has only one kind of matter in it; that matter may be an element or a compound.

An *element* is a pure substance that *cannot* be broken down into other elements. Examples of elements are hydrogen and oxygen. Ninety elements are found in nature. (Of the 108 known elements shown on periodic tables listing the elements, the first 92 are called "natural" elements. Two of these are not found in nature but must be constructed, or synthesized.)

An *atom* is the smallest piece of an element that is still recognized as an element.

A *chemical symbol* is a one- or two-letter abbreviation for an element. The chemical symbol for hydrogen is H, for oxygen O, and for calcium Ca.

A *compound* is a substance that contains two or more different elements bonded together in exact proportions. A compound can be broken down into its elements by using heat, light, or electricity. The properties of a compound differ from the properties of the elements it is composed of. Examples of compounds are water and table salt.

A *molecule* is the smallest unit of an element or a compound that can exist by itself. There are molecules of elements such as hydrogen (H_2) and oxygen (O_2) and molecules of compounds such as water (H_2O).

A *formula* tells the number of atoms of each element that combine to make a molecule. The formula for water is H_2O. Two atoms of hydrogen are shown by a **subscript**, a number to the right of and lower than the symbol. The fact that only one atom of oxygen is present is shown by the O with no subscript.

A *mixture* is a combination of two or more kinds of matter that are not chemically bonded to each other. A compound has a fixed proportion of components, but a mixture may have different proportions. There are mixtures of elements only, mixtures of compounds only, and mixtures of elements and compounds.

the **positive electrode**. The other wire, connected to the negative (–) pole of the battery, is called the **negative electrode**. Electrons move from the negative pole of the battery through the water to the positive pole of the battery.

ACTIVITY 1
Decompose water into its elements by electrolysis.

MATERIALS
- 1,000-mL beaker
- ring stand
- two 6-cm lengths of tubing (to connect syringe barrels)
- three 50-mL syringe barrels and plungers (plastic)
- 2 buret clamps
- 5 X 5-cm sheet of sandpaper
- two 20-cm lengths of insulated stainless steel wire
- masking tape
- 600 mL water
- 2 strong pinch clamps
- 2 alligator clips
- two 20-cm lengths of copper wire
- 6- or 9-volt battery
- 20-mL test tube
- 2 wood splints or broomstraws
- matches
- cobalt chloride paper

PROCEDURE
1. Setup the equipment as shown in Fig. 1–2.
   a. Place a 1,000-mL beaker on the base of the ring stand.
   b. Attach tubing to the small ends of the two syringe barrels. Attach a strong buret clamp to each tube. Clamp the syringe barrels to the ring stand.
   c. Use sandpaper to burnish (brighten) 10 cm at one end of each of the two pieces of stainless steel wire. Bend the burnished parts of the wires to fit into the syringe barrels. Burnish 3 cm at the other ends of the wires. Put one steel wire electrode into each barrel. Tape the wires to the barrels. Adjust the buret clamps on the syringe barrel so that the large, open end is at least halfway into the beaker.
   d. Add 600 mL of water to the beaker.
   e. Fill each syringe barrel with water by using another syringe to draw off the air. Clamp the tubes to hold the water in the syringe.
   f. Attach an alligator clip to one end of each of the two copper wires.
   g. Attach an alligator clip to one of the steel wires. Attach the other end of the copper wire to a pole of the battery. See Fig. 1–2.

2. Compare the volume of gas at the electrode connected to the positive (+) pole and the one connected to the negative (–) pole of the battery. Record your findings in your notebook.

3. When 8 to 10 mL of the water has been displaced in one barrel, attach a clean, dry syringe to the tubing on the syringe barrel above the clamp. Remove the clamp and draw off the gas to refill the the syringe barrel with water. Reclamp the tubing.

4. Remove the syringe containing the gaseous matter. Eject the contents of the syringe into a clean, dry test tube. See (A) in Fig. 1–3. Immediately place your

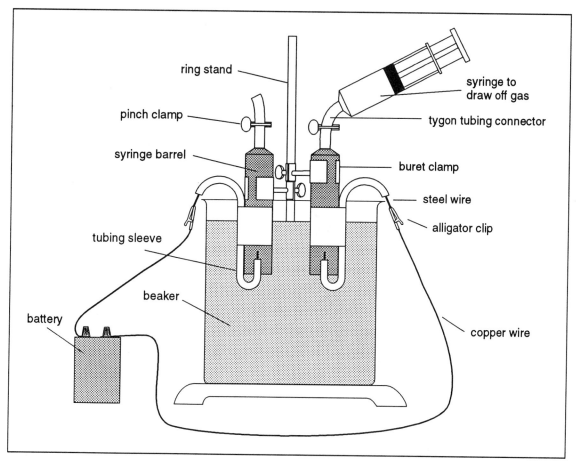

Fig. 1–2. Equipment for electrolysis of water

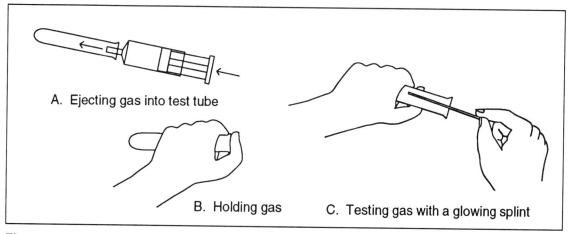

A. Ejecting gas into test tube

B. Holding gas

C. Testing gas with a glowing splint

Fig. 1–3. Procedure for testing collected gas

thumb over the end of the test tube so that the gas does not escape. See (B) in Fig. 1–3.

5. Perform the following tests to identify the gas in the test tube:
   a. Light a thin wooden splint or broomstraw. Blow out the flame but keep the tip end glowing.
   b. Holding the test tube at a slight angle away from you, remove your finger and insert the glowing splint or straw. See (C) in Fig. 1–3. Observe what happens. Record the results.
   c. If no reaction occurs, put your finger back over the end of the test tube. Light another splint or straw and thrust it into the test tube as in step (b).
   d. Examine the walls of the test tube for evidence of a chemical reaction. Record your observation. If any moisture forms, determine whether it is water by touching a piece of cobalt chloride paper to it. If it is water, the paper will turn pink.

6. When 8 to 10 mL of the water has been displaced in the second barrel, test its contents by repeating Procedures 5 and 6.

7. Make additional investigations.

QUESTIONS

Table 1–2 shows some physical properties of pure hydrogen (H_2) and oxygen (O_2). Atoms of some elements, such as hydrogen or oxygen, immediately react with each other to form molecules. Hydrogen forms H_2 molecules; oxygen forms O_2 molecules. Use this information as you answer the questions that follow.

1. What was the gas generated at the electrode connected to the positive (+) pole of the battery? Give your evidence.

2. What was the gas generated at the electrode connected to the negative (–) pole of the battery? Give your evidence.

3. How much gas formed at each electrode? How do the volumes of the gases compare? How might you explain any differences?

4. As you carried out the tests on the gases, was there evidence that water re-formed? If so, under what conditions?

5. Using the terms in Table 1–1, answer the following questions. Explain your reasoning in each case.
   a. Is water a molecule? A mixture? A compound?

Table 1–2. Physical properties of hydrogen, oxygen, and air

Gas	Density	Solubility in cold water	Combustibility
Hydrogen (H_2)	0.099 g/L	21 cm^3/L	burns in oxygen
Oxygen (O_2)	1.43 g/L	49 cm^3/L	supports combustion
Air ($O_2 + N_2$)	1.32 g/L	wide range	supports combustion

b. What elements are in water? What is the ratio of the elements in water?

c. What is the formula for water? What does each symbol in the formula for water mean?

Composition of Seawater

The most abundant elements in seawater are, of course, the elements of water—hydrogen (H) and oxygen (O). Together, these two elements account for about 96.5% of the mass of seawater. Because many elements and compounds have dissolved in seawater, it is a mixture of water molecules and other substances. See Fig. 1–4. When some compounds dissolve, they break up into charged particles called **ions**. (Ions are discussed in Topic 2.) But compound molecules and ions are all made of the atoms of elements, so we will discuss the components of seawater by talking only about its elements.

The elements occur in seawater in differing concentrations. **Concentration** is the number of grams of an element in 1,000 g of seawater. The symbol ‰ denotes concentrations in parts per thousand. For convenience, the elements in seawater are classified by their concentrations as major, minor, and trace elements. See Table 1–3.

The elements in seawater are listed in Table 1–4 from highest to lowest concentration. The six **major elements** in seawater

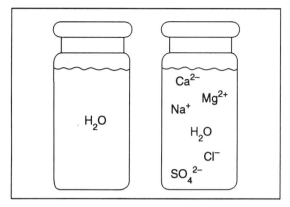

Fig. 1–4. Distinguishing between a pure substance and a mixture of substances

occur in concentrations greater than or equal to one-tenth gram per thousand grams of seawater (expressed as > 0.1 g/1,000 g of seawater or > 0.1‰). Sodium and chlorine (which make up common table salt, NaCl) account for almost three-fourths of the total dissolved content of seawater.

The **minor elements** in seawater have a concentration between one-tenth gram per thousand grams of seawater and one-thousandth gram per thousand grams of seawater (0.1 to 0.001g per 1,000 g of seawater, or 0.1 to 0.001‰). The **trace elements** in seawater have a concentration of less than one-thousandth gram per thousand grams of seawater (< 0.001 g/1,000 g of seawater, or < 0.001‰). Fig. 1–5 shows how to read the placement of the decimal for very small numbers.

Table 1–3. The concentration ranges of major, minor, and trace elements in seawater

Elements in seawater	Concentration range per 1,000 g seawater	Concentration range in parts per 1,000 (‰)
Major Minor Trace	> 0.1 g 0.1 g to 0.001 g < 0.001 g	> 0.1 ‰ 0.1 ‰ to 0.001 ‰ < 0.001 ‰

Table 1–4. Principal elements in seawater arranged by concentration

	Rank order of abundance in seawater	Element	Symbol	‰ in seawater (by mass)	Biological importance	Rank order of abundance in crust of the earth
	1	Oxygen	O	857.0	A	1
	2	Hydrogen	H	108.0	A	10
Major elements	3	Chlorine	Cl	19.5	V	15
	4	Sodium	Na	10.7	V	6
	5	Magnesium	Mg	1.287	V	8
	6	Sulfur	S	.885	A	13
	7	Calcium	Ca	.420	A	5
	8	Potassium	K	.380	V	7
Minor elements	9	Bromine	Br	.067	F	55
	10	Carbon	C	.028	A	14
	11	Nitrogen	N	.005	A	28
	12	Strontium	Sr	.007		18
	13	Boron	B	.004 6	F	51
	14	Silicon	Si	.003	F	2
	15	Fluorine	F	.001 3	F	17
Trace elements	16	Argon	Ar	.000 63		●
	17	Lithium	Li	.000 18		27
	18	Rubidium	Rb	.000 12		16
	19	Phosphorus	P	.000 06	A	11
	20	Iodine	I	.000 06	V	63
	21	Barium	Ba	.000 02		19
	22	Molybdenum	Mo	.000 01	M	38
	23	Zinc	Zn	.000 004 9	M	23
	24	Arsenic	As	.000 003 7	F	47
	25	Uranium	U	.000 003 2		50
	26	Vanadium	V	.000 002 5	F	22
	27	Aluminum	Al	.000 002	F ?	3

●   Inert gases, not found in the earth's crust
A   Essential to ALL living things, the basic building blocks of life
V   VERY essential to life
M   Essential to MOST organisms
F   Essential to a FEW specialized organisms

Table 1–4. (continued) Principal elements in seawater arranged by concentration

Rank order of abundance in seawater		Element	Symbol	‰ in seawater (by mass)	Biological importance	Rank order of abundance in crust of the earth
Trace	28	Copper	Cu	.000 002	M	25
elements,	29	Iron	Fe	.000 002	V	4
continued	30	Nickel	Ni	.000 001 7	M	24
	31	Titanium	Ti	.000 001		9
	32	Cesium	Cs	.000 000 4		40
	33	Chromium	Cr	.000 000 3	F	21
	34	Antimony	Sb	.000 000 24		58
	35	Manganese	Mn	.000 000 2	M	12
	36	Krypton	Kr	.000 000 2		●
	37	Selenium	Se	.000 000 2	M	69
	38	Neon	Ne	.000 000 12		●
	39	Cadmium	Cd	.000 000 1		66
	40	Tungsten	W	.000 000 1		26
	41	Cobalt	Co	.000 000 05	M	34
	42	Germanium	Ge	.000 000 05		41
	43	Xenon	Xe	.000 000 05		●
	44	Silver	Ag	.000 000 04		67
	45	Gallium	Ga	.000 000 03		37
	46	Mercury	Hg	.000 000 03		62
	47	Lead	Pb	.000 000 03		36
	48	Zirconium	Zr	.000 000 03		20
	49	Bismuth	Bi	.000 000 02		64
	50	Niobium	Nb	.000 000 01		33
	51	Tin	Sn	.000 000 01		30
	52	Thallium	Tl	.000 000 01		61
	53	Thorium	Th	.000 000 01		39
	54	Hafnium	Hf	.000 000 007		48
	55	Helium	He	.000 000 006 8		74
	56	Beryllium	Be	.000 000 005 6		44
	57	Gold	Au	.000 000 004		73
	58	Rhenium	Re	.000 000 004		77
	59	Lanthanum	La	.000 000 003		35
	60	Neodymium	Nd	.000 000 003		32

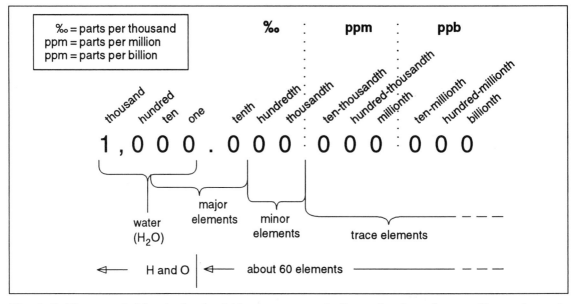

Fig. 1–5. Placement of the decimal point to show concentrations of major, minor, and trace elements in 1,000 g of seawater

ACTIVITY 2
Make a diagram showing the concentration of elements in seawater.

MATERIALS
• colored pencils (red, blue, green, yellow)

PROCEDURE
1. The 1,000 squares in Fig. 1–6 represent 1,000 g of seawater. (The table is 40 X 25 squares.) Each square represents 1 g. Use colors to represent the proportions of oxygen, hydrogen, and major, minor, and trace elements of seawater. Use the data on concentrations of elements in Table 1–3 for this procedure.
   a. Using a blue pencil, color squares in Fig. 1–6 to show how many represent the mass of the elements oxygen (O) and hydrogen (H) in seawater.
   b. Using a green pencil, color squares to show how many represent the mass of the major elements.
   c. Using a red pencil, color squares to show the proportion of the mass of the minor elements.
   d. Using a yellow pencil, color squares to show the proportion of the mass of the trace elements.
   e. Make a key at the bottom of the table to explain your color code.

QUESTIONS
6. Use as many terms as you can from Table 1–1 to describe seawater.

7. The average concentration of salt in seawater is 35‰. State this same concentration in parts per hundred (percentage, %).

8. Why do you suppose oceanographers use parts per thousand (‰) rather than parts

236

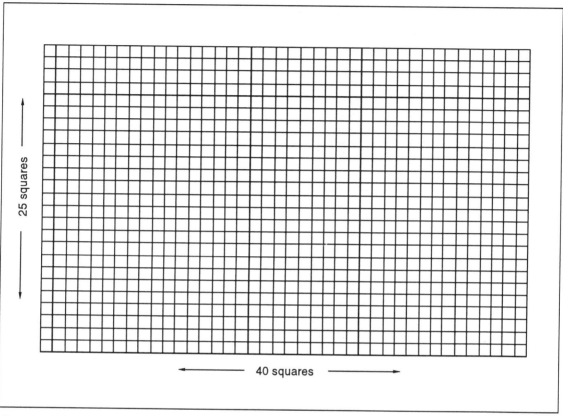

25 squares

40 squares

Fig. 1–6. Proportion of elements in 1,000 g seawater by mass Ⓦ

per hundred (%) to show concentrations of dissolved materials in seawater?

9. In seawater, what is the proportion of oxygen to hydrogen by mass? To determine the proportion, divide the mass of oxygen by the mass of hydrogen.

Chemical Symbols

Chemists abbreviate the name of each element with a one- or two-letter **chemical symbol**. Hydrogen (H), for example, is an element with a one-letter chemical symbol. Chlorine (Cl) is an element with a two-letter chemical symbol. Note that the first letter of a chemical symbol is always capitalized.

The symbol is usually the first letter or two of the common name of the element. But in some cases the letters in the symbol come from the Latin name of the element. For example, the symbol for sodium is **Na**, from *Natrium,* the Latin name of sodium. The symbol for gold is **Au**, from the Latin name *Aurum.*

So far, chemists have found 90 elements in nature. In recent years they have constructed many synthetic elements, extending the total to 108.

The first 92 elements are listed in alphabetical order in Table 1–5. Note that Table 1–5 also gives atomic numbers, which represent the number of protons or positive

Table 1–5. Names, symbols, and atomic numbers of elements found in nature

Name	Symbol	Atomic Number	Name	Symbol	Atomic Number	Name	Symbol	Atomic Number
Actinium	Ac	89	Holmium	Ho	67	Radon	Rn	86
Aluminum	Al	13	Hydrogen	H	1	Rhenium	Re	75
Antimony	Sb	51	Indium	In	49	Rhodium	Rh	45
Argon	Ar	18	Iodine	I	53	Rubidium	Rb	37
Arsenic	As	33	Iridium	Ir	77	Ruthenium	Ru	44
Astatine	At	85	Iron	Fe	26	Samarium	Sm	62
Barium	Ba	56	Krypton	Kr	36	Scandium	Sc	21
Beryllium	Be	4	Lanthanum	La	57	Selenium	Se	34
Bismuth	Bi	83	Lead	Pb	82	Silicon	Si	14
Boron	B	5	Lithium	Li	3	Silver	Ag	47
Bromine	Br	35	Lutetium	Lu	71	Sodium	Na	11
Cadmium	Cd	48	Magnesium	Mg	12	Strontium	Sr	38
Calcium	Ca	20	Manganese	Mn	25	Sulfur	S	16
Carbon	C	6	Mercury	Hg	80	Tantalum	Ta	73
Cerium	Ce	58	Molybdenum	Mo	42	Technetium	Tc	43
Cesium	Cs	55	Neodymium	Nd	60	Tellurium	Te	52
Chlorine	Cl	17	Neon	Ne	10	Terbium	Tb	65
Chromium	Cr	24	Nickel	Ni	28	Thallium	Tl	81
Cobalt	Co	27	Niobium	Nb	41	Thorium	Th	90
Copper	Cu	29	Nitrogen	N	7	Thulium	Tm	69
Dysprosium	Dy	66	Osmium	Os	76	Tin	Sn	50
Erbium	Er	68	Oxygen	O	8	Titanium	Ti	22
Europium	Eu	63	Palladium	Pd	46	Tungsten	W	74
Fluorine	F	9	Phosphorus	P	15	Uranium	U	92
Francium	Fr	87	Platinum	Pt	78	Vanadium	V	23
Gadolinium	Gd	64	Polonium	Po	84	Xenon	Xe	54
Gallium	Ga	31	Potassium	K	19	Ytterpium	Yb	70
Germanium	Ge	32	Praseodymium	Pr	59	Yttrium	Y	39
Gold	Au	79	Promethium	Pm	61	Zinc	Zn	30
Hafnium	Hf	72	Protactinium	Pa	91	Zirconium	Zr	40
Helium	He	2	Radium	Ra	88			

particles in an atom. Keep this list handy when you need to look up the chemical symbols of elements.

Periodic Table of the Elements

If the elements are arranged by their atomic numbers, they can be listed from left to right in a **periodic table**, as shown in Table 1–6. The periodic table is useful to chemists because it is organized into rows and columns according to certain properties of the elements. The columns are called **groups**; they indicate how these elements react. The rows are called **periods**; they show the increasing complexity of the atoms.

238

Table 1–6. Periodic table of natural elements showing atomic numbers and identifying those found in seawater

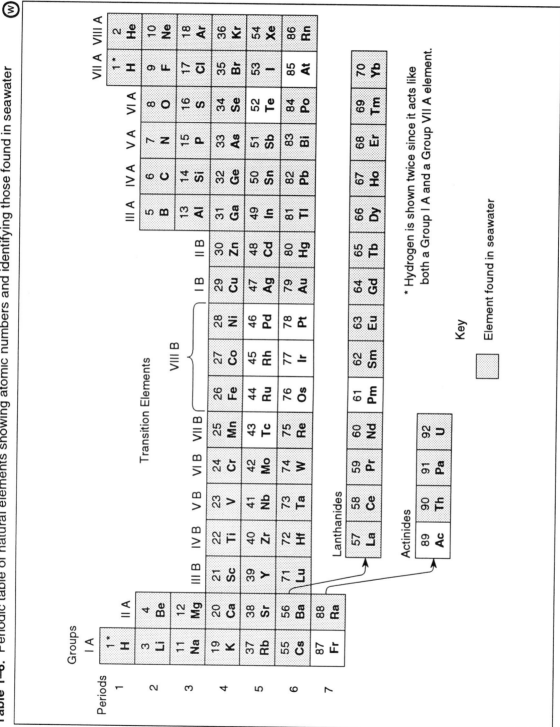

QUESTIONS

10. What is the name of the element with atomic number 7? Atomic number 16? Atomic number 33? See Tables 1–5 and 1–6.

11. What are the symbols for the elements gold, silver, platinum, and copper?

=================

ACTIVITY 3

Use a periodic table to show which elements are found in seawater as major, minor, and trace elements.

MATERIALS
• colored pencils (red, blue, green, yellow)

PROCEDURE
1. Refer to Table 1–4 for a list of the elements in seawater.

2. Color-code the periodic table, Table 1–6, as follows:
   a. With a blue pencil, color the box for each of the elements in the compound water
   b. With a green pencil, color the box for each of the major elements in seawater.
   c. With a red pencil, color the box for each of the minor elements in seawater
   d. With a yellow pencil, color the boxes of the trace elements in seawater.

3. Attach a key to describe your color code.

QUESTIONS

12. In which part of the periodic table are the major elements found? The minor elements? The trace elements?

13. Compare the abundant elements in seawater with the abundant elements in the earth's crust. See Table 1–4.
    a. How many of the ten most abundant crustal elements are among the ten most abundant seawater elements?
    b. From the data in Table 1–4, list the elements that are among the ten most abundant elements in seawater but not among the ten most abundant elements in the earth's crust.
    c. How might the differences in abundance be explained?

14. Compare the elements found in living organisms with those found in seawater.
    a. How many of the major and minor seawater elements are not biologically necessary?
    b. Which of the 35 most abundant elements in seawater are not biologically important?

15. Compare the elements found in living things with the crustal elements.
    a. How many of the biologically important elements are found in the 35 most abundant crustal elements?
    b. Which of the first 35 crustal elements are not biologically important?

16. Which hypothesis seems better supported—that life began in the sea or that life began on the land? What is your evidence?

2. Ionic Components of Seawater

We have seen that seawater is a complex mixture of many substances. In this topic we discuss a group of substances that dissolve to make seawater salty, the ionic components. To understand these components, we must first look at the structure of tiny atoms. Atoms are so small that we could not even see their outlines until powerful electron tunneling microscopes were invented in the 1980s. We get some idea of their size when we realize that it takes over 100 million (100,000,000) hydrogen atoms put end to end to equal 1 cm.

Atoms and Molecules

Recall from Topic 1 that pure forms of matter are of two kinds, elements and compounds. The simplest unit of both an element and a compound is called a **molecule**. Molecules of elements may contain one, two, or more atoms. The molecule of the gas helium (He) contains one atom. A molecule of the most abundant form of oxygen (O_2) is made of two atoms of oxygen; ozone (O_3), another form of oxygen, has three. A molecule of hydrogen (H_2) is made up of two hydrogen atoms. A chlorine molecule (Cl_2) is made up of two chlorine atoms. See Fig. 2–1.

Molecules of compounds are always made of atoms of two or more different elements. We have seen that a molecule of water (H_2O) is made up of two hydrogen atoms and one oxygen atom. A single drop of water contains billions of trillions of molecules of water. When different elements combine to form a compound, the

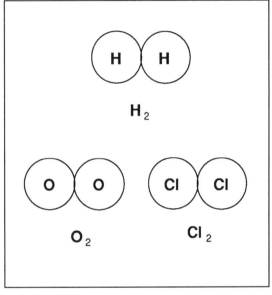

Fig. 2–1. Elemental molecules, such as hydrogen (H_2), oxygen (O_2), and chlorine (Cl_2), are made of atoms of only one element.

properties of the compound are very different from the properties of the separate elements. We found that the compound water is made up of hydrogen, an explosive gas, and oxygen, a gas that supports combustion.

Electrostatic Forces

What are atoms made of? What holds them together? To get a sense of how they hold together, we need to investigate static electricity—the kind that raises the hair on your arm when you open a big plastic bag or gives you a shock when the air is dry and you touch a doorknob.

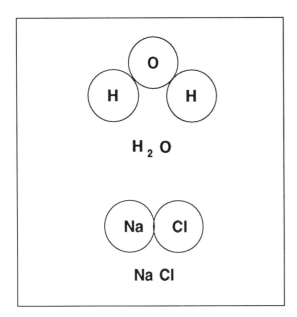

Fig. 2–2. Molecules of compounds such as water and sodium chloride are made of atoms of two or more different elements.

ACTIVITY 1

Determine how charged matter reacts with uncharged matter.

MATERIALS

- comb
- glass rod
- piece of silk or nylon
- 2 pith balls on nylon thread
- ring stand and ring
- paper
- strip of aluminum foil on nylon thread

PROCEDURE

1. Produce a negative (–) electrostatic charge on a comb by running it rapidly through dry, greaseless hair. Explore the interaction with different materials.
   a. Attach threads holding a pith ball and a strip of metal foil to a ring stand. See Fig. 2–3. Bring the charged comb near the ball and the foil and record your observations.
   b. Charge the pith ball and the foil by touching them with the charged comb. Record your observations.
   c. Bring the charged comb next to the charged pith ball. Approach the ball from various sides and from the bottom. Repeat with the foil. Record your observations.

2. Produce a (+) charge by rapidly rubbing a glass rod with a piece of silk or nylon. Explore the interaction with different materials.
   a. Discharge the pith ball and metal foil by touching them with your finger.
   b. Bring the (+) charged rod next to the pith ball and the metal foil. Record your observations.

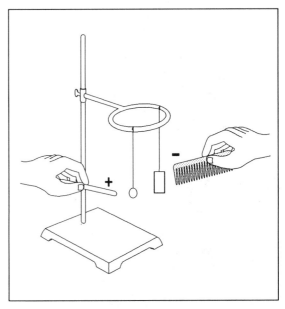

Fig. 2–3. Charging objects attached to a ring stand

c. Touch the pith ball and the foil with the rod to charge them. Record your observations.

d. Bring the charged rod next to the charged pith ball and foil. Approach the ball from various sides and the bottom. Record your observations.

3. Charge two pith balls, one with the comb (–) and one with the glass rod (+). Holding the threads, bring the two balls as close together as possible without letting them touch. Record your observations.

4. Discharge the pith balls by touching them with your finger. Charge both pith balls (–) by touching them with the charged comb. Holding the threads, bring the two balls as close together as possible without letting them touch. Record your observations.

5. Discharge the pith balls by touching them. Charge both pith balls (+) by touching them with the charged glass rod. Bring the two balls as close together as possible without letting them touch. Record your observations.

6. Make a small pile of torn bits of paper. Charge the comb and bring it near the paper. Record your observations. Charge the glass rod and bring it near the paper. Record your observations.

7. Explore other granular substances, such as dust and iron filings, as time allows. Record all observations.

QUESTIONS

1. How did the positively (+) and negatively (–) charged rods interact with paper and with discharged pith balls? What were the similarities and differences?

2. What charge, if any, was on the pith ball and the foil before the charged comb touched them? Explain your reasoning.

3. What charge, if any, was on the pith ball and the foil after the charged comb touched them?

4. Fill in Table 2–1. Use the terms *repel*, *attract*, and *no interaction*.

5. What can be said about the interaction of
   a. like charges?
   b. unlike charges?

6. From the information assembled in Table 2–1, what must have been the charges on the paper and the discharged pith balls? Explain your reasoning.

7. Paper is considered a nonmetallic substance. Aluminum foil is metallic. Do electrostatic charges interact differently or similarly with these two kinds of substances? Explain your answer.

Table 2–1. Interaction of charges   (w)

	Surface charged (+)	Surface charged (–)
Glass rod charged (+)		
Comb charged (–)		

Atoms and Their Parts

Atoms are held together in molecules by the electrical forces of attraction we have just explored. This occurs because atoms themselves are composed of three kinds of **subatomic particles**, each much smaller than the atom. They are the positively (+) charged **proton**, the negatively (–) charged **electron,** and the neutral **neutron.** See Fig. 2–4. As its name indicates, a neutron is neutral; it has no charge. Neutrons therefore neither attract nor repel charged particles.

Protons and neutrons are some 1,830 times more massive than electrons. Both neutrons and protons are in the **nucleus,** or center, of the atom, where they remain, even during the most violent chemical reactions. Together they account for almost all the mass and weight of an atom. But electrons are outside the nucleus and have little mass, so they are easily removed from or added to atoms. Electrons are located in regions called **shells** surrounding the atomic nucleus. They move around the way bees fly around a hive.

The numbers of electrons and protons and the location of electrons determine the ways atoms combine to form new compounds. Most of the chemical properties of elements and compounds can be explained in terms of the protons and electrons in the atoms that make them up. **Chemical properties** are the specific ways that substances react and the specific energies that they produce or use in reaction.

A single uncharged atom has an equal number of protons (+) and electrons (–). It is electrically neutral because the charges are of equal magnitude. The charges on equal numbers of protons and electrons exactly counteract each other.

Atomic Number and the Periodic Table

Elements are numbered from 1 through 108. See Table 2–2. The numbers are called the atomic numbers of elements. **Atomic numbers** tell us how many electrons or protons a neutral atom of an element has. A neutral hydrogen atom (H) with an atomic number of 1 has one electron and one proton. See Fig. 2–5. An atom of helium (He) has an atomic number of 2, so it has two electrons and two protons. Lithium (Li), with an atomic number of 3, has three electrons and three protons.

QUESTIONS

8. How many protons does each of the following atoms have? Refer to Table 2–2.
   a. oxygen (O)
   b. sodium (Na)
   c. chlorine (Cl)
   d. sulfur (S)

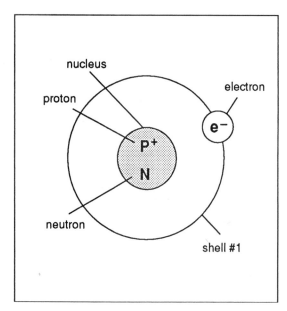

Fig. 2–4. The subatomic particles in an atom

Table 2–2. Periodic table showing metallic elements

Periods	Groups I A	II A	III B	IV B	V B	VI B	VII B	VIII B			I B	II B	III A	IV A	V A	VI A	VII A	VIII A
1	1* H																1* H	2 He
2	3 Li	4 Be											5 B	6 C	7 N	8 O	9 F	10 Ne
3	11 Na	12 Mg											13 Al	14 Si	15 P	16 S	17 Cl	18 Ar
4	19 K	20 Ca	21 Sc	22 Ti	23 V	24 Cr	25 Mn	26 Fe	27 Co	28 Ni	29 Cu	30 Zn	31 Ga	32 Ge	33 As	34 Se	35 Br	36 Kr
5	37 Rb	38 Sr	39 Y	40 Zr	41 Nb	42 Mo	43 Tc	44 Ru	45 Rh	46 Pd	47 Ag	48 Cd	49 In	50 Sn	51 Sb	52 Te	53 I	54 Xe
6	55 Cs	56 Ba	71 Lu	72 Hf	73 Ta	74 W	75 Re	76 Os	77 Ir	78 Pt	79 Au	80 Hg	81 Tl	82 Pb	83 Bi	84 Po	85 At	86 Rn
7	87 Fr	88 Ra																

Transition Elements

Lanthanides

57 La	58 Ce	59 Pr	60 Nd	61 Pm	62 Sm	63 Eu	64 Gd	65 Tb	66 Dy	67 Ho	68 Er	69 Tm	70 Yb

Actinides

89 Ac	90 Th	91 Pa	92 U

* Hydrogen is shown twice since it acts like both a Group IA and a Group VIIA element.

Key

Metallic elements (shaded)

	Hydrogen	Helium	Lithium
Atomic number	1	2	3
Atomic symbol	H	He	Li
Number of protons (+)	1+	2+	3+
Number of electrons (–)	1–	2–	3–
Atomic structure			

Fig. 2–5. The first three elements in the periodic table showing atomic numbers, atomic symbols, number of protons, number of electrons, and atomic structure

9. How many electrons does each of the following atoms have when it is neutral?
   a. oxygen (O)
   b. sodium (Na)
   c. chlorine (Cl)
   d. sulfur (S)

10. How many protons do elements with atomic numbers 12, 20, and 35 have? What are the elements with these atomic numbers?

11. If a neutral lead (Pb) atom has 82 electrons, how many protons does it have? Where are these protons located in the atom?

Electron Shells

As we have seen, protons remain in the nucleus of the atom, but electrons travel around the outside of the nucleus in regions called shells. A shell can contain only a certain number of electrons. When one shell fills to a certain number, electrons are added to a new outer shell. See Fig. 2–6. Hydrogen has one electron that moves in the first shell. Oxygen has eight electrons. Two of these electrons fill up the first shell; the rest travel in a second shell. Sodium requires three shells for all its electrons. A massive element such as lead (Pb), whose neutral atom contains 82 protons, has its 82 electrons distributed in six shells.

Periods

Now we can begin to understand the arrangement of the elements in the periodic table. See Table 2–2. The elements in each horizontal row have the same number of

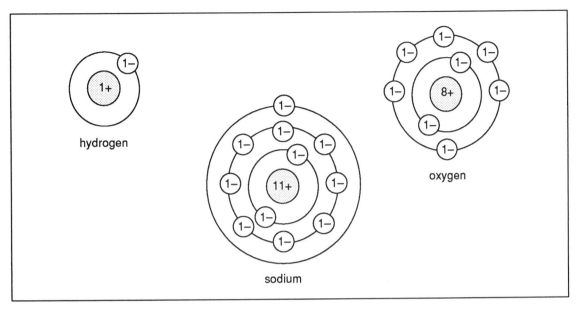

Fig. 2–6. Electron shells

shells. Each row is called a **period**. The period number tells how many shells are in the atoms of a particular row. All the atoms in Period 3 have three shells, those in Period 4 have four, and so on.

Groups

Elements with the same number of electrons in their outer shells are shown in **groups** or families. In the periodic table each group is shown in a vertical column. See Table 2–2. The group number of A-type elements tells us how many electrons are in the outer shell. Because Lithium (Li) and sodium (Na) have one electron each in their outer shells, they are in Group IA.

The number of electrons in the outer shell determines how each atom reacts, that is, how the atom combines chemically with other atoms. Atoms with the same number of electrons in their outer shells react similarly. Thus lithium (Li) and sodium (Na), with one outer-shell electron each, have

similar chemical reactions. The remaining **transition**, **lanthanide**, and **actinide** elements tend to have two electrons in their outer shells.

QUESTIONS

12. How many shells do the following elements have? What period are they in?
    a. nitrogen
    b. sodium
    c. calcium

13. How many electrons does a neutral atom of chlorine (Cl) have in its outer shell? What group is it in?

14. What elements react similarly to calcium? How do we know this?

15. What parts of an atom determine how it reacts?

247

Ions

We have said that atoms can easily gain and lose electrons. When they gain electrons, they become negatively (–) charged atoms. When they lose electrons, they become positively (+) charged atoms. A charged atom is called an **ion**. Elements in groups I A to III A tend to lose their electrons. Elements in groups V A to VII A tend to gain electrons to fill their outer shells to eight electrons.

As Fig. 2–7 shows, a neutral sodium atom (Na) that loses its one electron changes into a sodium ion (Na$^+$) with a charge of 1$^+$. A positive ion is named the same as the atom it is made of. The sodium atom (Na) thus becomes a sodium ion (Na$^+$).

A neutral atom of chlorine (Cl) tends to gain one electron and become a negatively charged chloride ion (Cl$^-$). The ion is negatively (1$^-$) charged because it has one more electron than it has protons. See (B) in Fig. 2–7.

The name of a negative ion differs from the name of the neutral atom. An **-ide**

replaces the last part of the name. Thus a chlorine atom becomes a **chloride ion**.

Some atoms can gain more than one electron. Sulfur (S), for example, can gain two electrons, becoming a sulfide (S^{2-}) ion with a charge of 2$^-$. The sulfide ion (S^{2-}) has two more electrons than it has protons.

QUESTIONS

16. What is the charge when a neutral fluorine atom (F) gains one electron? Write the symbol for this ion. What is its name?

17. What is the charge of a neutral lithium atom (Li) when it loses one electron? What is the charge of a magnesium ion after the neutral magnesium atom (Mg) loses two electrons? Write the symbols for these ions.

18. How many more protons than electrons has an ion with a charge of 2$^+$? A charge of 3$^+$? A charge of 4$^+$?

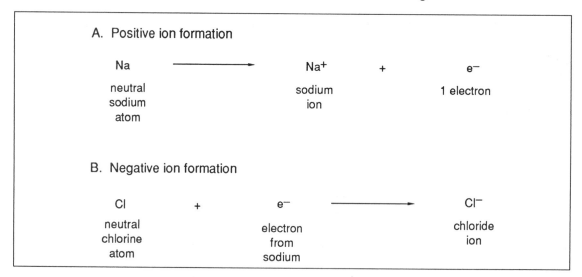

Fig. 2–7. Formation of positive and negative ions

19. Which particle, proton or electron, is in excess when the charge on an ion is 1⁻? When it is 3⁺? When it is 4⁻? How many particles are not electrically neutralized in each case?

Table 2–3. Some elemental ions found in sea- water   ⓦ

Positive ions			Negative ions	
1+	2+	3+	2–	1–
Li^+	Be	B	O	F^-
Na	Mg^{2+}	Al^{3+}	S^{2-}	Cl
K	Ca			Br
Rb	Sr			

Elemental Ions in Seawater

Table 2–3 shows a few elemental ions found in seawater. Notice the pattern that forms when ions are arranged in vertical groups according to their charges.

QUESTIONS

20. Complete Table 2–3 by adding charges to symbols for ions.

21. What are the names of the ions for which you added symbols for charges?

22. What is the relationship between the ionic charge and the group number?

ACTIVITY 2

Separate the substances in seawater by evaporation.

MATERIALS

- 10-mL graduated cylinder
- centigram balance
- seawater
- 100-mL beaker
- heat source
- thermometer
- microscope slide
- dissecting microscope

PROCEDURE

1. Find the mass of a 10-mL sample of seawater.
   a. Weigh a 100-mL beaker. Record the weight in Table 2–4.
   b. Using a graduated cylinder, measure out a 10-mL sample of seawater and pour it into the 100-mL beaker.

c. Weigh the beaker and water. Record in Table 2–4.
d. Subtract the mass of the beaker from the weight of the beaker and water together to find the weight of the water. Record in Table 2–4.

Table 2–4. Data from evaporation experiment   ⓦ

Mass of seawater and beaker		Mass of crystals and beaker	
Mass of beaker		Mass of beaker	
Mass of seawater		Mass of crystals	

249

2. Evaporate the water from the sample.
   a. Heat the beaker and water sample to not more than 60°C. Do not let the water boil.
   b. Let the water evaporate until the beaker is almost dry. Salt crystals will form on the sides and bottom of the beaker.
   c. When the water is almost gone, the crystals will be slightly wet because some of the salt crystals attract water. The crystals are said to be **hygroscopic**. To remove the remaining water, turn up the heat a little at a time until the salt crystals are as dry as you can get them. If the crystals begin sputtering, reduce the heat.

3. Find the mass of the crystals in the sample.
   a. Weigh the beaker and the dry crystals. Record in Table 2–4.
   b. Subtract the mass of the beaker (from 1.a.) from the weight of the beaker plus the salt crystals. Record in Table 2–4.

4. Describe the crystals in the beaker. How many kinds do there appear to be? What is the evidence for your answers?

5. Gently scrape different crystals onto a microscope slide or a small piece of cardboard. Examine the crystals under a dissecting microscope. Record your observations in your notebook.

QUESTIONS

23. What was the mass of the seawater sample before the water evaporated? What was the mass of the salts?

24. Using the values from Question 23, calculate the concentration of the salts in the seawater sample. Express the concentration in parts per thousand (‰).

25. What might have happened if the seawater had boiled during the evaporation? How would this have affected the results?

26. Is seawater a mixture or a compound? See Table 1–1. What is your evidence?

27. In what form are the salts when they are dissolved in the water sample? What happens when the water is removed from seawater during evaporation?

Ionic Compounds

When water is evaporated from a container of seawater, a mixture of solid crystalline compounds remains. Most of these solids are **ionic compounds**. They bond because their ions have opposite charges. The process by which ionic compounds form is called **electron exchange**.

Let's look at the electron exchange that takes place in the formation of the ionic compound sodium chloride ($NaCl$), or common table salt. A sodium atom collides with a chlorine atom. The neutral sodium atom (Na) gives up one electron, forming a positive sodium ion (Na^+), as shown in Fig. 2–7. The neutral chlorine atom (Cl) accepts the electron, becoming a negative chloride ion (Cl^-), as shown in Fig. 2–7. Once these two oppositely charged ions form, they can **bond** or hold onto each other by the attraction of their opposite charges. See (A) in Fig. 2–8. Because the two charges are equal and

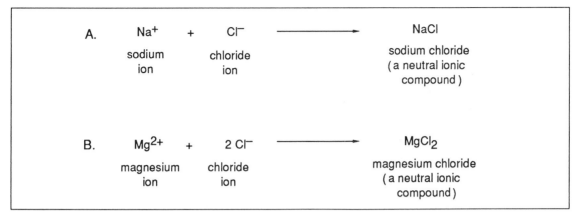

Fig. 2–8. Formation of an ionic compound

opposite, the ionic compound that forms has a zero charge and is called neutral.

In writing a chemical formula such as NaCl, we first write the symbol for the atom from the positive ion, then the symbol for the atom from the negative ion. Sometimes ions with different numbers of charges form ionic compounds. For example, a magnesium ion (Mg^{2+}) can combine with chloride ions (Cl^-) to form magnesium chloride ($MgCl_2$). See Fig. 2–8. Here it takes two negative chloride ions (Cl^-) to combine with one positive magnesium ion (Mg^{2+}).

Salts Are Ionic Compounds

When most people use the term *salt*, they mean a specific kind of salt, sodium chloride (NaCl), the common table salt we put on food. However, any ionic compound formed from a positive (+) ion (except H^+) and a negative (–) ion (except OH^-) is called a **salt.**

In a crystal of table salt, sodium and chloride ions are attracted to each other very closely. A single crystal will be composed of billions of trillions of sodium and chloride ions. Because of the way the ions are arranged, the sodium chloride crystal forms in the shape of a cube. See Fig. 2–9. In other ionic compounds the ions may be arranged differently, so their crystals may take a different shape. When the crystal of sodium chloride is put into water, the ions separate and mix or spread through the water. See Fig. 2–9. The crystal disappears or dissolves. New crystals can be re-formed by evaporating the water, as you did in the preceding activity.

Metal Ions

Salts from seawater contain many different ions. We know that seawater contains trace amounts of many of the naturally occurring elements; many of these elements are metals that form positive ions. Most salts that form when seawater evaporates contain metals. Some metals can form ions with two or more different charges. Iron (Fe), for example, can form both an iron II ion (Fe^{2+}) and an iron III ion (Fe^{3+}).

Polyatomic Ions

In addition to elemental ions, there are also **polyatomic** ions, or ions with more than one atom. Some polyatomic ions found in seawater are listed in Table 2–5. Polyatomic

251

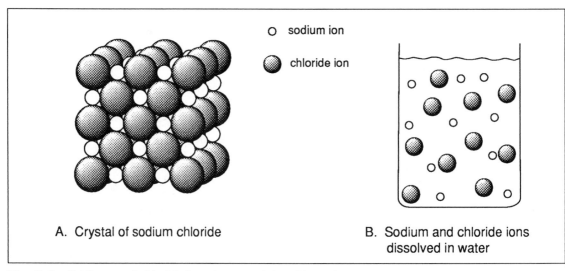

A. Crystal of sodium chloride

B. Sodium and chloride ions dissolved in water

Fig. 2–9. Sodium and chloride ions in a crystal and in water

ions act the same as elemental ions in forming compounds.

QUESTIONS

28. Potassium (K) is in the same atomic group as sodium (Na); bromine (Br) is in the same group as chlorine (Cl). Predict the structure of a potassium bromide crystal and give reasons for your prediction.

29. Nitrogen (N), phosphorus (P), and sulfur (S) are elements found in all living things. List the polyatomic ions from Table 2–5 containing each of these elements that are found in seawater.

FURTHER INVESTIGATION

Obtain crystals of salts of a number of different ionic compounds. Observe their shapes under a dissecting microscope. Draw and describe them. Report your observations to the class.

Table 2–5. Some polyatomic ions found in seawater

Polyatomic ions	Chemical name
NH_4^+	ammonium
CO_3^{2-}	carbonate
OH^-	hydroxide
NO_2^-	nitrite
NO_3^-	nitrate
PO_4^{3-}	phosphate
SiO_3^{2-}	silicate
SO_4^{2-}	sulfate
SO_3^{2-}	sulfite
HCO_3^-	hydrogen carbonate, bicarbonate*
HPO_4^{2-}	hydrogen phosphate
HSO_3^-	hydrogen sulfite, bisulfite*
	* common name

3. The Salty Sea

Seawater is more than just a mixture of water and dissolved substances. It is a dynamic chemical environment that interacts constantly with the land, the atmosphere, and living things. What do we know about this chemical environment? Is seawater unchanging? Can we human beings with our technologies change its chemistry? We begin by considering some of the processes that add dissolved substances to seawater and remove them.

Sources of Dissolved Substances in Seawater

Water is a highly active **solvent**—a substance capable of dissolving other substances. Water slowly dissolves the rocks and soil of mountains and flatlands. The salts in seawater come from the land or from the air. When rainwater flows over the land, it dissolves substances and picks up suspended sediments. Runoff then carries these materials into the oceans through streams and rivers. When winds and waves churn the ocean surface, atmospheric gases mix and dissolve into seawater. Rain falling into the ocean carries gases and small particles with it. Seawater constantly dissolves materials from the ocean bottom, including materials released by volcanoes on the seafloor. This constant addition of dissolved substances into the oceans over billions of years has made them quite salty.

The many ways that substances are added to seawater raise questions. For example, does seawater near the surface differ from seawater in the depths? Does seawater in cold climates differ from sea-water near the equator? How much does seawater from a coastal bay differ from seawater in the open ocean? To answer these questions, chemical oceanographers have analyzed seawater samples from many places.

Constancy of Salinity

After analyzing hundreds of thousands of samples from all oceans and all depths, oceanographers have found the chemical content of seawater astonishingly uniform. In the open ocean, **salinity**, the concentration of dissolved salts in seawater, averages 34.7‰; it ranges from 33‰ to 38‰. More astonishing, the ratios of the concentrations of the major elemental ions have been found to be constant. See Table 3–1. For example, for every 1.00g of chloride ion (Cl^-) there are 0.557g of sodium ion (Na^+) and .006g of magnesium ion (Mg^{2+}) dissolved in seawater, no matter where the sample is taken. We call this unvarying ratio the **rule of constant proportion** of seawater.

Calculating Constant Proportion

Because the ratio of dissolved ions of the oceans is constant all over the globe, oceanographers can determine salinity by using a single chemical test that measures only the concentration of the chloride ion (Cl^-) rather than all the salts. This measurement is called **chlorinity.** It is expressed as

$$\text{Chlorinity (Cl-‰)} = \frac{\text{grams of chloride ions (Cl-)}}{1{,}000 \text{ g seawater}}$$

Table 3–1. Constant composition ratios of the mass of common ions to the mass of chloride ions (Cl^-)

Most common ion	Symbol of ion	Ratio of ion mass to chloride ion mass (ion / Cl^-)	Average concentration in parts per thousand (‰) of seawater
Chloride	Cl^-	1.000	19.20
Sodium	Na^+	0.552	10.20
Magnesium	Mg^{2+}	0.066	1.29
Calcium	Ca^{2+}	0.021	0.410
Potassium	K^+	0.020	0.396

(Source: Data from G. Gross, *Oceanography,* 1987.)

It has been found that the ratio of concentration of all dissolved ions in seawater, that is, the ratio of salinity to chlorinity, is 1.81.

$$\frac{\text{Salinity}}{\text{Chlorinity}} = 1.81$$

Salinity = 1.81 X chlorinity

QUESTIONS

1. What is the salinity of seawater when
   a. chlorinity = 10.0‰?
   b. chlorinity = 25.0‰?

2. If the salinity of seawater is 30‰, what is its chlorinity?

Sample problem: What is the salinity when the chlorinity (the chloride ion concentration, Cl^-‰) is 22.0 ‰?

Step 1. Use this equation:

Salinity = 1.81 x chlorinity
= 1.81 x (Cl^- ‰)

Step 2. Substitute Cl^-‰ = 22.0 ‰ into Step 1 equation:

Salinity = 1.81 x 22.0 ‰
= 39.8 ‰

Fig. 3–1. Formula for calculating salinity from chlorinity measurements

Sample problem: What is the sodium ion concentration (Na^+ ‰) when chlorinity (the chloride ion concentration, Cl^- ‰) is 22.0 ‰?

Step 1. Obtain the constant ratio of Na^+ ‰ to Cl^- ‰ from Table 3–1:

$$\frac{Na^+ \text{‰}}{Cl^- \text{‰}} = 0.552$$

Step 2. Set up the equation:

Therefore Na^+ ‰ = 0.552 x Cl^- ‰

Step 3. Solve for the value:

$$Na^+ \text{‰} = 0.552 \text{ x } 22.0 \text{‰}$$
$$= 12.0 \text{‰}$$

Fig. 3–2. Using chlorinity measurements (Cl^-‰) to calculate the concentration of sodium ions (Na^+‰) in seawater

Rain, evaporation, and freezing do not change the ratio of major ions in seawater. Rain adds water, but not ions, to the ocean; evaporation and freezing remove water, but not ions, from the ocean. Adding or removing water changes the **concentrations** but not the **ratios** of the dissolved ions. Adding water dilutes the concentration of ions; removing water increases the concentration of ions.

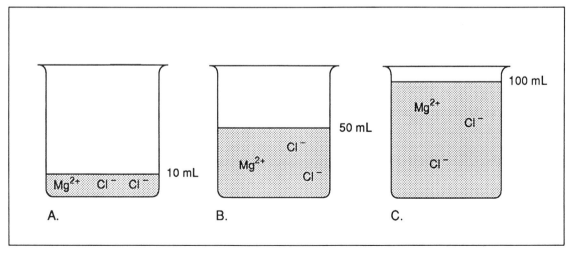

Fig. 3–3. Rain adds water to seawater and evaporation removes water from seawater, but the ratios of the major ions do not change.

QUESTIONS

3. When the Cl^- concentration is 22.0‰, what is the concentration of each of the ions listed?
   a. Mg^{2+}
   b. Ca^{2+}
   c. K^+

4. Why is the ion ratio of the chloride ion (Cl^-) given in Table 3–1 as 1.000?

5. An oceanographer obtained a sample of seawater, analyzed it, and found that its sodium ion concentration was 15‰. What was the concentration of each of the following ions?
   a. Cl^-
   b. Mg^{2+}
   c. Ca^{2+}

6. Suppose that you have an aerated seawater aquarium in your classroom. The weather has been warm, so you decide to check the salinity of the seawater in the aquarium and find it to be 40‰.
   a. What is the concentration of each of the major ions?
   b. What could have caused the salinity to increase?
   c. If you leave the water as it is, what are the ratios of each of the major ions?
   d. If you add fresh water to reduce the salinity back to 35‰, what happens to the ratios of each of the major ions? To their concentration?

Is Seawater Getting Saltier?

Every year nearly 4 billion tons (4×10^{15} g) of dissolved materials are added to the ocean. This mass is about 0.001% (one one-thousandth) of the total dissolved salts already in the ocean. It seems reasonable to believe that as the earth grows older, the ocean would become saltier. But does it?

To determine whether seawater is getting saltier, we need to know whether seawater was less salty thousands or even millions of years ago. Unfortunately, oceanographers have no direct evidence of the composition of seawater millions of years ago because they have been measuring it for only a hundred years or so. However, we can get indirect evidence from marine fossils preserved in rocks. These fossils are similar to organisms living in the oceans today. If we assume that similar seawater organisms require similar chemical environments, we can infer from fossil evidence that ancient seawater was chemically similar to seawater today. From this kind of evidence it appears that seawater is about as salty now as it was in ancient times.

Removal of Ions from Seawater

If natural processes steadily add substances to seawater, why hasn't the sea become saltier? Obviously, salt must be being removed somehow. We know some of the processes that remove salts from seawater, but research is needed to find others. A few of the processes are listed here.

1. The dissolved ions in seawater react in complex ways with the layers of sediment on the ocean floor. These sediments remove ions from seawater to form solids. Seawater reacting with hot volcanic rocks also removes ions, such as those of magnesium (Mg^{2+}).

2. Occasionally, small bodies of seawater become separated from the ocean by the movement of continents. The water evaporates from these basins, leaving

large salt deposits called **evaporites**.

3. Solid materials precipitate out of seawater. Crystal-growing is a familiar example of the formation of a solid precipitate from a saturated solution. Although seawater is not a saturated solution, precipitates form in it by processes that are not well understood. See Topic 8.

4. Salts are continuously removed from the ocean by waves washing ashore and winds blowing sea spray onto land. When the water evaporates, salts are deposited on land.

5. Calcium (Ca) and silicon (Si) are removed by living plants and animals. Their skeletons sink and are buried or are washed up on shore.

Skeleton-Building Elements

The one process we understand in some detail is the biological process of calcium and silicon removal. Marine animals and some plants use calcium (Ca) or silicon (Si) to build their skeletons. Most marine and land animals build skeletons of calcium carbonate ($CaCO_3$). Because the dissolved calcium ion (Ca^{2+}) is abundant in seawater, sea organisms have an ample supply. Two kinds of marine plants, called **coralline algae** and **calcareous algae**, build calcium carbonate into their body structure. Animals such as corals and foraminifera get their calcium directly from dissolved calcium in the seawater, but most animals get it by eating plants or other animals that contain it.

A few organisms use silicon (Si) rather than calcium (Ca) to make their skeletons. Organisms that use silicon are microscopic in size but abundant in the oceans. They in-

clude the diatoms (one-celled plants) and radiolarians (one-celled animals). See Fig. 3–4.

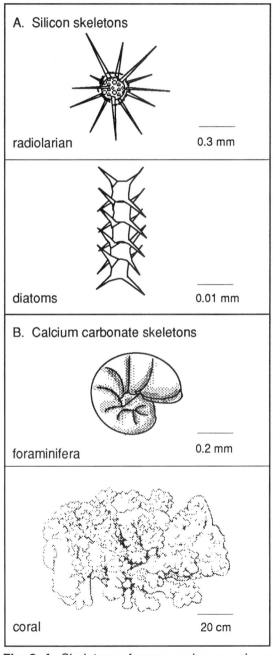

A. Silicon skeletons

radiolarian   0.3 mm

diatoms   0.01 mm

B. Calcium carbonate skeletons

foraminifera   0.2 mm

coral   20 cm

Fig. 3–4. Skeletons of some marine organisms

In the open ocean countless trillions of microscopic foraminifera, diatoms, and radiolarians live in the surface water. When they die, their tiny skeletons sink to the seafloor and become part of the mud. Seafloor sediment that is composed of 30% or more of the skeletons of any one kind of organism is named after that organism. Thus we have foraminiferal mud, diatomaceous mud, and radiolarian mud. Of these, the silicon muds are more abundant because silicon compounds do not redissolve in seawater as readily as calcium compounds.

Residence Time

To account for the apparent steady state of seawater composition, oceanographers use a concept called **residence time**, the average time an ion stays in the ocean from the moment it enters until it leaves. Residence time is calculated as follows:

$$\text{Residence time} = \frac{\text{total amount in the ocean}}{\text{amount added per year}}$$

To calculate residence time, we will use data from Table 3–2.

Table 3–2. Data for calculating residence time

Element	Amount now in ocean $\times 10^{21}$ g	Amount added to ocean / yr $\times 10^{13}$ g / yr	Residence time $\times 10^6$ yr
Sodium (Na^+)	14.4	20.7	69.5
Magnesium (Mg^{2+})	1.9	13.3	
Potassium (K^+)	0.5	7.4	
Calcium (Ca^{2+})	0.6	48.8	
Silicon ($SiO_2{}^{2-}$)	0.008	42.6	
Chlorine (Cl^-)	26.1	25.4	
Iron (Fe^{3+})	0.000 001 4	2.2	
Copper (Cu^{2+})	0.000 001 4	0.007	

ACTIVITY

Represent the residency time of major seawater components graphically.

MATERIALS

• colored pencils
• ruler

PROCEDURE

1. What are the residence times for the ions listed in Table 3–2? Complete Table 3–2.

2. Complete the bar graph in Fig. 3–5. Show each ion with a pair of bars. On the first bar mark the amount added to the ocean in a year. On the second bar mark the residence time. Lightly shade in the bars for residence time.

QUESTIONS

7. How might you explain that the sodium (Na$^+$) and chlorine (Cl$^-$) ions are the most abundant ions in seawater?

8. What process seems to be the most active in removing ions from seawater? Explain your reasoning.

9. Suggest reasons for assuming that similar seawater organisms require similar chemical environments.

10. If natural processes were not removing substances from seawater each year, how long would it take for the salinity to double? Explain your answer.

FURTHER INVESTIGATIONS

1. How might data on residence time help us calculate how long industrial pollutants will stay in seawater?

2. Matter can be neither created nor destroyed. Write an imaginary biography of a calcium ion (Ca$^+$) discharged into an estuary. What might happen to it over a hundred years?

3. In reference books find out how oceanographers have measured or calculated the data shown in Table 3–2. Report your findings to the class.

4. Analyze the ion concentrations in a sample of seawater—for example, in a seawater aquarium.
   a. Use a hydrometer to measure the density of the seawater sample. Record the density.
   b. Refer to Unit 3, Topic 3, "Measuring Salinity." Using Fig. 3–2, the temperature-density-salinity graph, estimate the salinity of the seawater sample.
   c. Calculate the concentrations of the major ions in the sample.

5. In a chemical handbook or other reference look up the solubility of each of the ions of the major and minor elements in seawater. What relationship, if any, is there between the solubility of ions and their concentration in seawater? What other factors might affect the concentration of ions in seawater?

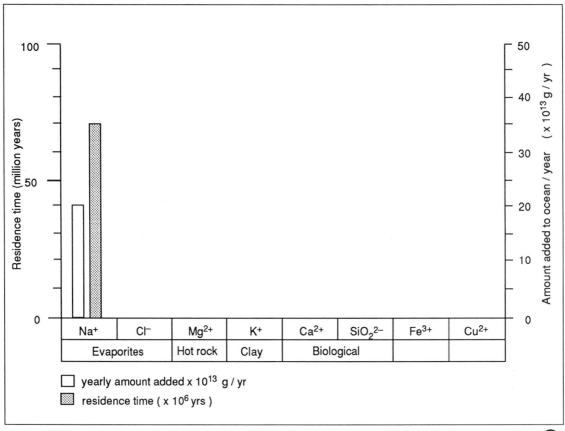

Fig. 3–5. Residence time and quantity of ions added to ocean annually

4. Water as a Solvent

Water has been called the "universal solvent" for its unusual ability to dissolve large quantities of many kinds of substances. In this topic we look at the special chemistry of the water molecule that gives it its solvent properties, then investigate some examples of those properties in operation.

Covalent Bonds

The atoms in a water molecule are held together in a different way from those in an ionic compound such as sodium chloride (NaCl). Recall that in forming the salt NaCl, sodium atoms transfer electrons to chlorine atoms, producing positive Na^+ ions and negative Cl^- ions. In water formation there is no electron exchange. Instead, hydrogen and oxygen atoms collide and share electrons.

Ionic salts are held together by the opposite electrostatic forces of their positively and negatively charged ions. In a water molecule the hydrogen and the oxygen atoms hold on to each other's electrons; they are bonded together like two children trying to pull a stick away from each other. This kind of bond in which different atoms jointly hold on to electrons is called a **covalent bond**.

Ionic salts are composed of positive ions, which are almost always metals, and negative ions, which are usually composed of nonmetals. In contrast, compounds with covalent bonds are composed mostly of nonmetals. A table of stick symbols of nonmetal elements that form covalent bonds is shown in Table 4–1. The number of bonds that each element is able to form is shown by its number of sticks. Use of these stick symbols is shown in Fig. 4–1. Note that in the formation of water each oxygen atom has two bonds that it can form and each hydrogen atom has one; therefore the formula for water is H_2O. In the formation of a hydrogen molecule each hydrogen atom forms a single bond, producing a molecule with the formula H_2. In the formation of the oxygen molecule each atom of oxygen forms two bonds, producing the molecule O_2. In carbon dioxide (CO_2) two double bonds are formed between the carbon and the two oxygen atoms.

Table 4–1. Stick symbols of nonmetal elements

			H –
– Ċ –	– N –	O –	F –
– Ṡi –	– P –	S –	Cl –
	– As –	Se –	Br –
		Te –	I –

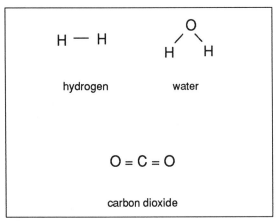

Fig. 4–1. Some models of covalent compounds using stick symbols

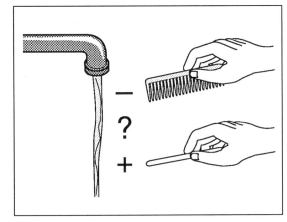

Fig. 4–2. Determining the apparent charge on water

Water and Electrostatic Forces

Covalent bonding imparts some interesting properties to water, one of which is its response to electrostatic forces.

ACTIVITY 1

Determine electrostatic forces on liquids.

MATERIALS
• running tap water
• comb
• glass rod
• piece of silk or nylon
• seawater
• alcohol
• oil

PROCEDURE

1. Turn on a water faucet and adjust the water flow so that a thin, steady stream comes out. See Fig. 4–2.

2. Predict what will happen to the stream of water of when
   a. a negative (–) electrostatic charge is brought near it.

   b. a positive (+) electrostatic charge is brought near it.

3. Record your predictions on Table 4–2 using the terms *repel, attract,* and *no reaction.*

4. Determine what happens when a negative electrostatic charge is brought near the stream of water. Record your observations in Table 4–2.
   a. Put a negative (–) electrostatic charge on a comb by running it through dry, greaseless hair.
   b. Bring the charged comb near the stream of water. Observe what happens to the water.

5. Determine what happens when a positive (+) electrostatic charge is brought near the stream of water. Record your observations in Table 4–2.
   a. Put a positive (+) charge on a glass rod by rubbing it with silk or nylon
   b. Bring the charged rod near the stream of water. Observe what happens to the water.

262

Table 4–2. Interactions between a flowing stream of water and electrostatic charges

	Movement of water	
Charges	Predicted	Observed
Comb charged (–)		
Glass rod charged (+)		

6. As time allows, run further investigations on seawater, oil, alcohol, and other liquids. Small streams can be produced with a buret.

QUESTIONS

1. What charge does water appear to have, if any? What is your evidence?

2. Why might seawater act the same way as water?

Polarity

Both positive and negative electrostatic charges attract the thin stream of pure water and the stream of ionic seawater. However, electrostatic charges do not seem to have much, if any, effect on oil. This compound, like water, is also made of covalently bonded nonmetal atoms. How can a seemingly non-ionic compound such as water have the same reaction to an electrostatic charge as a solution of ions does when other covalent compounds don't react as water does?

The world of atoms and molecules is not always what it seems at first glance. Notice that the two bonding points on the oxygen atom are a little off to one side, so that the hydrogens are slightly bunched together on the molecule. See Fig. 4–3. Further, measurements of the relative attraction of oxygen and hydrogen for their shared electrons show oxygen to have the stronger pull. Oxygen, being stronger, pulls all electrons closer to itself and becomes slightly negatively charged. The hydrogen atoms, having partially lost the battle over the electrons, become slightly positively charged. We say that the water molecule becomes electrically **polar** because one end has a slight positive charge and the other end has a slight negative charge. It is this polar water molecule that is attracted by electrostatic forces.

Polar covalent molecules exist whenever there is an **asymmetry**, or uneven distribution of electrons, in a molecule and one or more of these asymmetric atoms pulls electrons more strongly than do the other atoms. See Fig. 4–3 for examples of polar and nonpolar molecules.

You should notice one other point from the experiment: Pure water and other water solutions, including seawater, are attracted by both positive and negative electrostatic forces. This happens because the ions and polar covalent molecules in a liquid are so mobile that they can instantly orient themselves in any direction in response to a force.

QUESTION

3. How do your observations of the interaction between the stream of water and electrostatic charges tend to demonstrate
   a. that water is a polar substance?
   b. that the water molecule has a slight excess of negative charges at one end and a slight excess of positive charges at the other end?

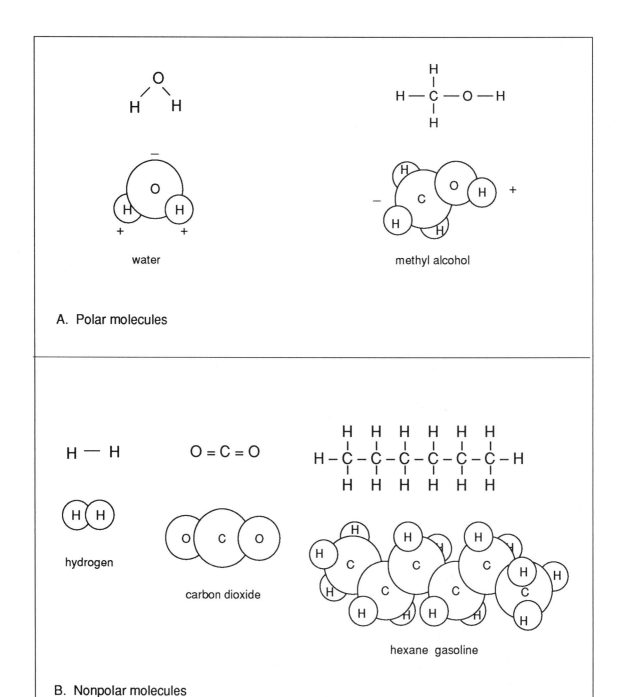

Fig. 4–3. Polar and nonpolar molecules

Comparison of Water with Other Liquids

Table 4–3 lists five liquid solvents with information on their polarity and the kind of bonding between their atoms. Of those listed, oil, alcohol, and detergents are potential pollutants of world water systems. In the activity that follows, we will investigate the capacity of water to dissolve other materials.

Table 4–3. Chemical structure of selected liquids

Liquid	Polarity	Bonding type
Distilled water	Highly polar	Covalent
Ethyl alcohol	Very slightly polar	Covalent
Oil*	Nonpolar	Covalent
Salt water	Highly polar	Covalent and ionic
Detergent solution	Nonpolar	Covalent and ionic

*Oils are usually mixes of different kinds of molecules.

ACTIVITY 2
Compare how well polar, slightly polar, and nonpolar liquids dissolve substances.

MATERIALS
- distilled water
- ethyl alcohol
- oil
- salt water
- detergent solution
- sodium chloride
- sugar
- starch
- powdered detergent
- 10-mL graduated cylinder
- stopper to fit graduated cylinder
- 10 small jars or beakers
- masking tape
- waterproof marking pen

PROCEDURE
1. Determine how much solid each liquid can dissolve.
   a. Your teacher will assign a solvent liquid to be tested. Record the name of your liquid in Table 4–4.
   b. For the liquid you are testing, predict how much of each solid it will dissolve. Using the terms *all*, *some*, and *none*, record your predictions in Table 4–4.
   c. Put 2 mL of salt into a 10-mL graduated cylinder; then fill the graduated cylinder to the 10-mL line with your solvent liquid.
   d. Stopper the cylinder, shake the contents, and let the mixture stand until settling stops.
   e. Determine how much of the solid dissolved. Record your observations as *all*, *some*, or *none*.
   f. Save the solid-liquid mixture for later conductivity tests. Put the solutions in containers and label them.
   g. Wash out the graduated cylinder and rinse it with distilled water. Then repeat steps (b) to (f) for each of the other solids.

2. Transfer your data to a classroom data chart that lists all the liquids.

3. Determine the capacity of each solvent liquid to dissolve other liquids.
   a. For your assigned solvent liquid, predict how much of each of the other liquids it can dissolve. Using the terms *all*, *some*, and *none*, record your predictions in Table 4–5.
   b. Put 2 mL of test liquid into a 10-mL graduated cylinder; then fill the graduated cylinder to the 10-mL line with your solvent liquid. Stopper the cylinder, shake the contents, and let the mixture stand till settling stops.
   c. Observe how the solvent liquid dissolved the test liquid.
   d. If there is a separation of the liquids, measure the volume of the bottom layer. Record the volume and identity of the bottom layer in Table 4–5.

Table 4–4. Ability of a liquid to dissolve solids ⓦ

Solvent liquid:_____		
	Solubility	
Solids	Predicted	Observed
Salt		
Sugar		
Starch		
Powdered detergent		

QUESTIONS

4. How do you know when
   a. a liquid has completely dissolved a solid?
   b. a liquid has completely dissolved another liquid?

5. How is it possible that salt water is
   a. both covalent and ionic?
   b. highly polar?

6. What statements can be made about polar liquids and their ability to dissolve
   a. polar liquids?
   b. nonpolar liquids?
   c. ionic substances?

7. What statements can be made about
   a. nonpolar liquids and their ability to dissolve polar, nonpolar, and ionic substances?
   b. slightly polar liquids and their ability to dissolve polar, nonpolar, and ionic substances?

8. Minerals dissolve and are carried from the land in stream water. Most of these minerals are ionic compounds. Why is water an effective solvent for minerals?

How Does Water Dissolve Other Substances?

In our experiment we found that water readily dissolves many ionic salts and many polar covalent compounds such as alcohol. It is far less effective as a solvent for nonpolar covalent compounds such as oil. But the list of trace elements in seawater suggests that water can dissolve small quantities of almost any substance.

To understand how water dissolves substances, let us concentrate first on com-

Table 4–5. Ability of a liquid to dissolve other liquids Ⓦ

Liquid tested: _____				
	Solubility		Bottom layer	
Test liquid	Predicted	Observed	Volume	Material
Distilled water				
Ethyl alcohol				
Oil				
Saltwater solution				
Detergent solution				

pounds that water dissolves easily, the ionic and polar covalent compounds. With these compounds it is the exceptionally strong polarity of water that gives it its dissolving power. The ionic salt sodium chloride (NaCl) is a good model of how this dissolving takes place.

Clusters of water molecules are attracted to and surround sodium ions (Na^+) and chloride ions (Cl^-) on the surface of the salt crystal. Positive polar ends of water molecules are attracted to the chloride ions (Cl^-), and their negative polar ends are attracted to the positive sodium ions (Na^+). See Fig. 4–4. The bonding between the ions and water is strong, and shortly the ions are as strongly attracted to the water as to each other. As other water molecules collide with the ion-containing clusters, they knock them off, casting them into the body of the solution. An ion surrounded by water is called a **hydrated ion**.

A similar process occurs in the dissolving of polar covalent compounds, except that the water is attracted to the poles of the dissolving polar compound.

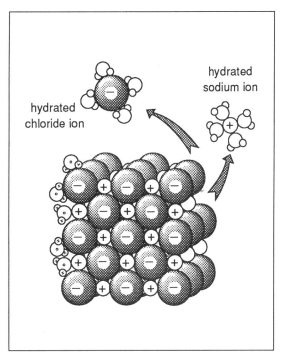

Fig. 4–4. Water dissolving a salt crystal

Nonpolar Molecules in Water

Molecules of nonpolar compounds such as oil and gasoline when mixed into water tend to separate from the water and rejoin to form a single liquid. However, gasoline readily dissolves oil. We can make the generalization that like molecules tend to dissolve each other. Since the molecules of gasoline and oil have the same general structure, they easily slide between each other in the constant jostling of the liquids and become evenly mixed or dissolved. Water molecules tend to hold on to each other and squeeze out nonpolar oil and gasoline.

In our discussion of readily soluble substances, we must not forget that small quantities of low-solubility substances such as oil remain in a solvent such as water, either as droplets or as single suspended molecules. For example, wind and waves at sea eventually break up an oil slick into particles and distribute them far and wide. Molecules of nonpolar substances such as the vital gases of air, oxygen (O_2) and nitrogen (N_2), dissolve in sufficient quantity in water to sustain all living things in our rivers, lakes, and oceans. At 25°C a liter of seawater holds 5 mL of oxygen (.007 g/L) and 10 mL of nitrogen (.012 g/L).

Detergents and Water

Detergents are an interesting class of compounds that permit large quantities of nonpolar compounds to dissolve in water. The molecules of detergents are long, with one ionic end and one nonpolar end. The molecule is so long that its ionic end does not affect its nonpolar end. When a detergent molecule contacts a nonpolar compound such as oil, it slides its nonpolar end between the nonpolar molecules of the oil. In this way it can surround small droplets. Since its nonpolar end is attracted to the oil, its ionic end faces outward and attracts water molecules. Such detergent-surrounded oil droplets are readily carried into the water solution. See Fig. 4–5.

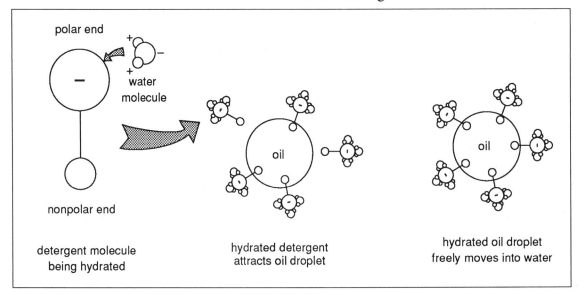

Fig. 4–5. Water, oil, and detergent molecules

Conductivity

Let us test the **conductivity** of some liquids to get a sense of their ability to carry an electric current. We will use a battery and a light bulb as shown in Fig. 4–6. If the liquid conducts electricity, the bulb will light.

ACTIVITY 3

Compare the conductivity of polar, slightly polar, and nonpolar liquids.

MATERIALS

- three 20-cm pieces of insulated copper wire
- scissors
- wire stripper (optional)
- 5 X 5-cm sheet of sandpaper
- 7.5-volt threaded flashlight bulb
- 9-volt battery
- tape (optional)
- 10-mL graduated cylinder
- watch glass or Petri dish
- distilled water
- ethyl alcohol
- oil
- salt water
- detergent solution
- salt
- 1/4-tsp measuring spoon
- 8-1/2 X 11-in sheet of paper
- glass stirring rod
- solutions saved from Activity 2

PROCEDURE

1. Make a conductivity-testing device like the one shown in Fig. 4–6.
   a. Obtain three pieces of insulated copper wire about 20 cm long. Gently remove 5 cm of insulation from both ends of each wire. Use scissors, or a

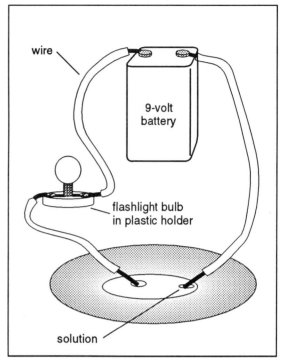

Fig. 4–6. Conductivity-testing device

wire stripper if available, to cut through the insulation only. Pull the insulation off the ends of the wires.
   b. Burnish the bare wire with sandpaper until it is bright.
   c. Wrap the ends of one wire around the screw-track of the bulb holder. Attach a second wire to the other screw-track.
   d. Attach the second wire to the battery. Twist the wire around a terminal. If necessary, secure it firmly with a piece of transparent tape. Attach the third wire to the other terminal of the battery.
   e. Test your device by touching the two free ends of the wires together. If the testing device works, the light will burn brightly.

269

Table 4–6. Conductivity of liquids   Ⓦ

Liquid	Predicted conductivty	Observed conductivty
Distilled water		
Ethyl alcohol		
Oil		
Salt water		
Detergent		

2. Predict the conductivity of each solution in terms of the amount of light it will produce. Record your predictions in Table 4–6. Use these terms:
Good conductor (bright light)
Poor conductor (dim light)
Nonconductor (no light)

3. Test the conductivity of each liquid. Record your data in Table 4–6.
   a. Pour 10 mL of the liquid into a watch glass or Petri dish.
   b. Touch the base of the bulb to one pole of the battery.
   c. Put the bare ends of the contact wires close together (within 2 mm from each other) in the liquid in the watch glass.
   d. Observe the brightness of the bulb. Record your observation of the conductivity of each liquid.
   e. Wash the watch glass and contact wires and rinse them with distilled water between tests. The wires may need to be burnished with sandpaper if material sticks to them.
   f. Repeat steps 2.a. to 2.d. to test the remaining liquids.

4. Measure eight 1/8-tsp portions of salt. Place each portion on a small piece of paper.

5. Test the conductivity of different concentrations of salt water.
   a. Measure 10 mL of distilled water and pour it into a watch glass. Test the conductivity of the water as in Procedure 3. Record the conductivity in Table 4–7.
   b. Add 1/8 tsp of salt to the water. Mix with the stirring rod until the salt is dissolved.
   c. Test the conductivity and record the relative brightness in Table 4–7. Use the terms in Procedure 2.

Table 4–7. Conductivity of saltwater solutions
  Ⓦ

Tsp salt	Conductivity
1/8	
1/4	
3/8	
1/2	
5/8	
3/4	
7/8	
1	

d. Increase the salt concentration by adding salt to the solution 1/8 tsp at a time. Mix well and test for conductivity after each addition. Continue until no more salt will dissolve in the solution.

6. If time permits, test the conductivity of the solutions you made in Activity 2. Make a data table like Table 4–6.
   a. Predict which mixtures will conduct electricity. Record your predictions.
   b. Pour about 10 mL of each mixture into a watch glass and test it for conductivity as in Procedure 2. Record the observed conductivity.

QUESTIONS

9. What kinds of bonds do compounds that conduct electricity have?

10. Oceanographers use conductivity meters to determine the salinity of seawater. Explain how this is possible.

FURTHER INVESTIGATIONS

1. Water is a very unusual chemical compound in many respects. Invite a chemist or a chemical oceanographer to class to talk about water, what makes it so remarkable, and how its uniqueness affects us.

2. In 1989 a large oil tanker ran aground off the coast of Alaska. Using library references, find out what chemical substances and techniques were used to clean up the oil and to contain its spread. What makes oils spills so difficult to control? Apply what you know about the chemistry of water to explain the actions taken in a major oil spill.

3. It is said that electrons do not flow through the water in electrolysis. Find out what this statement means.

4. Most materials corrode in seawater. Some dissolve in the water; others react with the dissolved ions. Find out what kinds of materials are used
   a. to prevent rapid corrosion of ship hulls and offshore oil rigs.
   b. to protect bridges, wharfs, and other structures that are partially embedded in water.
   c. to provide durable, noncorrosive equipment for sailors and others who work at sea.

5. Design and carry out further experiments to answer such questions as these:
   a. How does water temperature affect the solubility of substances?
   b. How is the solubility of a substance affected by other dissolved substances in water?

5. Water, Energy, and the Water Cycle

Ice floats on water. Why doesn't it sink in its own liquid, as other substances do? Clouds form on a cool day, and rain falls. How can water form clouds when it doesn't boil until 100°C? We heat a pan of water to boiling, but it doesn't instantly become steam. Instead, it boils away. In this topic we investigate how the structure of the water molecule makes it respond in unique ways to energy changes.

Why Does Ice Float?

To understand why ice floats, we need to get a sense of the architecture of an ice crystal. For a moment, let's become molecular engineers reduced in size so that we can supervise construction of an ice crystal. Water molecules shaped something like lumpy V-shaped beams made of Tinkertoys are our only building materials. At the point of the V, the oxygen atom provides a negative electrical bonding point, and the hydrogen atoms provide positive bonding points. By maneuvering oppositely charged ends of the beams together, we assemble them into great hexagonal galleries all running parallel to each other. See Fig. 5–1. The center of these galleries is open, and air molecules periodically come bouncing through the empty spaces. Compared with the liquid water in which it floats, our ice occupies 11% more volume.

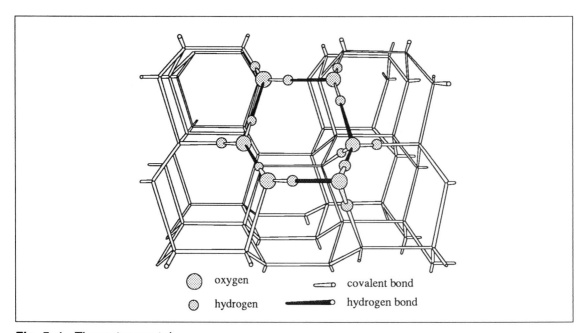

oxygen   covalent bond

hydrogen   hydrogen bond

Fig. 5–1. The water crystal

Water's crystalline arrangement is unique among common molecules. Most molecules, ions, and single atoms collapse together into a smaller space when they form solids. Because the density of these solids is greater than the density of their liquid form, they sink in their own liquids.

Evidently some assemblage of water molecules into larger structures begins be-fore the freezing point. At 4°C, pure water being cooled starts to expand, indicating that the water molecules are beginning to build on each other.

Freezing and Melting

Ice also forms in seawater. In the following activity we investigate what happens as ice forms in fresh water and salt water.

ACTIVITY 1

Investigate the properties of freshwater and saltwater ice.

MATERIALS

- 1,000-mL beaker
- centigram balance
- table salt
- 100-mL graduated cylinder
- stirring rod
- fresh water
- two 1-qt milk cartons
- scalpel
- masking tape
- waterproof marking pen
- centimeter ruler
- pencil
- newspapers
- rubber bands
- freezer
- ice pick or screw driver
- hammer
- marking pens or labels
- three 250-mL beakers
- heat source
- thermometer
- hydrometer

PROCEDURE

1. Prepare a saltwater solution having about the same salinity as seawater. Using table salt (NaCl), make a 35‰ salt solution as follows:
   a. Place a 1,000-mL beaker onto a centi-gram balance. Weigh it.
   b. Leave the beaker on the balance. Add 35 g of salt to the beaker.
   c. Remove the beaker. Add 1,000 mL of water to the beaker. Stir with a stirring rod until all salt is dissolved.

2. Prepare ice samples.
   a. Use a scalpel to cut the top ends off two 1-qt milk cartons. Rinse the insides of the cartons if necessary. Using mask-ing tape and a waterproof marking pen, label one carton "fresh water" and the other carton "salt water."
   b. Measure and pour 900 mL of fresh water and 900 mL of salt water into the appropriate cartons.
   c. Measure the distance from the bottom to the surface of the liquid in each carton as shown in Fig. 5–2. Use a pencil to mark the water height on the

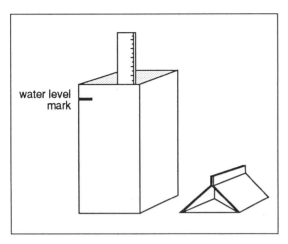

Fig. 5–2. Measuring the distance from the bottom to the surface

outside of each carton. Record the water heights in centimeters in Table 5–1.

d. Wrap the cartons in newspaper to insulate the bottom and the sides so that cold air contacts only the exposed surface of the liquids. Hold the newspaper in place with rubber bands or tape.

e. Freeze the liquids in both cartons by putting them into the freezer.

Table 5–1. Height of liquids and ice in cartons ⓦ

Liquid sample	Height (cm)	
	Fresh water	Salt water
Start (liquid)		
Finish (ice)		
Change		

3. After the liquid has frozen solid, remove the cartons from the freezer.
   a. Measure the height of the ice from the bottom to the surface. Record the height of the ice in Table 5–1. Calculate any difference in height between the liquid salt water and the saltwater ice.
   b. Look for differences in texture, clarity, and other physical characteristics of the two blocks of ice. Record your observations in your notebook.

4. Compare sections of the blocks of ice.
   a. Return the freshwater ice block to the freezer.
   b. Spread newspaper over the working surface.
   c. Tear or cut away the carton from the saltwater ice.
   d. Using an ice pick or a screw driver and a hammer, carefully break the ice into three horizontal blocks of about equal volume. See Fig. 5–3. Separate and label the top, middle, and bottom

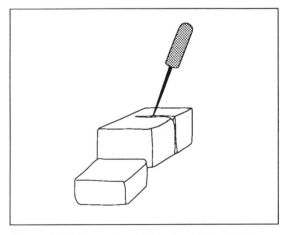

Fig. 5–3. Using an ice pick to break ice into three blocks

sections. Label the newspapers to identify the samples. Break each block into smaller chunks.

e. Put a small chunk of ice from the top block into a 250-mL beaker filled with fresh water. Observe whether the chunk floats or sinks. Record your observation in your notebook. Repeat this step using small chunks of ice from the middle and bottom sections.

5. Measure the temperature and density as follows:
   a. Place a beaker containing about 250 mL of ice chunks from the top block onto a heat source. Gently heat the beaker until all but about one-tenth of the ice in the beaker has melted.
   b. Remove the beaker from the heat source and stir its contents until the remaining ice melts. While stirring the contents of the beaker, take temperature readings every 30 sec until the ice has melted. Record the data in Table 5–2.
   c. Pour the liquid sample into a 100-mL graduated cylinder. Use a hydrometer to measure the density of the liquid. Record the temperature and the density in Table 5–3.

Table 5–2. Temperature during melting

Seconds	Temperature (˚C)					
	Top block		Middle block		Bottom block	
	Fresh water	Salt water	Fresh water	Salt water	Fresh water	Salt water
0						
30						
60						
90						
120						
150						
180						
210						
240						
270						
300						

Table 5–3. Temperature and density of liquids (W)

	Density (g/mL)	
	Fresh water	Salt water
Liquid from top block temperature:___		
Liquid from middle block temperature:___		
Liquid from bottom block temperature:___		

Table 5–4. Saltiness of ice blocks from the top, middle, and bottom of the saltwater ice (W)

	Top block	Middle block	Bottom block
Most salty			
In between			
Least salty			
Same as			

d. Repeat steps (a) to (c) for the middle and bottom sections. Record your data in Tables 5–2 and 5–3.

6. Ask your teacher for permission to taste the melted liquids from the top, middle, and bottom blocks. Compare their tastes. Put check marks in Table 5–4 to describe your observations.

7. Repeat Procedures 4 and 5 using the freshwater ice sample.

QUESTIONS

1. How does a block of frozen fresh water compare with a block of frozen salt water?

2. What happens to the volume of water as it freezes? Be as quantitative in your answer as possible. Explain how you determined your answer. Show your calculations.

3. Where does ice form first, at the top or at the bottom of a water sample? What evidence do you have to support your answer?

4. Describe what happens when a carton of salt water freezes. Describe differences, if any, in the top, middle, and bottom portions of the saltwater ice in terms of density and saltiness.

5. What is the effect of melting ice on the temperature of the surrounding liquid water?

6. What happens to the ions in the water as salt water freezes? What evidence supports your answer?

7. At what temperature did the fresh water melt? The salt water? Explain any differences in the melting points of the two water samples.

8. In terms of covalent bonding, how might it be explained that water reaches its greatest density just before it freezes at 4°C?

9. It is said that buckets of seawater will warm a house in northern climates during below-freezing weather. How is this possible?

Sea Ice

We have seen that salt in water lowers the melting point below that of fresh water. The more salt, the lower the melting point. In freezing homemade ice cream, we put salt and ice together around the ice cream container. Why? Because the salted ice melts at a lower temperature than the freezing point of milk, the milk freezes.

In polar regions where ice forms on the surface of the ocean, the ice is almost free of salt. The top layer of your frozen saltwater ice in the carton had far less salt than the bottom layer. As the ice crystals form, they exclude the salt ions. These excluded ions create a denser, saltier solution below the ice, lowering the freezing point still further. For this reason ocean water has no fixed freezing point. Though the salt exclusion process is effective, small pockets of salt solution are incorporated into the ice, producing a slight salinity.

Heating and Cooling Water

Fig. 5–4 shows the results of a heating experiment. One gram of freshwater ice was heated in a small container. Miniature instruments were used to measure how much heat energy was introduced to get each degree of temperature change. The experiment started with ice at a temperature of –10°C and stopped when all the water boiled away. Here the unit of heat used to measure energy was the calorie. One **calorie** (cal) is the amount of heat needed to raise the temperature of 1 g of water 1°C.

The graph shows that it took only 5 cal to heat the ice from –10°C to 0°C. That is 0.5 cal per gram of ice. From 0°C it took 80 cal just to melt the ice, and the temperature did not change during the melting. Both the ice and the liquid water were at 0°C. Then, with the melting of the last bit of ice, the temperature suddenly rose again very regularly, requiring 100 cal to go from 0° to 100°C. Again at 100°C the temperature stopped rising, and it took 540 cal more to boil the water completely away as steam.

The process was then reversed. One gram of steam was condensed into liquid water at 100°C and slowly cooled to –10°C. The graph reveals that the same amount of heat put in to raise the temperature from –10°C through boiling the water away had to be removed from the steam to restore the temperature to –10°C. See Fig. 5–5.

What happened to the water during this process? When the ice was being heated from –10°C to 0°C, the molecules in the ice crystal were caused to vibrate more and more. See (A) in Fig. 5–6. This movement of the molecules was measured as a change in temperature. Then at 0°C the molecules, having reached their vibrational limits in the crystal, used all the additional heat energy to break the hydrogen bonds that held them in place in the crystal. During this time there was no increase in temperature.

When all the bonds of the crystal were broken, the unattached molecules of the liquid water were free to move about, and the additional heat caused them to move faster. See (B) in Fig. 5–6. As the molecules moved faster, the temperature rose. Then at 100°C the molecules reached their liquid movement limitation. Before they could increase their speed again, they had to break the

277

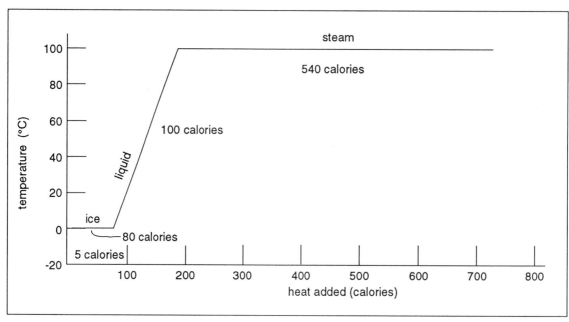

Fig. 5–4. Heating experiment

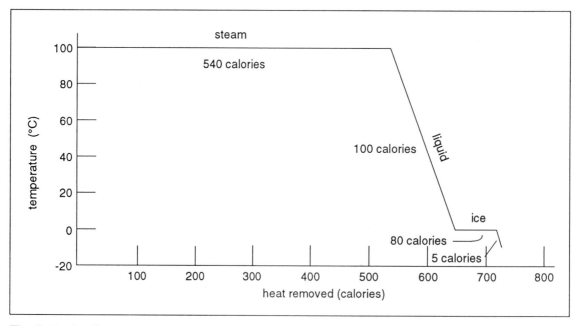

Fig. 5–5. Cooling experiment

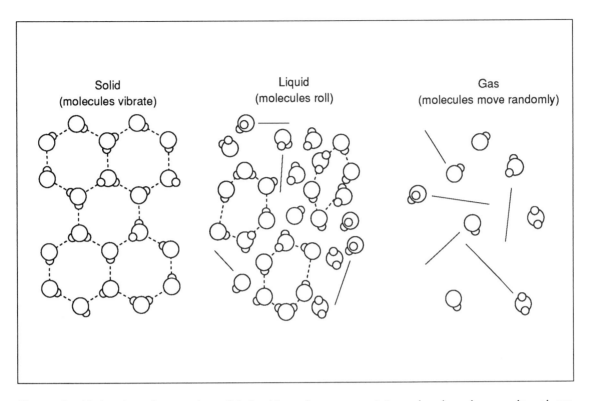

Fig. 5–6. Molecules of water in solid, liquid, and gaseous states, showing changes in volume occupied by the molecules

strong attractions that still held them together as a liquid. They had to become part of the gas we call **steam**, in which there is very little attraction for anything. See (C) in Fig. 5–6. However, it took an additional 540 cal to break the bonds of the liquid and release all the molecules as steam. As in the melting of ice, the temperature remained constant until all the liquid bonds were broken.

To condense 1 g of steam at 100°C back into liquid water, 540 cal of energy had to be removed. An additional 100 cal then had to be taken out to get the water back to 0°C, and 80 cal more had to be removed to freeze the

water again. Finally, 5 cal more had to be removed to lower the ice to the starting temperature of –10°C. The same amount of heat energy had to be taken out of the 1 g of steam as had been added to convert the ice to steam.

Rain in a Bucket

In our simulated heating experiment we found that the 1 g of water in our beaker boiled dry at 100°C with the addition of 540 cal of heat. But we know that water evaporates from a freshly mopped floor or wet clothes at much lower temperatures. How do we account for this?

279

ACTIVITY 2

Make fresh water from seawater.
Distill water at temperatures below boiling.

MATERIALS

- sodium chloride (table salt)
- balance
- 200 mL fresh water
- two 100-mL graduated cylinders
- hydrometer
- metal baking sheet with rims
- 2 ring stands with rings
- heat source with low temperature range
- sand
- 2 aluminum pie pans (300-mL capacity or larger)
- two 1-gal cans with both ends removed
- 2 small tin cans with one end removed
- two 250-mL beakers
- two 30 X 30-cm sheets of plastic wrap
- 2 rubber bands
- 2 weights (small stones)
- thermometer

PROCEDURE

1. Prepare 100 mL of simulated seawater.
   a. Weigh 3.5 g sodium chloride (NaCl).
   b. Place the sodium chloride crystals in a 100-mL graduated cylinder.
   c. Add water to the sodium chloride until the total volume is 100 mL.
   d. Mix until dissolved.

2. Use the hydrometer to measure the density of the simulated seawater. Record in Table 5–5.

3. Pour 100 mL of fresh water into the second graduated cylinder. Measure the density of the fresh water. Record in Table 5–5.

4. Set up the heating system as shown in Fig. 5–7.
   a. Center the flat metal baking sheet on the heat source. Support the ends of the sheet with ring stands.
   b. Cover the sheet with sand about 0.5 cm deep. The sand distributes the heat.
   c. Place two pie pans on the sand at equal distances from the center of the heat source.

5. Make two stills.
   a. Pour 100 mL of fresh water into one pie pan and 100 mL of salt water into the other pie pan. Label each pan.

Table 5–5. Distillation data using the still Ⓦ

		Fresh water	Salt water
Density (in g/mL)			
	Starting (in pan)	pan: _____	pan: _____
	Ending (in beaker)	beaker: ___	beaker: ___
Temperature (°C)			
	Starting	pan: _____	pan: _____
		beaker: ___	beaker: ___
	After 30 min	pan: _____	pan: _____
		beaker: ___	beaker: ___
	Ending	pan: _____	pan: _____
		beaker: ___	beaker: ___
Condensation rate (in mL/hr)			
Taste*			

*Obtain your teacher's permission.

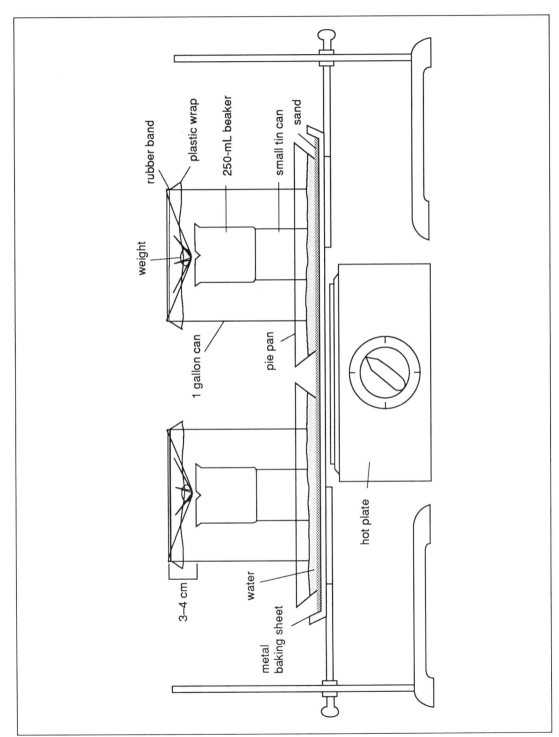

Fig. 5-7. Still

281

b. Place a 1-gal can with the ends removed in each pie pan.

c. Place a small tin can in the center of each big can.

d. Place a clean beaker on top of each small tin can. Check to make sure the top of the beaker is 3 to 4 cm below the rim of the gallon can. If necessary, use a smaller beaker. See Fig. 5–7.

e. Loosely cover the top of each gallon can with plastic wrap. Seal with a rubber band.

f. Put a weight in the center of the plastic wrap so that a cone-shaped depression forms. Make sure that the bottom of the depression is over the beaker and that the plastic wrap is not touching the beaker. Completed stills should look like Fig. 5–7.

6. Adjust the heat to a low setting that keeps the temperature of the water in the pan at about 40°C.

7. Measure the starting temperature of the liquid in each pan. Record data in Table 5–5.

8. After 30 minutes, again measure and record the temperatures of the liquids in the pans. Also determine the number of milliliters per hour condensing in the still.

9. If the still can be watched during the day, allow it to operate until about 20 mL of liquid collects in the beaker. If the still cannot be left on during the day, turn up the heat until 5 to 10 drops are produced per minute. Measure and record the highest temperature of the liquid in each pan. Do not let it exceed 90°C.

10. At the end of the distillation period, turn off the heat. Remove the weight and the plastic wrap.

a. Measure the temperature and density of the distilled liquid in the beaker. Record in Table 5–5.

b. Measure the density of the liquid remaining in the pan.

11. After getting your teacher's permission, taste the contents of the beaker and the pan. Record your observations in Table 5–5.

12. If time permits, repeat the experiment, this time using the sun as a heat source. Prepare a table similar to Table 5–5. Record your observations and measurements.

QUESTIONS

10. Explain how the still works.

11. What could be done to make the device produce more water per minute?

12. In what way, if any, did the results of heating fresh water differ from the results of heating salt water? Give your evidence.

13. Define the following terms:
a. condensation
b. distillation

14. What techniques might be used to
a. purify water?
b. obtain fresh water from salt water?
c. obtain fresh water from moist soil?

Evaporation

In the closed system of our low-temperature still, water changes into vapor and vapor condenses at temperatures well below the 100°C boiling point. This finding demonstrates that not all the molecules in a water sample behave the same at any given temperature. In fact, in any sample of water at any temperature, some molecules will be moving very fast and some very slowly. **Temperature** is a measure of the average motion of molecules.

The range of movement of the water molecules in a sample can be explained by the fact that molecules collide when they move. When they collide, their rate or energy of motion may speed up, slow down, or change very little. At any time, some molecules at the water's surface will have sufficient energy to break free and escape from the liquid. Most of the molecules that escape will be driven back into the liquid when they collide with air molecules above the liquid, but a few will not. As the temperature rises, more and more molecules gain the energy to escape. In the summer near the seashore, or in a marine air mass inland, we often feel this escaped moisture. We call it **humidity**.

As high-energy molecules leave the surface of the water, the molecules left behind have less energy. In this way, evaporation cools the surface of the water, just as it cools our skin when we are exposed to the wind after perspiring. The mechanical bombardment of the wind on the moisture of our bodies carries off high-energy water molecules, lowering our temperature.

QUESTIONS

15. Explain how water can be boiled in a paper cup over a campfire.

16. What happens to the temperature of the liquid left behind when water evaporates?

17. How does perspiring help to cool us down?

18. A wet towel hung outside in freezing weather turns stiff, yet it dries if left there long enough. How might this be explained?

Condensation

We saw condensation in the still. Water vapor condensed into liquid droplets on the surface of the plastic covering, then ran down the slope of the sheet and dripped into the collecting container. How did this happen?

Once water molecules have broken the bonds of the liquid, they must lose their bond-breaking energy before they can again become part of a liquid. Because the plastic covering was in contact with the cooler air outside the still, the plastic was cooler than the water vapor inside the still. When hot material contacts cooler material, the hot material loses heat while the cooler material gains heat. Thus, when the gaseous water molecules struck the plastic, the cool surface accepted their bond-breaking energy, and they condensed back into a liquid.

As we saw when we evaporated the water off salt water in Topic 2, the salt was left behind. In the still the same thing happened. Water evaporated without carrying the salt with it. We produced pure water vapor, which condensed as pure **distilled** liquid water.

Precipitation

Our still simulated the continuous process that evaporates water from rivers, lakes, and oceans and sends it to all parts of the world in the form of precipitation. It is the unusual properties of the water molecule that keep life-sustaining moisture distributed around the earth's surface.

The water molecule is little more than half as massive or as heavy as molecules of oxygen (O_2) and nitrogen (N_2), the major gases in air. Therefore, when water evaporates and saturates a body of air, that moist air is less dense than dry air. This lighter moist air tends to rise. As it travels upward, its water molecules eventually collide with particles of salt and dust in the air. When they collide, the molecules give up their bond-breaking energy and condense on the particles. The air also cools as it rises. At cooler temperatures other water molecules condense on the same particles until tiny water droplets form. We see this process in cloud formation.

Sometimes clouds evaporate as the droplets lose their water molecules to bombardment by rising warm air. But if the droplets keep growing until they reach a mass that the atmospheric winds can no longer support, they fall earthward as **precipitation**—fog, rain, hail, or snow, depending on the temperature. By the time the droplets precipitate and fall, winds may have carried water molecules great distances— across a quarter or half a continent, across a whole continent, even beyond it out to sea.

Specific Heat

Specific heat is the amount of heat it takes to raise or lower the temperature of 1 g of a substance 1°C. The specific heat of liquid water is 1 cal per gram per 1°C (1 cal/g/°C). The specific heat of ice is 0.5 cal/g/°C. But soil, rocks, and metals have specific heats of about 0.2 cal/g/°C. The difference is important ecologically.

When the sun shines, rocks, soil, and buildings on land warm faster than the ocean and other bodies of water do. For example, the rocks around a tide pool may be painfully hot to our bare feet while the shallow water in the pool is only warm. During the night, rocks, soil, and buildings lose their heat faster than bodies of water do. Night chills the rocks around a tide pool while the water remains relatively warm.

Water temperatures near the ocean surface range from a little below 0°C in Arctic and Antarctic regions to about 30°C in the Red Sea. Most tropical waters stay at a fairly constant 28°C. By contrast, temperatures over the land range from –70°C to 60°C. Though the water receives the same amount of sunlight as the land, water's high specific heat keeps its temperature within a relatively narrow range.

Coastal Breezes

In coastal regions along an ocean or fronting on large lakes, summer brings day and night breezes. During the day, cooler, denser air above the ocean or lake sweeps in over the shore as air warmed by the land rises. Because of these breezes, on a hot summer day the beach area is much cooler than inland areas. During the night, breezes blow off the land as the warmer air over the ocean rises. See Fig. 5–8.

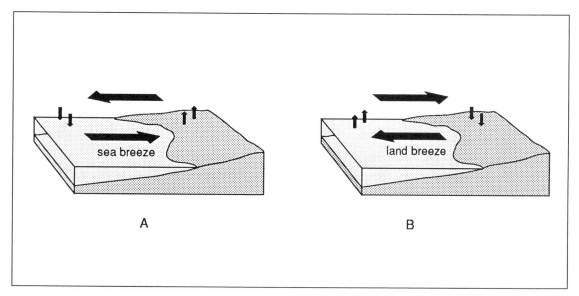

Fig. 5–8. Sea breeze (A) and land breeze (B)

Winds that come off the ocean tend to keep nearby coastal lands relatively warm in winter and cool in summer. San Francisco, with ocean water on three sides, seldom gets cooler than 10°C or warmer than 18°C. But in a midcontinent city such as Lincoln, Nebraska, temperatures range from –10°C to 40°C.

QUESTIONS

19. Some coastal regions are said to have **maritime climates** characterized by cool summers and relatively warm, wet winters. Inland climates, on the other hand, are characterized by hot, dry summers and cold winters. Applying what you know about the properties of water, explain how the ocean affects maritime climates.

20. How does water act to stabilize temperature?

Water on the Earth

Earth is the only known place where life exists as we know it. It is unique in the solar system. It has water in all three states:

• as a *liquid* in great quantities in the oceans, lakes, rivers, and clouds
• as *solid ice and snow* on the surface of the earth
• as *gaseous water vapor* in the atmosphere

None of the other planets in our solar system has such an abundance of water. Even if one did, water couldn't exist in all three states on any of them. Some planets are too hot, so water would boil off; others are too cold, so water would freeze solid and remain that way. Of all the planets, only the earth is positioned at just the right distance from the sun so that its global temperatures permit water to continuously evaporate and condense.

Water is essential to living things, serving as the solvent in which all the chemicals necessary for life are able to interact. From the simplest single-celled organisms to our own complex bodies, all living organisms are composed primarily of water.

Global Distribution of Water

Of all the water on earth, over 97% is in the oceans. See Table 5–6. An additional 2% is held in the great polar ice caps and glaciers. The remainder, less than 1% of the total water, is used to run all the processes of land-based life; to fill our rivers, lakes, and underground reservoirs; to erode hillsides and farms; and to build the great cloud masses of the sky.

Because the land and the atmosphere hold so little water, vast areas of the world are arid; some are deserts. Beyond our personal need for water, modern industrial and agricultural needs make the control of fresh water a major national and international problem. How we use existing freshwater sources and whether we decide to recover water from the sea will determine where major population centers will be situated in the next century.

QUESTIONS

21. What percentage of the total water on earth is available as liquid fresh water? List the sources
    a. in order of abundance.
    b. in order of how easy they are to obtain.

22. Explain this statement: The temperature range on the surface of the earth permits water to exist in all three states.

23. How can you account for the fact that a very small percentage of the fresh water exists on land?

Table 5–6. Global distribution of water

Location	Percentage of global water	
	Subtotal	Total
Oceans *(liquid)*		97.2
Ice caps and glaciers *(solid)*		2.15
Surface water *(liquid)*		0.017 1
Freshwater lakes	0 .009	
Saline lakes and inland seas	0 .008	
Rivers and streams	0 .000 1	
Subsurface water *(liquid)*		0.625
Soil moisture	0 .005	
Shallow groundwater	0 .31	
Deep groundwater	0 .31	
Atmosphere *(gas)*		0.001

The Water Cycle

The constant exchange of water between the earth, the oceans, and the atmosphere is known as the **hydrological cycle**, sometimes simply called **the water cycle.** See Fig. 5–9.

Water vapor, which makes up only a tiny portion of the water on earth, is the critical link for distributing fresh water worldwide. The sun provides energy to drive the system as it heats the earth, causing evaporation of liquid water. Evaporation takes place from the surface of all the bodies of water on the earth as well as from soil and living organisms. As plants transport water from their roots, much of the water evaporates through the leaves into the atmosphere. This process is called **transpiration.** Daytime transpiration from a tropical forest produces a volume of water vapor as great as the volume of vapor escaping from the surface of a lake.

Water vapor remains in the atmosphere only a short time. It rises into the atmosphere, cools, condenses, and forms tiny droplets of water in clouds. These are blown by the winds over the surface of the earth. Eventually the moisture-laden clouds release the water in the form of rain, snow, hail, dew, or fog, collectively called **precipitation**. Most precipitation falls back into the ocean, where it quickly mixes with seawater.

When precipitation falls onto land, some of it evaporates directly back into the atmosphere. When the surface soil cannot absorb all the water from rain or melting snow, the excess precipitation flows off the land. This is known as freshwater **runoff**. It then flows over land surfaces into small streams, which form larger streams and rivers. Eventually it reaches a lake or an ocean. Surface water has a short residence time in rivers, moving relatively quickly through them as it flows to the ocean.

Water that seeps or **percolates** down into the soil is called **groundwater**. It drains downward until it reaches a saturated area called a **water table.** Generally, the level of a water table follows the surface features of

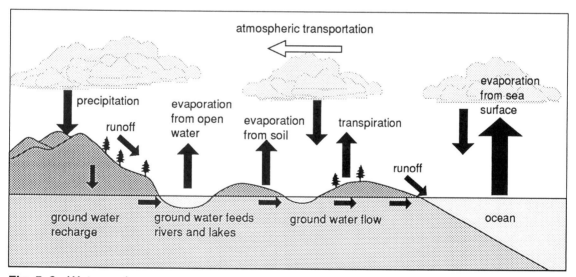

Fig. 5–9. Water cycle

an area. Where the water table is very close to the surface, water seeps out of rocks and forms springs. If there is a lot of rain and the water table rises, shallow groundwater flows into streams and lakes, sometimes causing them to flood their banks. Where the water table is deep in the earth, wells must be dug to reach water.

QUESTIONS

24. How are evaporation and condensation related to the water cycle?

25. In what ways does a still serve as a model of the water cycle? What parts of the water cycle does it demonstrate? What parts of the water cycle does it not demonstrate?

26. Is the water cycle of the earth a closed system or an open system? Give reasons for your answer.

FURTHER INVESTIGATIONS

1. Design experiments to determine how the following environmental factors affect evaporation:
   a. soil moisture
   b. wind speed
   c. the surface area of a lake or pond
   d. wave action on a lake or pond

2. Design and conduct an experiment to measure the effect of different concentrations of salt on the temperature at which salt water boils and freezes. Compare your findings with the boiling point and freezing point of fresh water. How might this difference be explained?

3. Steam irons often require distilled water or deionized water. Why?

4. Consult library references to explain the meaning of relative humidity.

5. Read about global temperatures in the ocean and on land and report on average temperatures worldwide for summer and winter and for day and night.

6. Fresh water is one of our most precious natural resources. Report to the class on one or more of the following topics:
   a. ways used to find, store, and deliver supplies of safe water
   b. how urbanization has changed the natural patterns of precipitation, run-off, and soil percolation
   c. efforts to conserve and use our water resources wisely
   d. the effects of lowered water tables in places where consumption of water exceeds the natural processes of replenishing the water supply
   e. salinization of the soil and its possible long-term consequences

7. Scientists have found evidence that great glaciers have formed periodically, covering vast areas of the northern continents. Report on
   a. evidence for the periodic advance and retreat of glaciers.
   b. evidence that sea level also has risen and fallen periodically.
   c. evidence that sea level is related to the formation of glaciers.

6. Acid Rain and the Greenhouse Effect

Several of our major environmental problems arise from interactions between water and the atmosphere. One problem is acid rain, which affects large areas of the United States, Canada, and Europe. **Acid rain** forms when certain air pollutants dissolve in raindrops or in lakes and streams. The acid in the rain damages many plants, sometimes entire forests. It alters the quality of streams and lakes, harming aquatic organisms. Runoff from acid rain pollutes estuaries and seeps into groundwater. The acid also damages artifacts, the products of human activity. Steel bridges, limestone buildings, and marble statues are being eroded by acid rain.

How does acid rain form? To answer this question we need to know some **acid-base** chemistry.

Acids and Bases

We can think of **acids** as compounds that dissolve in water and release hydrogen ions (H^+). **Bases** are compounds that dissolve in water to release hydroxide ions (OH^-). When there are more H^+ ions than OH^- ions in a water solution, it is **acidic**. **Basic** solutions have more OH^- ions than H^+ ions. Some common acids and bases and the ions they form in water are listed in Table 6–1. Note that other definitions of acids and bases exist. The ones used here are the ones that are most helpful in describing acid-base chemistry in seawater.

Pure water is neither an acid nor a base. It is **neutral**, meaning that it contains equal amounts of H^+ and OH^- ions. Since water is a covalent molecule, it does not readily dissociate into ions. But among the billions and billions of molecules in a container of water, strong polar attractions break a few apart, forming a small but equal number of H^+ ions and OH^- ions. These ions readily reform into water, so the reaction is said to be **reversible**. See Fig. 6–1.

The pH Scale

The **pH scale** shown in Fig. 6–2 gives a sense of the concentration of hydrogen ions in a solution.

• *Neutral solutions have a pH of 7.* At pH 7 there are equal numbers of H^+ ions and OH^- ions. Pure water is neutral.

• *Acid solutions have low pH readings.* Strong acids have pHs of 2 or less; weak acids range from 2 to less than 7.

• *Basic solutions have high pH readings.* Strong bases have pHs of 12 or more; weak bases range from more than 7 to less than 12.

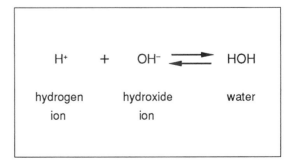

Fig. 6–1. Reversible water-ion reaction

Table 6–1. Some common acids and bases

Acid or base	Common name (Chemical name)	Ions formed in water		
Strong acids				
HCl	Hydrochloric acid (Hydrogen chloride)	H^+ hydrogen ion	+	Cl^- chloride ion
HNO_3	Nitric acid (Hydrogen nitrate)	H^+ hydrogen ion	+	NO_3^- nitrate ion
H_2SO_4	Sulfuric acid (Hydrogen sulfate)	H^+ hydrogen ion	+	HSO_4^- hydrogen sulfate ion
Weaker acids				
$HC_2H_3O_2$	Acetic acid, vinegar (Hydrogen acetate)	H^+ hydrogen ion	+	$C_2H_3O_2^-$ acetate ion
H_2CO_3	Carbonic acid (Hydrogen carbonate)	H^+ hydrogen ion	+	HCO^{3-} bicarbonate ion
$H_2SO_3^-$	Sulfurous acid (Hydrogen sulfite)	H^+ hydrogen ion	+	HSO_3^- hydrogen sulfite ion
Strong bases				
KOH	(Potassium hydroxide)	K^+ potassium ion	+	OH^- hydroxide ion
NaOH	Lye (Sodium hydroxide)	Na^+ sodium ion	+	OH^- hydroxide ion
Weak bases				
NH_4OH	Household ammonia (Ammonium hydroxide)	NH^+ ammonium ion	+	OH^- hydroxide ion
$Ca(OH)_2$	Slaked lime (Calcium hydroxide)	Ca^{2+} calcium ion	+	$2OH^-$ hydroxide ions

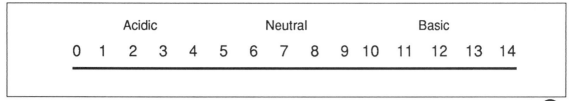

Fig. 6–2. pH scale

An acid is **neutralized** when excess H^+ ions are chemically tied up or removed from the solution, leaving equal numbers of H^+ and OH^- ions. One way to neutralize an acid (H^+) is to add enough base (OH^-) to form water (H_2O). Another way is to add certain metals to the acid. The acid reacts with the metal, converting the H^+ ions to gaseous hydrogen (H_2), which then escapes. See Fig. 6–3.

Measuring pH

Electrical **pH meters** give precise measures of pH. A less precise but faster method uses **pH paper** strips with indicator dyes in them. Different concentrations of acid turn the paper different colors. We will use pH paper in Activity 1. The paper has a range of pH 1 to pH 14.

ACTIVITY 1

Determine the pH of common substances and list them in order on a pH scale.

MATERIALS

- substances from Table 6–2
- small beakers or watch glasses
- glass stirring rod
- pH test papers with standard color chart
- colored pencils or pens

PROCEDURE

1. Determine the pH of common substances by testing as follows:
   a. To determine the pH of a liquid substance, put a few drops in a small beaker or on a watch glass. Dip the end of a clean glass stirring rod into the liquid. Touch the moist end of the

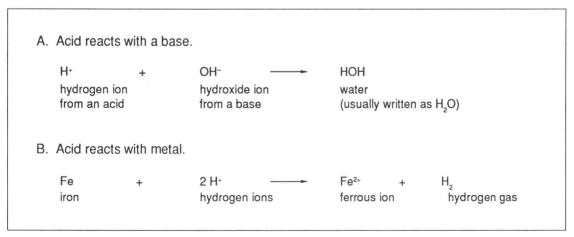

A. Acid reacts with a base.

H^+ + OH^- ⟶ HOH
hydrogen ion   hydroxide ion   water
from an acid   from a base   (usually written as H_2O)

B. Acid reacts with metal.

Fe + $2 H^+$ ⟶ Fe^{2+} + H_2
iron   hydrogen ions   ferrous ion   hydrogen gas

Fig. 6–3. Two ways to neutralize an acid

Table 6–2. Approximate pH of common substances ⓦ

Substance	pH
Ammonia	
Apple juice	
Baking soda	
Battery acid	1.0
Bleach	
Blood	7.3–7.5
Carrots	5.0
Cola	
Cow's milk	
Crackers	7.0–8.5
Distilled water	7.0
Lemon juice	
Lye (drain opener)	13.0
Milk of magnesia	10.5
Saliva (human)	
Seawater	
Tap water	
Tomatoes	
Vinegar	

stirring rod to a small piece of pH test paper. Compare the color on the pH test strip with the standard colors. Determine the pH. Record data on Table 6–2.

b. To determine the pH of a solid substance, put a small piece of the solid in a beaker. Add a few drops of distilled water, mash the material, and stir it into the water. Test for pH as you did in step (a).

2. If time permits, test other substances, such as foods, beverages, cosmetics, household cleaning substances, and aquarium water.

3. Sketch the pH scale from Fig. 6–2 in your notebook. Write the names of the substances above the line in order of their increasing pH. Include all the substances listed in Table 6–2 and any others you tested.

4. Using colored pencils, color-code the pH scale to show acids, neutral substances, and bases. Make a key to explain your code.

QUESTIONS

1. Explain why pure water is described as neutral.

2. When is a substance said to be acidic? When is it said to be basic?

3. Judging from your observations and the information in Table 6–2, are most common foods neutral, acidic, or basic?

4. How do the pH values compare
   a. between seawater and distilled water?
   b. between distilled water and tap water?

pH of Rain

Pure water itself is neutral, but rainwater is not pure water. Rainwater is naturally slightly acidic, ranging in pH from 5.0 to 6.0. The falling drops in rain wash the air of particles and soluble gases. Carbon dioxide (CO_2) dissolves in the raindrops, forming carbonic acid (H_2CO_3), a weak acid. See Fig. 6–4.

Acid rain is any form of water precipitation (rain, fog, snow) having a pH lower than normal rainwater. It forms when certain gaseous air pollutants dissolve in atmospheric water droplets. In Europe, the eastern United States, and eastern Canada, acid rain

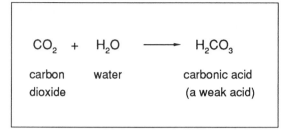

Fig. 6–4. Carbon dioxide dissolves in water, forming a weak acid.

is common in the range of pH 4.0 to pH 4.6 and occasionally as low as pH 2.

Acid rain is linked to the water cycle. It may fall from clouds near where it forms or hundreds of miles away. When it falls on land, the acid percolates into the soil or flows as runoff into streams and lakes. Some bodies of water are also acidic from the natural presence of decaying vegetation; some become acidic from farm fertilizer runoff and waste from mines and other industries.

Air Pollutants That Form Acid Rain

Two of the the major substances that form acid rain are sulfur dioxide (SO_2) and nitrogen dioxide (NO_2). Small amounts of these gases are produced naturally by soil bacteria and volcanoes. These compounds of nitrogen and sulfur are needed to sustain life, so small quantities benefit the environment. But in excessive quantities they form destructive acid rain.

Excess sulfur dioxide and nitrogen dioxide are produced by industrial power plants burning coal and gas. Oxides of nitrogen are also produced by motor vehicles. On smoggy days, reddish layers of nitrogen dioxide (NO_2) gas are sometimes visible over urban areas, particularly during heavy traffic.

The chemical reactions that produce acid rain are complex. Simplified summaries of the reactions are shown in Fig. 6–5. Both **ozone** (O_3), a gas, and water must be present in the air to produce nitric acid

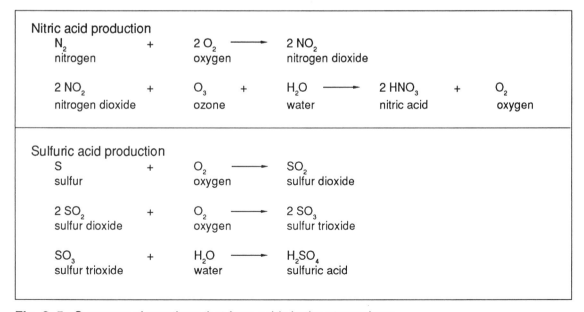

Fig. 6–5. Summary of reactions that form acids in the atmosphere

(HNO$_3$) from nitrogen dioxide (NO$_2$). Sulfuric acid (H$_2$SO$_4$) forms in the atmosphere when gaseous sulfur dioxide reacts with oxygen and water.

Neutralizing Acid Rain

Acid rain can be neutralized by reaction with calcium (Ca) and magnesium (Mg) compounds in soil. Limestone (CaCO$_3$), a substance common in soil, neutralizes acids when H$^+$ ions replace calcium-producing Ca^{2+} ions. See Fig. 6–6. Deep soils rich in metallic compounds have a greater capacity to neutralize acid rain than shallow soils or soils composed of nonmetals do. If the acid rain is not neutralized, the acid percolates into the ground or flows into lakes and streams.

Changes in the pH of water have damaging effects on aquatic life, including microorganisms, plants, and animals living in the lakes. All aquatic organisms have a pH **tolerance** or range they can live within. See Table 6–3. They soon die in water outside their tolerance. Some organisms appear to be more tolerant of acidic environments than others, and some adult organisms may be more tolerant than their eggs and embryos

Table 6–3. Preferred pH tolerance for some freshwater aquatic organisms

Organism	pH tolerance
Frog & toad embryos	
American toad	5.0 to 6.5
bullfrog	5.0 to 6.5
woodfrog	4.5 to 6.5
Fish	
flathead minnow	6.5
pumpkinseed sunfish	5.5 to 6.5
smallmouth bass	6.0 to 6.5
brown trout	5.5 to 6.5
rainbow trout	6.0 to 6.5
brook trout	5.0 to 6.5
yellow perch	5.0 to 6.5
Others	
clam (some species)	6.5
crayfish	6.0 to 6.5
snail	6.5
spotted salamander embryo	5.5 to 6.5

are. Ocean animals tolerate a pH range that is more basic than freshwater animals can tolerate. The pH at the ocean surface is 8.1 to 8.3. In the midocean column it is close to pH 7.

$$CaCO_3 \quad + \quad H^+ \quad \longrightarrow \quad Ca^{2+} \quad + \quad HCO_3^-$$

calcium carbonate (limestone)   hydrogen ion (from acid)   calcium ion   bicarbonate ion

Fig. 6–6. An acid can be neutralized by reacting with limestone. (This equation shows only the reacting compounds and ions. The H$^+$ ion could have been contributed by any acid, for example, the air pollutant HNO$_3$. In this kind of equation the charges on either side of the arrow must balance.)

Other Effects of Acid Rain

Acid rain appears to contribute to the rapid dying off of forests since 1960 in some areas of Europe and the eastern United States and Canada. About 40% of the maple trees in some Canadian forests and 50% of the red spruce in mountainous areas of New England have died. Findings show that acid rain may cause nutrient deficiency by depriving roots of necessary trace metals through acid-induced leaching. It may decrease photosynthesis through direct damage to leaves and needles. Weakened plants are less resistant to disease and rot, and they are less able to withstand such natural stresses as drought and cold.

Acid rain also damages our human creations. Because acids corrode metals, acid rain weakens bridges. It discolors paint and dissolves marble and limestone buildings. Ancient Greek temples that have withstood centuries of weathering are deteriorating rapidly as acid rain dissolves the stone from which they are built.

QUESTIONS

5. What is meant by acid rain? What causes it? What problems does it cause?

6. In what way is acid rain related to
   a. the water cycle?
   b. the chemistry of water?
   c. the chemistry of soil?

7. How is acid rain neutralized in nature?

Acid Rain and the Oceans

Acid rain has little effect on seawater for several reasons. Acid rain falling on the ocean is quickly diluted, and the acids react with seawater, which is naturally basic. In addition, seawater is a **buffered** solution, meaning that its chemical reactions can keep the pH of seawater quite constant, somewhere between 8.1 and 8.3.

The ocean's major buffering system is the **carbonate buffering system**. This buffer system has two components. The first is the weak acid, carbonic acid (H_2CO_3), which forms when carbon dioxide (CO_2) from animal and plant respiration and from the atmosphere dissolves in seawater. By a **weak acid** we mean one that tends to ionize slightly and release only a little of its hydrogen component as H+ ion.

The second component is the carbonate ion (CO_3^{2-}) Carbonate ions come from carbonate components dissolved in seabed muds, from carbonates in the skeletons of coral and other animals, and from carbonate minerals washed into the sea from land.

Nitric acid (HNO_3) and sulfuric acid (H_2SO_4), the major acids in acid rain, are called **strong acids**. Strong acids readily ionize in water, releasing their hydrogen as H^+ ions. The carbonate (CO_3^{2-}) ions in the seawater tend to react with the hydrogen ions (H^+), making the weak acid carbonic acid (H_2CO_3). Since carbonic acid is a weak acid that holds its hydrogen tightly, H^+ ion is removed from the water and the pH rises. See Fig. 6–7.

This buffer system also works to neutralize excess hydroxide ions. If, for example, there is a sudden excess of hydroxide (OH^-) ions from a spill of a sodium hydroxide (NaOH) solution, the weak carbonic acid (H_2CO_3) will produce the hydrogen ions (H^+) necessary to neutralize the excess OH^- ion, reducing the pH. See Fig. 6–7.

Acid reaction								
CO_3^{2-}	+	H_2SO_4	$\longrightarrow$	H_2CO_3	+	SO_4^{2-}		
Net acid reaction								
CO_3^{2-}	+	$2\,H^+$	$\longrightarrow$	H_2CO_3				
Base reaction								
H_2CO_3	+	$2\,NaOH$	$\longrightarrow$	$2\,H_2O$	+	$2\,Na^+$	+	CO_3^{2-}
Net base reaction								
H_2CO_3	+	$2\,OH^-$	$\longrightarrow$	$2\,H_2O$	+	CO_3^{2-}		

Fig. 6–7. The carbonate buffer interacting with an acid and a base

QUESTIONS

8. Explain what is meant by a buffer solution.

9. In what ways do the following act to keep pH relatively constant?
   a. seawater
   b. calcium carbonate sediments
   c. green plants

10. What changes in pH might cause the ocean
    a. to release carbon dioxide into the atmosphere?
    b. to convert carbon dioxide into other substances?

11. Compare fresh water and seawater in terms of their buffering capacity.

ACTIVITY 2

Design an experiment that simulates acid rain.

MATERIALS

- plastic cups or beakers
- one or more weak acids (a carbonated drink can be used)
- a strong acid (pH of 2 or less)
- pH paper
- metal objects: coins, nails, bits of metals, pieces of wire
- chalk, chunks of coral, pieces of limestone or marble
- forceps or spoons
- seawater

PROCEDURE

1. Use pH paper to determine the pH of the acids you use. If you use a carbonated drink for your weak acid, test its pH immediately after opening it and again after it has gone flat, that is, when all bubbles have escaped. Record your data in your notebook.

2. Design an experiment investigating a specific problem related to pH and acid rain. Refer to Table 6–4 for suggestions. Carry out the steps listed below.
   a. With your team members, make a written research plan. State your hypothesis or research question.

b. List the materials or equipment you will need.

c. Write out your procedure and construct the data tables you will use to record your observations.

d. Review your plan with your teacher and others in the class.

e. Obtain your teacher's approval before beginning the experiment.

3. Report the results of your investigation.

a. Organize your results in data tables and graphs.

b. Write your conclusions.

c. Prepare an oral report for the class. Use charts and diagrams to explain your experiment and its results.

4. Take notes on reports of experiments conducted by others in the class. Use this information to answer the questions that follow.

Table 6–4. Suggestions for investigating pH and acid rain

1. Simulate the effects of acid rain on metal.
   a. Test the effect of acid on different types of metals. Determine which metals react the most, the least, and not at all.
   b. Test the effect of acid on combinations of two or more different metals in contact with each other.
   c. Determine how the metal affects the acid, if at all. Measure the pH before and after the reactions with metals.

2. Test what acid rain does to materials made of calcium carbonate. Substances that contain calcium carbonate are chalk, coral, seashells, marble, and limestone.
   a. Devise a test that compares how acids react with solid substances containing calcium carbonate. Observe reactions after 14 to 20 minutes and after 24 hours. Record your data.
   b. Determine how the calcium carbonate affects the acid. When the acid stops reacting with the calcium carbonate, measure the pH of the final liquid.

3. Simulate acid rain being diluted in progressively larger bodies of fresh water. Start with a raindrop added to a puddle, then to a small pool, and then to a larger pool. Determine how pH changes when an acid is diluted from 100% to 10%, to 1%, to 0.1%, and to 0.01%. Measure the pH of each dilution.

4. Compare the effects of acid rain on
   a. fresh water,
   b. hard water (water containing high quantities of dissolved calcium), and
   c. seawater.
   Obtain a 100-mL sample of each liquid. Measure its pH. Add 5 mL of "acid rain," stir, then measure the pH.

5. Make a study of the pH of bodies of water in your community. Collect and test samples of rainwater and water from puddles, ponds, lakes, the ocean, and other bodies of water.

QUESTIONS

12. How does the pH of an acid change when the acid is diluted? When it is concentrated?

13. Some rain in a region may be acid. Other rain may be freshwater rain. How would light and heavy freshwater rain affect acid rain already in a rain gauge?

14. On the basis of your experiments, what statements can you make about reactions between acid rain and
    a. metallic objects?
    b. calcium carbonate objects?

15. What objects in our environment would be damaged by acid rain? What is your evidence?

Global CO_2 Problems

Another gaseous substance that can damage the environment when there's too much of it is carbon dioxide. Carbon dioxide (CO_2) is one of the naturally formed gases that make up the atmosphere. Natural processes that constantly release CO_2 into the atmosphere are shown by solid arrows in Fig. 6–8. Each year about 77 trillion tons of CO_2—about 280 parts of CO_2 per million parts of air—are released into the atmosphere by such natural processes as

- respiration by plants and animals,
- decay of organic matter,
- weathering of rocks and skeletons,
- release of dissolved CO_2 from water, and
- natural forest fires.

All plants and animals in their respiration return both CO_2 and water vapor to the

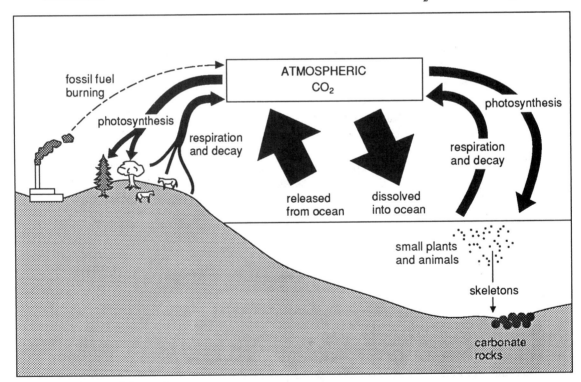

Fig. 6–8. Global CO_2 cycle

air. **Respiration** produces energy by combining carbohydrates from food with oxygen from the air according to this equation:

$$C_6H_{12}O_6 + 6 O_2 \longrightarrow 6 CO_2 + 6 H_2O + energy$$

Carbohydrate + oxygen $\longrightarrow$
carbon dioxide + water + energy

Processes that remove CO_2 from the atmosphere are also shown by solid arrows in Fig. 6–8. They include

• photosynthesis by green plants on land and by algae in the ocean.
• the dissolving of CO_2 molecules from the air into water.

Green plants on land such as grasses, shrubs, and trees use water from the soil and carbon dioxide from the air in the process of **photosynthesis** to manufacture new carbohydrates. In the ocean small plants called algae carry on the same process. They make more carbohydrate in photosynthesis than they consume in respiration. The excess carbohydrate produced by plants becomes the food consumed by animals. In the photosynthetic process plants convert the radiant energy of the sun into chemical bond energy to make the carbohydrates and produce oxygen as a byproduct. The oxygen is used by animals and plants to oxidize food and by industry to oxidize fuel. The equation for photosynthesis is

$$Energy + 6 CO_2 + 6 H_2O \longrightarrow C_6H_{12}O_6 + 6 O_2$$

Energy + carbon dioxide + water $\longrightarrow$
carbohydrate + oxygen

In addition, human activities, primarily the burning of **hydrocarbon fuels** (ones containing carbon, such as wood, coal, natural gas, gasoline, and oil) also add to the amount of CO_2 in the atmosphere. See the dashed arrow in Fig. 6–8.

Because all natural fuels—wood, oil, gasoline, coal—come from once-living things, they are made from carbon and hydrogen, which release carbon dioxide (CO_2) and water (H_2O) when they burn. For example, the gasoline component octane burns as follows:

$$2 C_8H_{18} + 25 O_2 \longrightarrow 16 CO_2 + 18 H_2O$$

Octane (gas) + oxygen $\longrightarrow$
carbon dioxide + water

Recent studies of gases in the atmosphere show that the amount of CO_2 has increased steadily over the past hundred years. See Fig. 6–9. Analyses of gases trapped in ice show similar increases in CO_2 levels at both poles. See Fig. 6–10. Most of the rise comes from the tremendous increase in the burning of hydrocarbon fuels by utility companies, other industrial plants, motor vehicles, and airplanes.

To complicate matters, many plants that once removed CO_2 from the atmosphere to make food have been destroyed. As trees are cut for fuel, forests are cleared for agriculture, and vegetation is destroyed to build cities and towns, the amount of leaf surface acting to remove CO_2 from the atmosphere has dropped sharply.

Some scientists believe that seawater has reached the limit of its capacity to dissolve atmospheric CO_2. If they are right, CO_2 will continue to build up in the atmosphere.

QUESTIONS

16. What was the average atmospheric concentration of CO_2 in 1958? In 1985?

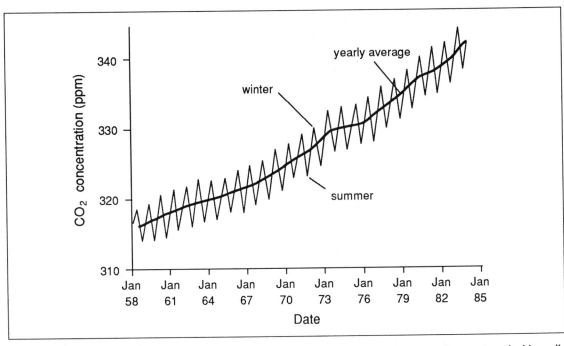

Fig. 6–9. Concentrations of atmospheric CO_2 measured at the Mauna Loa observatory in Hawaii

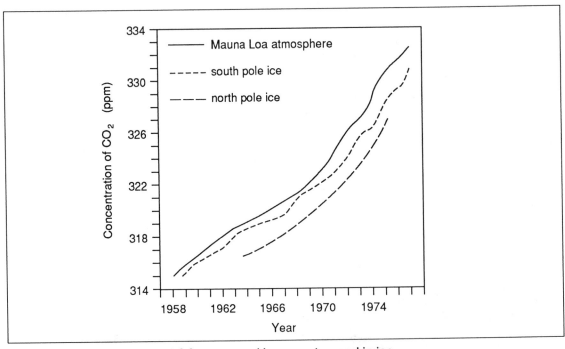

Fig. 6–10. Concentrations of CO_2 measured in gases trapped in ice

17. What is the average yearly increase in the atmospheric concentration of CO_2? Show your calculations.

18. What natural processes might account for the high concentration of CO_2 in the winter and its low concentration in the summer?

The Greenhouse Effect

When gases like CO_2 accumulate in the atmosphere, they have the effect of a greenhouse. They warm the earth the way glass holds in radiant energy, warming the interior of a greenhouse. By holding in the heat, the layer of CO_2 raises the temperature of the air, the land, and the water. The natural concentration of CO_2 in the atmosphere is enough to keep the earth at a habitable average temperature of 15°C. But human uses of hydrocarbon fuels could increase the concentration enough to cause an "enhanced," or magnified, greenhouse effect that could warm the earth enough to cause global problems. See Fig. 6–11.

QUESTIONS

19. What would be the average global temperature in °F
    a. if there were no greenhouse effect?
    b. if there were only the natural greenhouse effect?
    c. if the atmospheric carbon dioxide were to double?

20. In °F, how much warmer
    a. is the earth now because of the natural greenhouse gases?
    b. would the earth become if atmospheric carbon dioxide doubles?

21. Explain the difference between the greenhouse effect and the "enhanced" greenhouse effect.

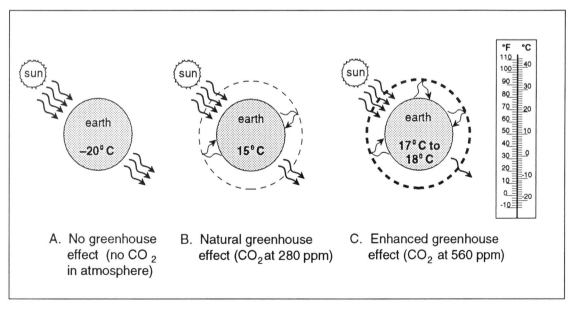

A. No greenhouse effect (no CO_2 in atmosphere)

B. Natural greenhouse effect (CO_2 at 280 ppm)

C. Enhanced greenhouse effect (CO_2 at 560 ppm)

Fig. 6–11. CO_2 levels and average temperatures at the earth's surface

Other Greenhouse Gases

CO_2 is the chief culprit in the greenhouse effect, but other gases from industry and agriculture add to it. These include

- methane (CH_4), a gas produced by bacterial decomposition of organic plant and animal matter in such places as landfills, marshes, mudflats, flooded rice fields, sewage treatment plants, and the guts of cattle and termites.
- nitrogen oxides from the runoff of nitrogen-based fertilizers and as a by-product from the burning of hydrocarbons.
- ozone (O_3), a gas normally present in trace amounts in the atmosphere but also produced in industrial processes.
- chlorofluorocarbons (CFCs), synthetic gases used in cleaning solvents, refrigerants, and plastic foam.

Scientists have made computer models to predict the consequences of the greenhouse effect. They say an increase of 2°C to 3°C in the earth's temperature could cause one or more of the global changes listed in Table 6–5. Fig. 6–12 shows three predictions of rise in sea level.

Scientists warn that we do not yet have enough information to make firm predictions about the greenhouse effect. Global temperature records have been kept for only 100 years. The warmest years were in the latter part of the twentieth century. Furthermore, the average global temperature for landmasses has climbed more than 0.7°C since the 1880s. Whether we are seeing the beginning of a global warming or whether these are temporary changes in global temperature we do not yet know.

Table 6–5. Predicted global consequences of the enhanced greenhouse effect

- The volume of ocean surface water will increase.
- Sea levels will rise.
- Low-lying islands, coasts, estuaries, marshes, and deltas (including farmlands and cities) will be flooded.
- Rich, productive coastal ecosystems (including bayous, salt marshes, and mangrove swamps) will be destroyed.
- Domestic and agricultural water systems will be disrupted.
- The snowpack that supplies freshwater reservoirs will be reduced.
- Global patterns of weather and precipitation will change.
- Temperature zones in the northern hemisphere will move north.
- Agricultural areas will move north with changes in climate.
- The number of days with temperatures over 37°C will increase.
- Ocean water will evaporate faster, producing more clouds, rain, and snow in some places.
- Some deserts will get heavy rain; some fertile areas will dry up.
- Storms will be more frequent, and hurricanes will be more severe.
- Some plants and animals will become extinct.
- Photosynthesis and plant growth will accelerate.

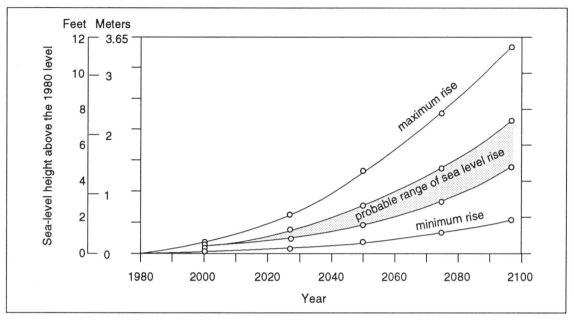

Fig. 6–12. Predictions of rises in sea level because of an enhanced greenhouse effect

Some scientists studying the data on the burning of hydrocarbons make a reverse prediction. They think that pollutants in the atmosphere could block sunlight, just as particles from forest fires and volcanic eruptions do. If that happens, the blockage could offset the warming effect of the increase in carbon dioxide.

ACTIVITY 3

Analyze a coastal map to predict shoreline changes due to the greenhouse effect.

MATERIALS

• colored pencils, pens, or crayons

PROCEDURE

1. Examine the map in Fig. 6–13 showing two imaginary coastal towns, "Seaside City" and Baytown"

2. Using colored pencils,
   a. find and draw in sea level.
   b. shade the river that carries water to the towns.
   c. find and color the major highways into and out of the towns.
   d. find the airport and color-code it.

3. Imagine that the greenhouse effect causes sea level to rise. See Fig. 6–12.
   a. Shade the area(s) that will be flooded if the most probable (average) sea-level rise occurs.
   b. Shade the area(s) that will be flooded if the maximum predicted sea-level rise occurs.
   c. Shade the contour lines for sea-level rises of 1 m, 2 m, and 4 m.

4. Attach a key to the map.

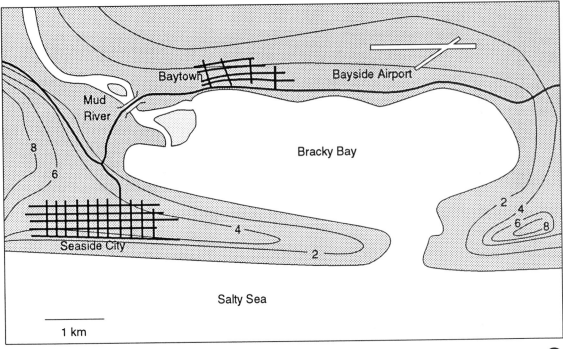

Fig. 6–13. Map of imaginary coastal towns (elevation in meters)

QUESTIONS

22. How far inland does the coastline move with
    a. a 1-m rise in sea level?
    b. a 2-m rise in seal level?
    c. a 4-m rise in sea level?

23. How would the most probable rise in sea level affect
    a. homes and business buildings in the towns?
    b. coastal roads and airports?
    c. the sources of fresh drinking water for coastal areas?
    d. coastal wildlife?

24. How would the maximum sea-level rise affect these areas?

What Can Be Done?

Many suggestions have been made for reducing the CO_2 content of the atmosphere:
- Reduce CO_2 emissions by reducing the consumption of fossil fuels.
- Switch from burning oil or coal to burning fuels (such as hydrogen) that produce less CO_2 or none.
- Increase the use of solar, wind, and geothermal energy.
- Replant and restore forests.

QUESTIONS

25. List the things that you, your family, and the people in your community could do to reduce the buildup of CO_2.

26. What are businesses, industries, and

304

governments in your region doing to reduce the causes of the greenhouse effect?

27. If the sea level begins to rise, what might be done to minimize
    a. damage to coastal structures?
    b. disruption of coastal wildlife?

FURTHER INVESTIGATIONS

1. Study the pH of water in your community. Include water in your home, in swimming pools, in puddles, and in lakes or streams. What evidence, if any, do you find of acid rain? How might you account for your findings?

2. Read library references on acid rain. Learn more about ways to reduce pollutants that produce acid rain. Report to the class.

3. Read library references on the greenhouse effect.
    a. Look for computer predictions of changes in precipitation, sea level, and regional, climatic, and atmospheric temperature.
    b. Read about international conferences on the greenhouse effect. Report actions that have been called for to control CO_2 emissions.

4. Ozone (O_3) is a greenhouse gas, but scientists are also concerned about its depletion in the upper atmosphere, exposing life on earth to additional harmful rays from the sun. Find out more about this and report to the class.

5. Read and report on which government agencies are trying to solve environmental problems such as acid rain and the greenhouse effect. Who monitors the environment? Where do the data go? How are decisions made, and by whom?

6. Learn more about computer models that predict environmental change. What information goes into the computer? How reliable are computer-generated maps? What are their limitations?

7. Water Pollution

Dumping wastes into lakes, rivers, and oceans seems an easy way to get rid of them. Water can **dilute** some liquid wastes by mixing with them, thereby reducing their concentration. Waves and currents **disperse**, or scatter and carry away, some materials that do not dissolve. But the capacity of bodies of water to **recycle** wastes in natural processes is limited, so the waters are becoming polluted.

A **water pollutant** is anything in water that can harm organisms, including human beings. **Water pollution** is any change in the physical or chemical condition of water or any change in its biological content that limits or prevents our use and enjoyment of the water. Water pollutants can alter the taste, odor, or color of water; they can affect marine and aquatic life by reducing the dissolved oxygen concentration or introducing substances hazardous to life; they can threaten human health by contaminating our water supply and our swimming sites with disease-causing microorganisms and hazardous materials.

Almost any material that enters lakes, rivers, bays, estuaries, harbors, or the ocean may become a water pollutant. The major sources of pollutants are farms, homes, mines and factories, and land and sea vehicles. **Agricultural pollutants** include fertilizers, pesticides, herbicides, and animal wastes from farms and ranches. **Domestic pollutants** include chemicals, debris, sewage, and wastes generated by people living in rural and urban areas. **Industrial pollutants** include debris and chemicals from mines, refineries, and manufacturing plants. Pollutants from vehicles on land or at sea include fuel emissions, oil spills, and ordinary trash. Boats and ships also discharge sewage and bilge water, the wastewater used to wash out the inner hull.

ACTIVITY 1
Investigate water pollution.

MATERIALS
• pencil

PROCEDURE
1. Study the diagram in Fig. 7–1. Identify as many sources of water pollution as you can. List the sources in Table 7–1. Add others that you think of.

2. What pollutants are generated by each source? List them in Table 7–1. Refer to the descriptions of pollutants in Table 7–2.

3. Identify and record the way each source releases pollutants into water. Use the terms in Table 7–3.

4. Classify each source listed in Table 7–1 as a *point* source or a *nonpoint* source of pollution. A **point source** is a specific place. A **nonpoint source** is an indefinite or undefined place, often a variety of places.

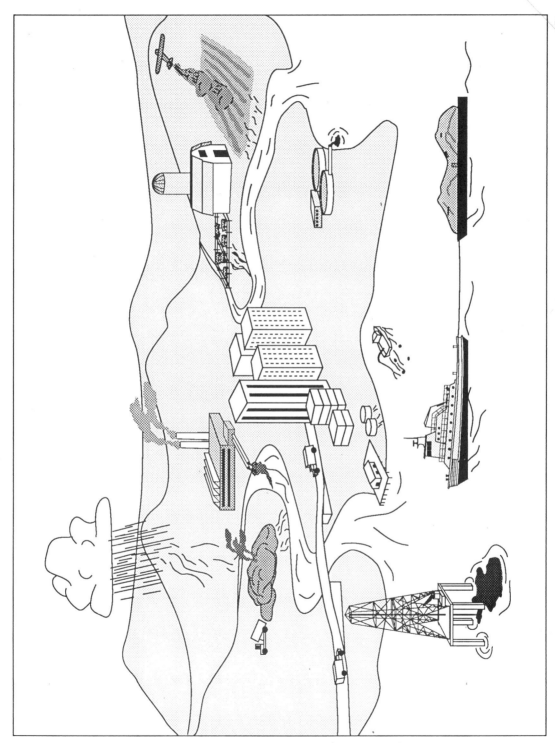

Fig. 7-1. Some sources of water pollution

Ⓦ

Table 7–1. Sources of pollutants Ⓦ

Source	Pollutant	Method of release	Point or nonpoint?	Intentional or unintentional?

5. Decide whether the pollution is done intentionally or unintentionally. Record your decision in Table 7–1.

QUESTIONS

1. There is an old saying, "The solution to pollution is dilution." When and where would this approach be effective in preventing water pollution? When would it not be an acceptable approach?

2. Give an example of how water
   a. dilutes pollutants.
   b. disperses pollutants.

3. Which sources of pollutants could affect
   a. freshwater ponds, lakes, streams, and rivers?
   b. groundwater?
   c. bays, estuaries, and inlets?
   d. nearshore coastal waters?
   e. the open ocean?

4. How could specific sources of pollution be reduced or eliminated?
   a. What specific actions could people take to reduce the problems of marine pollution?
   b. What kinds of laws might reduce pollution?

5. Which of the major categories of pollutants
   a. would be the easiest to reduce, control, or eliminate?
   b. would be the most difficult to reduce, control, or eliminate?
   Give reasons to support your answers.

6. "Water pollution is caused directly or

Table 7–2. Major categories of water pollutants

Heated water, also called **thermal pollution**. Warmed water discharged by power plants and other industries that have used it to cool equipment.

Inorganic matter. Toxic metals, salts, acids, sediments, and radioactive material.

Microorganisms. Bacteria, viruses, and other microorganisms that can cause disease in humans and other organisms.

Biological wastes. (a) Sewage, (b) animal wastes, (c) remains of plant or animal matter, and (d) some industrial wastes, such as those produced by food-processing and paper-pulp industries.

Petroleum and its products. Oil, gasoline, diesel and heating fuels, greases, waxes, lubricants, detergents, pesticides, plastics, and other materials made from oil derivatives.

Table 7–3. Mechanisms by which pollutants enter the environment

Dumping. Discharging of sewage, sludge, industrial wastes, and dredged material in marine sites, landfills, or hazardous-waste-disposal sites.

Littering. Discarding solid materials without burial. The materials may be called **debris**.

Pipeline discharge. Discharging fluids from factories and municipal sewage plants into waterways or coastal waters.

Runoff. Washing of agricultural, rural, and urban wastes into streams, rivers, and lakes by rainwater.

Seepage. Leaking of substances into water or ground, often over a long period.

Spills. Accidental and unintentional sudden release of substances.

indirectly by the actions of humans." Decide whether you agree or disagree with this statement.

a. If you agree, give evidence that supports the statement.
b. If you disagree, rewrite the statement to make it one you can agree with.

Biological Responses to Water Pollutants

Fertilizers washed by runoff into waterways promote **biostimulation**, the swift growth of populations of aquatic plants and animals. Biostimulation is similar to fertilizing a lawn or garden to increase the growth of grass or other plants. Fertilizers in water cause a rapid growth of aquatic plants, called an **algal bloom**. When aquatic animals eat the abundant plants, they too thrive and multiply. Predators then eat these animals and increase in number. If the increase in aquatic plants and animals overtaxes the supply of dissolved oxygen, some organisms may suffocate, particularly at night, when photosynthesis stops. Bacteria consume dead organisms, multiply rapidly, and further exhaust the dissolved oxygen supply. **Oxygen depletion**, then, is a water pollution problem associated with biostimulation.

In U.S. coastal waters, continuous discharge of sewage and sludge has created dead zones off the New York-New Jersey coast and in the Gulf of Mexico. In a **dead zone**, fish, mollusks, and crustaceans suffocate.

Sewage contains disease-producing bacteria, viruses, and other microorganisms. Drinking sewage-contaminated water can make people sick or kill them. Swimming in sewage-polluted water can cause eye and skin infections and lung problems. Sewage dumping has been blamed for causing fin rot in saltwater fish and is suspected of causing diseases in other marine and aquatic organisms. Many recreational waters in the United States are monitored for quality, and warnings are posted when contamination becomes dangerous.

Heavy metals like lead (Pb) and mercury (Hg) can harm or kill life. In uncontaminated seawater, most metal ions occur in quanitites too small to damage marine life. In fact, all organisms require minute quantities of certain heavy metals to survive. Arsenic (As), for example, is toxic in large quantities, even though all organisms need it in minute quantities for survival. Modern technology uses the toxic properties of metals by deliberately adding them to marine paints to prevent **biofouling**, the unwanted growth of organisms on boat and ship hulls.

Bioaccumulation

Toxic metals in water threaten larger organisms when they move up the food chain. Many plants incorporate dissolved toxic metals into their body structures. Animals that eat these plants then incorporate the toxic metals and pass them along the food chain to larger animals. Large animals are said to **bioaccumulate** metals, or store them in their bodies in heavy concentrations. Because they eat many plants or smaller animals, the concentration of metals builds up with each organism they consume. Once taken in, toxic heavy metals tend to stay in animal tissue. People who eat organisms that have bioaccumulated toxic metals can become ill.

Bioaccumulation also occurs with other substances, such as chlorinated pesticides and radioactive materials.

QUESTIONS

7. Which bodies of water are most susceptible to biostimulation?

8. Green plants use sunlight energy in photosynthesis to produce oxygen. How then can large numbers of green plants living in water deplete the supply of dissolved oxygen?

9. Explain how toxic metals and hazardous substances like pesticides can
   a. be passed up a food chain.
   b. bioaccumulate.
   c. be more concentrated in predator organisms than in their prey.

10. What commonsense guidelines should be followed in deciding whether to collect and eat food from coastal waters?

11. As an alternative to dumping sewage in bodies of water, what might be some of the advantages and disadvantages of devising technologies for using sewage
    a. to fertilize forests and public lands?
    b. to provide nutrients for aquaculture?

12. Under what circumstances might bioaccumulation be
    a. harmful to humans?
    b. useful to humans?

Fate of Marine Debris

Although ships at sea dump an estimated 6 million tons of debris into the ocean each year, about 85% of all ocean pollution can be traced to human activities on land, not on the sea. About 90% of all marine debris remains in coastal waterways. What happens to the debris? Where does it go?

Liquid and gaseous wastes quickly mix with seawater. Solids must be **degraded**, that is, eaten by other organisms or broken down by other processes, in order to be recyled in a freshwater or ocean environment. The fate of solid debris depends largely on its chemical composition. Biological wastes are **biodegradable,** meaning that they are either eaten by scavenger organisms or digested by decomposers. In small quantities biodegradable materials can benefit the environment by enriching the food supply, but in large quantities they can overwhelm the capacity of organisms to use them.

Plastic, metal, and glass debris are not food for consumers or decomposers, so these are described as **nonbiodegradable.** Nonbiodegradable debris is removed from the environment by **physical processes** that break it into small pieces and by **chemical processes** that alter the material, making it easier to degrade into simpler substances. Nonbiodegradable materials are described as **persistent pollutants** because of their residence time in the ocean. Nonbiological degrading processes can take many years. See Table 7–4.

The fate of nonbiodegradable debris is in part determined by its density. Metal and glass sink; plastics float at the surface or are suspended in the water column. Glass and metal are less degradable than plastics. Their sinking removes them from sight, but not from the environment.

Plastics that float or are washed ashore are exposed to sunlight, particularly ultraviolet light, and turn brittle. Some plastics break down into smooth pellets about the size of rice grains; others break into sharp-edged shards. Plastic sheeting tears into shreds. Because plastics that float in midwa-

Table 7–4. Estimated residence time of non-biodegradable materials

Material		Residence time in years
Aluminum cans		100 to 400
Plastic particles on beach		5 to 50
Nets drifting in the ocean		2 to 10
Sunken nets		5 to 50
Brittle plastics (in sunlight)		2 to 4

ter or sink to the seafloor are not exposed to sunlight, they last much longer than plastics at the surface.

Floating plastics cause two kinds of environmental concern:

1. Plastics can damage or kill marine animals through ingestion, entanglement, or entrapment. **Ingestion** of plastics can choke animals, block their digestive tracts, cause toxic reactions, and weaken them by filling their stomachs with non-food substances. **Entanglement** in plastic debris creates drag on their bodies, making it harder to swim or capture food. Entanglement in packing bands, wires, and rope can constrict and cut into an animal's body. **Entrapment** in nets kills air-breathing animals. Nets lost at sea continue to trap fish and other organisms. See Table 7–5.

2. Plastics are the chief culprit in shoreline litter, which is an aesthetic problem, an economic burden, and a health hazard. Volunteers who pick up shoreline debris give us some idea of the immensity of the problem of marine debris. They bagged an average of 100 to 200 lb of litter per mile of U.S. beaches. Some states, such as Maine, had relatively little debris— 50 to 100 lb per mile. New Jersey and New York had as much as 1,000 lb per mile; Texas, about 4,000 lb per mile.

Water pollution and marine debris have major **economic consequences**. Closed beaches spoil recreational opportunities. Such businesses as restaurants, hotels, beach concessions, and charter-fishing boats lose income. (People living in Long Island who heard about hospital wastes washing up on their beaches all but abandoned the beaches during the summer of 1988.) The costs of monitoring and cleaning up the environment come out of taxpayers' pockets. (The cost of cleanup and lost business for just one episode off Long Island was estimated at $30 million.) Environmental interactions are so complex that the value of lost biological resources cannot even be estimated.

Hospital wastes in particular pose **health hazards**. Some wastes contain medicines called antibiotics. If these chemi-

Table 7–5. Examples of harm that plastic debris causes marine life

Birds that mistake plastic pellets for food may feel full but starve. Ingested plastics can choke them, block their digestive passages, tear their body tissues, and cause toxic reactions. Birds can become entangled in monofilament lines, plastic six-pack carriers, and Styrofoam cups. Perhaps the most serious danger to birds is drowning in "ghost" nets—lost fishing nets that keep trapping fish. The birds apparently see the fish but not the nets.

Fish too suffer from eating plastic particles and getting caught in netting. Many fish have been found with plastic pellets in their stomachs. Some fish, including manta rays and bottom-dwelling fish, have been entangled in debris. An unknown loss occurs from free-floating ghost nets and fish traps. Abandoned purse-seine nets and gill nets that wash ashore usually have fish carcasses in them.

Turtles ingest and choke on plastic bags, probably mistaking them for jellyfish. Of the seven marine turtle species, four are known to ingest plastic. People have reported seeing sea turtles swimming wrapped in plastic.

Marine mammals apparently can see the marine debris. In fact, they appear to seek it out, sometimes as a potential food source, sometimes as an object to play with. Their inquisitiveness, unfortunately, leads them into entanglement, injury, and even death.

Endangered species such as the Hawaiian monk seal and the West Indian manatee have been found entangled in ghost nets. Some 50,000 to 90,000 deaths of northern fur seals every year are attributed to debris entanglement.

Seafloor organisms. Plastic debris sinks and rolls around the ocean floor or becomes tangled on corals or rocky bottoms. We know little about the effects on seaweeds, corals, or other bottom-dwelling life.

Human beings. We do know that human life can be threatened by marine debris. Scuba divers must be wary of ghost nets. Ships whose rudders or propellers get entangled in floating debris become disabled. Entangled research submersibles and military submarines may be unable to surface.

cals are dumped into a municipal sewer system, they can kill off decomposer organisms that play a vital role in breaking down and recyling biological wastes. Used hypodermic needles and blood plasma bags have washed ashore, posing health hazards if they are contaminated with human diseases.

We cannot continue to use the oceans as a global garbage can. The oceans have an enormous capacity to dilute, disperse, and recycle substances, but the strain on natural biological and chemical processes is becoming so great that the oceans can no longer cope with the enormous quantities of materials dumped into them. The nonbiodegradable manmade pollutants we so unthinkingly cast into the sea are accumulating in the water, on the seafloor, and on shorelines. To cope with pollution, we now have only two remedies: reducing the kinds and quantities of wastes, and recycling as many materials as we can.

QUESTIONS

13. What are some possible explanations for the volunteers' findings that there is more marine debris on the beaches in some states than in other states?

14. What actions to reduce the quantity of marine debris can be taken
    a. by individuals?
    b. by coastal communities?
    c. by marine industries?
    d. by nations?

15. What is meant by the following terms?
    a. pollution
    b. biodegradable

16. Why do persistent pollutants tend to accumulate in the environment?

ACTIVITY 2
Conduct a shoreline debris study.

MATERIALS
• map
• tide chart
• watch or stopwatch
• compass
• 20-m line marked off in meters
• 2 wooden stakes
• notebook or clipboard
• pencil
• gloves
• tongs
• 4 heavy-duty degradable plastic bags
• bucket with handle
• bathroom scale
• anemometer (optional)
• camera (optional)

PROCEDURE
1. Plan a field study of marine debris.
    a. Study a map of the area you select and consult a tide chart. Plan to begin the study just after a high tide. Select a moderate to steep sand or gravel beach. Avoid boulder and bedrock shorelines (where debris becomes hidden in crevices) and flat, muddy areas (where it becomes buried in mud or tangled in vegetation).
    b. Divide the class into teams. Review the procedures below and decide how to divide assignments within the team. Each team should be responsible for assembling its equipment, taking it to the beach, and returning it to the classroom.
    c. Plan to wear tie-on shoes and heavy gloves during the field study.

2. At the beach observe and record condi-

tions before starting to collect litter.

a. Map the study area. Note the beach slope.

b. Record the tide height. Check the tide chart and observe the beach to determine whether the tide chart agrees with your observations.

c. Observe and record wave conditions. Estimate wave height. Measure the wave period.

d. Look for evidence of a longshore current. If there is one, small objects washing in and out with the waves will move along the beach. If you are uncertain, toss a floating object into the water beyond the waves and note where it goes.

e. Observe and record wind speed and direction. Use a compass to determine the direction the wind is blowing from. If an **anemometer** (a wind-speed measuring device) is available, measure the wind speed. If not, estimate wind speed.

f. If possible, photograph the study area.

3. Conduct the marine debris study.

a. Measure off a 20-m section for each team and mark its boundaries with wooden stakes.

b. Weigh the empty bucket on the bathroom scale. If you get no reading, weigh yourself first, then weigh yourself holding the bucket. Subtract your mass from the total.

c. Weigh the four plastic bags on the bathroom scale in the same way. Divide their total mass by four to find the mass of each bag.

d. Collect all nonbiodegradable litter items found in your assigned section between the water's edge and the vegetation line (usually just above extreme high tide). Use tongs to pick up broken glass and put it in the bucket. Wear gloves to handle all other objects and put them in the plastic bags. Record your counts in Table 7–6.

Table 7–6. Marine debris found during beach study   Ⓦ

Type of debris	Number of items	Mass (g)	% of total debris by mass
Plastic			
Styrofoam			
Synthetic lines and nets			
Rubber			
Glass			
Wood			
Metal			

4. Sort the materials, using the categories in Table 7–7.
   a. Weigh the material in each category. Weigh yourself on the bathroom scale. Then weigh yourself holding one bag or bucket at a time. Subtract your mass and the mass of the container from the total. Record the mass of the debris.
   b. Make a pie chart showing the contribution of each category of debris to the total mass.

5. Closely examine the plastic materials. Record your data in Table 7–7.
   a. Determine the probable original use for each item (for example, plastic sheeting used as a sandwich bag).
   b. Look for signs that the plastic is degrading.
   c. Imagine that you are a hungry bird or marine organism. Which of the plastic items might you mistake for food? What kind of food?

6. If you can, return in 2 weeks or a month. Repeat the study. Determine the rate at which marine debris is deposited on the beach.

QUESTIONS

17. How much litter did you find
    a. in your study area?
    b. in the class study site?

18. Which type of litter was most prevalent? Answer in terms of
    a. types of litter by count.
    b. types of litter by percentage of total mass.

19. Where along the beach was most of the beach litter deposited? Did wind, waves, tides, currents, or beach slope appear to contribute to piling or sorting the debris on the beach? Explain.

20. Where do you think most of the litter came from? What was it originally used for? What is your evidence?

21. What actions could be taken to prevent or reduce litter and debris?
    a. For what plastic products could paper, wood, or cloth serve as substitutes?
    b. What kinds of laws might encourage people to recycle wastes instead of littering?

Table 7–7. Composition of plastic litter (W)

Number	Item	Original use of item	Description of degradation	What food does it resemble?

c. What could you and your family do now to reduce litter and recycle materials?

22. What evidence did you find that natural processes are breaking down the litter?

23. How does the shoreline you studied compare with other shorelines in the United States? Calculate the beach litter in pounds of debris per mile. Show your calculations.

ACTIVITY 3

Predict the fate of marine debris dumped at sea.

Determine the density of objects commonly found in shoreline debris.

MATERIALS
- marine debris
- gloves or tongs
- seawater
- bucket

PROCEDURE

1. Use the samples of marine debris you collected in Activity 2, or simulate marine debris by obtaining pieces of materials commonly found in beach litter. Table 7–8 lists objects that might be lost or discarded from a small boat. See Fig. 7–2.

2. Identify the items you think are biodegradable. Remove them from the collection. Devise and carry out an experiment to determine whether they are biodegradable. Record your results.

3. Imagine that all the nonbiodegradable items were discarded overboard about 10 km offshore. Predict the fate of each object as follows:
   a. Determine its density by putting it (or a piece of it) in seawater. Observe and record whether it floats at the surface (FS), tends to float in midwater (FMW), or sinks (S).
   b. Predict where the materials would go

Fig. 7–2. Debris lost or discarded from a recreational boat

Table 7–8. Potential marine debris

Potential beach litter	Biodegradable?	Density	Fate if discarded at sea
Bread in plastic bag			
Sandwich meat wrapped in wax paper			
Cheese in plastic bag			
Margarine in aluminum foil wrapper			
Box of crackers			
Bag of chips			
Salad in plastic container			
Jar of pickles (with screw cap)			
Canned soda			
Bottled beverage			
Canned pudding			
Plastic fork, spoon, and knife			
Styrofoam cup			
Sun lotion in plastic bottle			
Sunglasses			
Rubber slippers			
Comb			
Beach towel			
Newspaper			
Fishing line			
Fish hooks			
Cooler			

and what would happen to them if they were dumped overboard.

QUESTIONS

24. How did you test whether items were biodegradable? What is your reasoning? Which items are biodegradable?

25. Of the nonbiodegradable items,
    a. which would be carried toward shore by currents?
    b. which would be exposed to ultraviolet sunlight?
    c. which would sink and might be buried?
    d. which would remain the longest in the environment?

26. How do the following affect the problems of marine debris?
    a. wind
    b. currents
    c. seawater temperature
    d. waves
    e. sandy shorelines
    f. rocky coasts
    g. sunlight

FURTHER INVESTIGATIONS

1. Adopt a beach or a section of a beach and clean it regularly. If you do not have access to a beach, adopt a section of shoreline along a stream, river, or lake.
   a. Record what you find, following the procedures in Activity 2. Send the data to local environmental organizations concerned with environmental cleanup. Also mail a copy of your data to The Center for Marine Conservation (1725 DeSales Street, NW, Washington, D.C. 20036), an organization that collects marine debris data nationwide.
   b. Acting on what you observed, recommend ways of preventing or reducing litter–for example, by placing trash receptacles in key locations.
   c. If you need a fund-raising event, work with your teacher to organize a cleanup campaign in which sponsors in the community pledge money for every pound of trash you collect.

2. List sources that might pollute the waters of a local lake, river, marsh, estuary, or bay. Make a map showing these sources of potential pollution. Invite a speaker to talk to the class about potential pollution problems, about the laws regulating dumping of wastes into waterways, and about efforts to prevent contamination of the water. What could you and your classmates do to prevent future water pollution?

3. Test the degradability of objects that manufacturers say are biodegradable or recyclable. Expose pieces of such objects to conditions that simulate environmental processes. For example, see what happens when you burn them, bury or compost them, tear or shred them, expose them to sunlight, or soak them in fresh water or seawater.

4. Study the effects of toxic metals that inhibit biofouling. Two possibilities are given here, but you may modify the procedures.
   CAUTION: Follow the manufacturer's directions for handling these toxic paints.
   a. Obtain two samples of each type of metal, including copper, steel, alumi-

319

num, and other metals. Set one sample aside to serve as a control. Suspend the other into fresh water, brackish water, or seawater, perhaps off a dock or pier. Observe the metals at least once a week, comparing the experimental metals with the control samples. Report the results to the class.

b. Test how well marine paints prevent biofouling. Talk with a marine supplier for suggestions. Obtain samples of different kinds of marine paints. Paint two pieces each of wood, fiberglass, aluminum, or other materials used in boat hulls. Test as described above.

5. How is pollution affecting marine organisms? Read reports to find what effects, if any, pollution has had on
   a. the shellfish industry, including mollusks (clams, mussels, and oysters) and crustacea (shrimp, crabs, and lobsters).
   b. recreational fishing and the fishing industry.
   c. porpoises and other mammals.
   d. turtles and seabirds.

6. Invite someone from the Coast Guard to talk to the class about water pollution regulations. What cleanup methods does the Coast Guard use? What laws regulate pollution? What penalties do the laws impose? What happens after a major oil spill?

7. Learn about laws governing packaging and disposal of

a. used oil.
b. pesticides.
c. glass bottles.
d. styrofoam.
e. plastics.

8. Learn about statutes and treaties
   a. seeking to prevent or control the disposal of harmful substances in the ocean, including
      1) the London Dumping Convention.
      2) the MARPOL Protocol of 1973 related to preventing pollution from ships.
      3) the Marine Protection, Research and Sanctuaries Act of 1972.
      4) the Federal Water Pollution Control Act.
      5) the Resources Conservation and Recovery Act of 1976.
      6) the 1988 International Convention for the Prevention of Pollution from Ships.
   b. prohibiting the capturing or killing of animals, including
      1) the Marine Mammal Protection Act.
      2) the Fur Seal Act.
      3) the Endangered Species Act.
      4) the Migratory Bird Treaty Act.
   c. establishing the conservation and management of fisheries, including the Magnuson Act.
   d. limiting pollution problems, including
      1) the Federal Water Pollution Control Act.
      2) the Comprehensive Environmental Response, Compensation, and Liability Act.

8. Mineral Resources

As we use up the mineral resources of the land, those in the ocean will become more and more important to us. Ocean **minerals** include substances dissolved in seawater and substances that have precipitated out of it, such as salt crystals, manganese nodules, and cobalt crusts. Oil and gas, which form in deposits under the seafloor, are also classified as minerals.

Many of the world's mineral resources on land are rapidly being exhausted. Faced with shortages—or even a total lack—of metals extracted from these minerals, industrialized nations now import and stockpile certain **strategic metals**—ones critical to military and industrial technology. See Table 8–1.

Because of shortages, the United States and other nations have begun to explore the oceans for new sources of these metals and to develop new technologies for recovering them. See Fig. 8–1. Obtaining minerals from the ocean takes huge investments of money. So far, only a few of the known ocean mineral resources can be profitably mined.

QUESTION

1. Why might an industrialized nation want its own source of strategic metals? What could happen if it has none?

Minerals from the Sea

Let's look at some of the mineral resources in the sea. Refer to Table 8–2 and Fig. 8–2 as you complete this topic.

Table 8–1. Some strategic metals now imported by the United States that could be recovered from the ocean

Mineral	Percentage that must be imported	Sources
Manganese (Mn)	99	South Africa, France, Gabon, Brazil
Cobalt (Co)	95	Zaire, Namibia, Canada, Japan
Nickel (Ni)	74	Canada, Australia, Norway, Botswana
Zinc (Zn)	67	Canada, Peru, Mexico, Australia
Cadmium (Cd)	66	Canada, Australia, Mexico, Peru
Copper (Cu)	21	Chile, Canada, Mexico, Peru
Lead (Pb)	18	Canada, Mexico, Australia, Peru

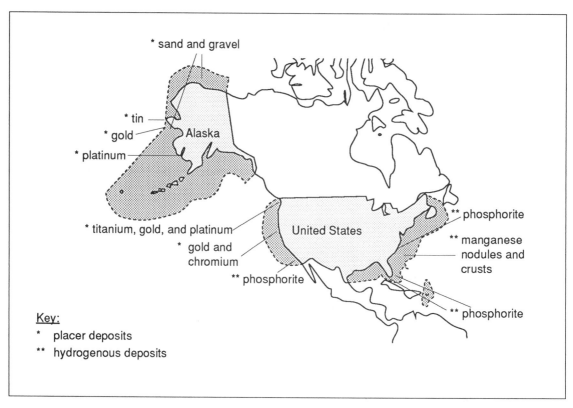

Fig. 8–1. Mineral resources in the EEZ of the United States

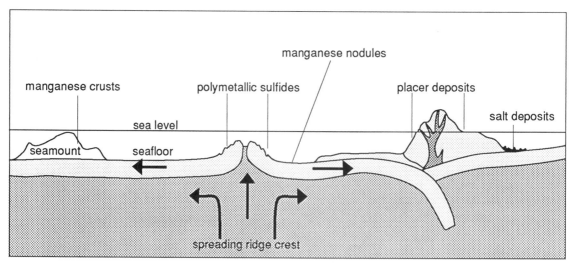

Fig. 8–2. Types of mineral resources (Source: Adapted from B. McGregor and M. Lockwood, *Mapping and Research in the Exclusive Economic Zone*, 1985.)

Table 8–2. Major chemical resources from the ocean

Material	Source	Some uses
Bromine (Br_2)	Extracted from seawater brine	Anti-knock compound in gasoline; industrial chemicals
Cadmium*	Associated with zinc in polymetallic sulfide deposits	Metal alloys; nickel-cadmium batteries
Chromium (Cr)	Placer deposits	Steel alloys, particularly hard stainless steel; electroplating to make bright, shiny surfaces; industrial chemicals
Cobalt (Co)*	Seafloor, manganese nodules, crusts, and polymetallic sulfide deposits	High-quality steels with temperature- and wear-resistant properties for high-speed cutting tools; permanent magnets; industrial chemicals
Copper (Cu)*	Manganese nodules, crusts, and polymetallic sulfide deposits	Wire, cable, pipes, tubes, jewelry; mixed with zinc to make brass and with tin to make bronze
Gas and oil	Biological sediment	Fuels, fertilizers, plastics, pesticides, and industrial chemicals
Gold (Au)**	Seafloor and placer deposits	Money, jewelry, dentistry; electrical and electronic applications
Iodine (I_2)	Extracted from seawater brine	Antiseptics; chemicals for photography, printing, and industry
Iron (Fe)	Manganese nodules, crusts, and polymetallic sulfide deposits	Steel and other alloys
Lead (Pb)*	Polymetallic sulfide deposits	Batteries, radiation shielding, bullets, plumbing alloys, and industrial chemicals

Table 8–2. (continued) Major chemical resources from the ocean

Material	Source	Some uses
Magnesium (Mg)	Extracted from seawater brine	Alloy for lightweight metals; industrial chemicals
Manganese (Mn)*	Manganese nodules, crusts, and polymetallic sulfide deposits	Steel alloys and alloys of non-iron metals to improve strength and pliability
Molybdenum (Mo)	Cobalt crusts	Steel alloys giving toughness
Nickel (Ni)	Seafloor, manganese nodules, and crusts	Money; steel alloys giving strength, hardness, and toughness; industrial chemicals
Phosphorus (P)	Phosphorite	Agricultural fertilizers, detergents and cleaners, phosphoric acid, pesticides, and plastics
Platinum (Pt)*	Seafloor, placer deposits, and manganese crusts	Jewelry, scientific apparatus, surgical tools, electrical contacts, and catalysts to speed up chemical reactions
Sand and gravel	Placer deposits	Construction materials; replenishing eroded beaches
Table salt (NaCl)	Crystallized from seawater and mined from salt deposits	Food additive, food preservative, and source of industrial sodium (Na) and chlorine (Cl)
Tin (Sn)	Placer deposits	Plating, solder, copper alloys
Titanium (Ti)	Placer deposits	High-strength alloys for airplanes and submarine construction; opaque white paint pigments
Zinc (Zn)*	Polymetallic sulfide deposits	Batteries, alloys, and industrial chemicals

* Strategic metal   ** Precious metal

Salts

As we have seen, seawater contains the ions that can form salts. For thousands of years, table salt has been recovered by evaporating it. The seawater is pumped into shallow ponds called **evaporating basins**, constructed in sunny, dry environments where air movement promotes evaporation. Table-salt crystals are the first to precipitate from the concentrated salt solution, called **brine**. The brine concentration is controlled so that other salts do not precipitate. Most salts today are mined from natural deposits that formed on land when ancient shallow seas evaporated.

QUESTION

2. What might explain salt deposits in a desert?

Placer Deposits

Placer deposits are loose accumulations of sand or gravel on continental shelves. Fig. 8–1 shows some placer deposits in the EEZ of the United States. They probably formed when rivers eroded the surface of the land and carried sediment to the ocean. Through the millennia, changes in climate caused sea levels to rise and fall, sometimes exposing placer deposits as beaches, sometimes covering them. Ocean waves and currents sifted and sorted the sediments, creating pockets of sand, gravel, and sometimes such metals as gold (Au), platinum (Pt), chromium (Cr), and titanium (Ti).

The most profitable undersea placer deposits for mining are sand and gravel, both used in the construction industry. Even though sand and gravel are plentiful on land, they are costly to transport, and land mining may be legally restricted to limit environ-mental damage. So mining sand and gravel offshore can be highly profitable.

Precious metals such as gold (Au) and platinum (Pt) bring such high prices that ocean mining has become profitable in spite of its cost. But metals such as titanium (Ti) and chromium (Cr), important for industry and the military, do not bring a high enough price to make mining them from placer deposits worth the investment.

QUESTIONS

3. Why might heavy metals accumulate in the sand deposits in some places on the continental shelf but not in others?

4. Heavy precious metals are eroded from land and carried to the ocean as particles. Why might deposits in the ocean be easier to mine than deposits on land?

5. What laws, if any, do you think are needed to regulate mining of placer deposits?

Hydrogenous Sediments

Minerals that precipitate from seawater form **hydrogenous sediments**—sediments produced in water. Three types of hydrogenous mineral deposits are known: phosphorite, manganese nodules, and cobalt crusts. Scientists do not know how these precipitates form. When they understand the precipitation process, they may be able to control it to obtain minerals on demand.

Phosphorites, also called **phosphate rocks**, are hydrogenous sediments that seem to be associated with upwelling, the process that brings nutrient-rich seawater from the depths to the surface near the edge of a continental shelf. Phosphorite deposits are also found on dry land in ancient marine deposits. This rock is used in fertilizers and in phosphorus compounds for industry.

Manganese nodules are small lumps of minerals about the size of potatoes that lie scattered on the seafloor. Scientists hypothesize that they precipitate from seawater with the aid of biological organisms. As Fig. 8–3 shows, some parts of the seafloor contain few nodules while other parts are almost covered. The nodules are found where sediment accumulation is low.

Manganese nodules average 55% manganese (Mn), 35% iron (Fe), and varying amounts of nickel (Ni), cobalt (Co), copper (Cu), and other minerals. See Fig. 8–4. The nodules are valued mainly for their manganese content, though the trace metal cobalt has potential value. Nodules in the Atlantic Ocean tend to be lower in cobalt content than those in the Pacific Ocean. Technologies have been proposed for scooping up nodules from the seafloor and extracting their metals, but the process is still too costly to be profitable.

Manganese crusts rich in cobalt coat the sides of seamounts, ridges, and plateaus in the Pacific. The crusts are believed to form in a natural precipitation process similar to electroplating. They coat the sides and tops of seamounts and volcanic islands. The crusts, which range from very thin to about 10-cm thick, contain iron (Fe), manganese (Mn), cobalt (Co), nickel (Ni), platinum (Pt), copper (Cu), and molybdenum (Mo). New technologies will have to be developed before hard crusts can be removed profitably and without too much damage to the environment.

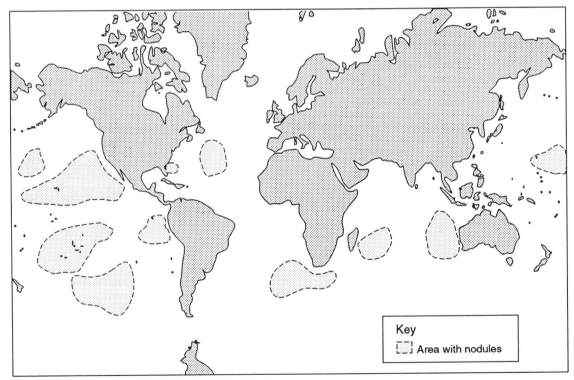

Fig. 8–3. Manganese nodule distribution

Key
Area with nodules

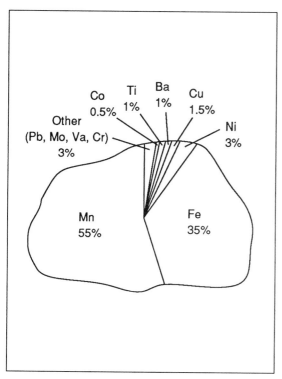

Fig. 8-4. Metallic content of manganese nodules from the Pacific Ocean

QUESTIONS

6. How abundant is phosphorus in seawater? How important is it to plants and animals? Refer to Topic 1.

7. How does the metal content of manganese nodules compare with the content of cobalt crusts?

Biological Sediments

Natural gas and oil are the most valuable resources taken from the seafloor. They form from decomposed plant and animal matter accumulated on the seafloor over millions of years. They are produced in **sedimentary rock**, which forms when underwater gravel and sand are compressed. Because sandstone and limestone are relatively porous, oil and gas can rise until they are trapped by harder, nonporous rock layers like shale and salt. See Fig. 8–5.

Geologists exploring for oil look for hard cap rocks that trap oil and gas in reservoirs. Seismic profiling techniques similar

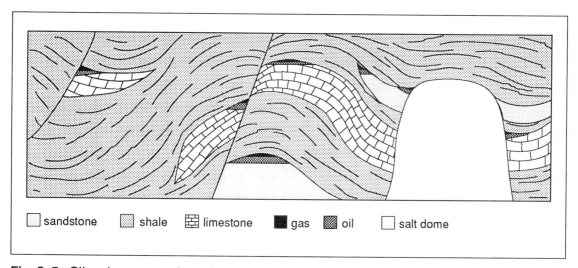

sandstone   shale   limestone   gas   oil   salt dome

Fig. 8–5. Oil and gas move through permeable sedimentary rock and are then trapped beneath impermeable cap rock.

to those discussed in Unit 1 are used to gather data about the types of rocks in the seafloor. Because shock waves traveling through the seafloor reflect differently off each type of rock, geologists can use shock waves to produce pictures of the earth's crust showing formations where oil and gas may be trapped.

Exploratory **oil-drilling rigs** are used to find whether a promising geological forma-tion contains oil. See Fig. 8–6. The template rig (A) is the simplest, but it is difficult to move. Semisubmersibles (B) travel on floats and are stabilized by partial submer-gence. Drill-ships (C) are held in place by propellers. If oil is found, huge platforms are set on the seafloor to drill into the reservoirs. See Fig. 8–7. The oil is pumped up, pro-cessed, and refined for use in fuels, lubri-cants, and raw materials for plastics.

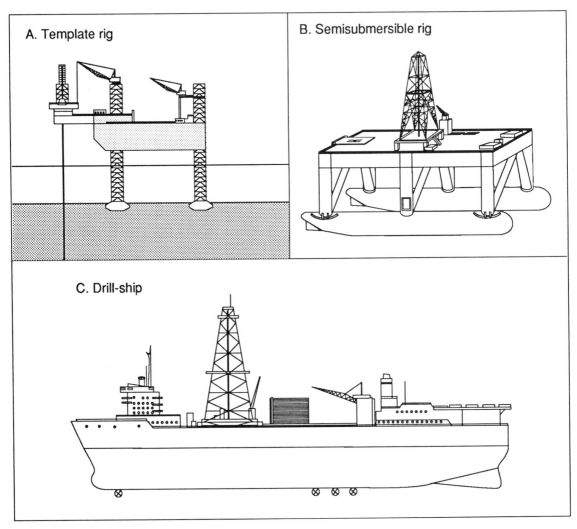

Fig. 8–6. Exploratory oil-drilling rigs

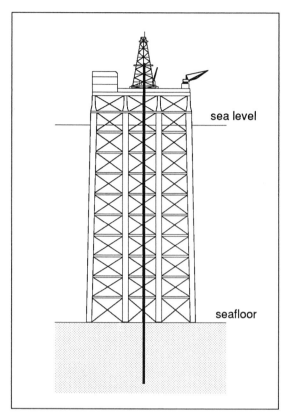

Fig. 8–7. Oil-drilling platform

Fig. 8–8 shows the sedimentary basins with potential oil and gas resources within the EEZ of the United States.

QUESTIONS

8. Why are oil and gas classified as minerals?

9. What makes natural gas and oil the most valuable resources taken from the seafloor?

Hydrothermal Vents

Hydrothermal vents, openings in the seafloor through which hot fluids flow, occur in volcanically active areas such as midocean ridges and hot spots. Cold seawater sinks through fractures and crevices into the earth's crust, where volcanic magma superheats it. The hot water dissolves sulfides of metals, including copper (Cu), lead (Pb), zinc (Zn), iron (Fe), manganese (Mn), and cobalt (Co). The mineral-laden seawater then shoots through the seafloor in

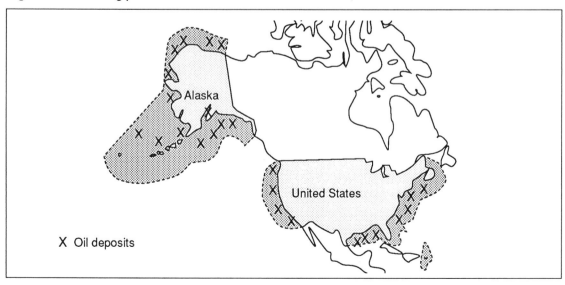

Fig. 8–8. Oil deposits in the EEZ of the continental United States

underwater geysers called **smokers**. On contact with cold, deep-ocean seawater, minerals precipitate out of solution, forming **polymetallic sulfide deposits** (**poly** means "many"). See Fig. 8–9. Large, irregular, chimneylike structures, often brightly colored from the mineral deposits, develop around the vents.

Analyses of the vent deposits show some promise for mining. Samples from the Galapagos Ridge contained 14% copper. (Land deposits contain only about 0.1% copper.) Before mining can begin, however, we need to know more about the extent of crustal deposits and about the hazards of mining near active underwater volcanoes. The copper, too, must bring a high enough price to cover the cost of mining hydrothermal vents.

QUESTIONS

10. What problems might be encountered in mining polymetallic sulfides?

11. Businesses cannot survive unless they make a profit. What conditions do you think an offshore mining operation must meet if it is to be profitable?

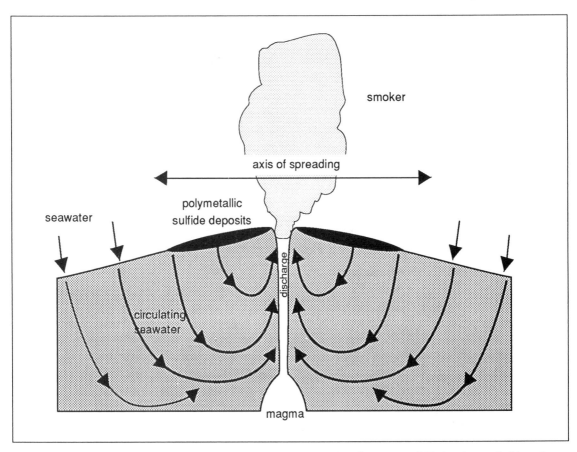

Fig. 8–9. Hydrothermal vents (Source: Adapted from B. McGregor and M. Lockwood, *Mapping and Research in the Exclusive Economic Zone*, 1985.)

Environmental Impact

All underwater mining operations disturb the environment. Fig. 8–10 shows damage caused by dredging or cutting. Environmental questions about seabed mining include the following:

- How will the killing of organisms affect the ecological balance of the seafloor?
- Once a mining operation stops, will the mined areas recover biologically?

- Will removal of nearshore sediments change wave formations? Will new wave patterns affect shoreline erosion?
- Will mining operations on steep slopes contribute to submarine landslides? Will such landslides damage cables or pipes or drilling platforms?

Until researchers can answer these questions and engineers can design safe technologies, it is not feasible to mine crustal deposits.

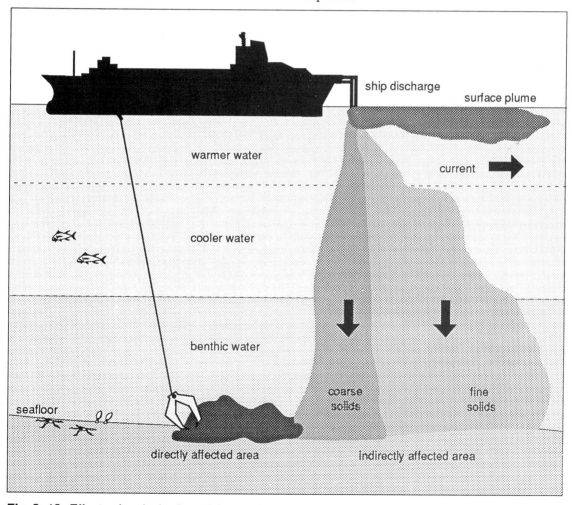

Fig. 8–10. Effects of grab-dredge mining on the ocean environment (Source: Adapted from Satellite Planning Committee, *Marine Minerals: Exploring Our New Ocean Frontier*, 1987.)

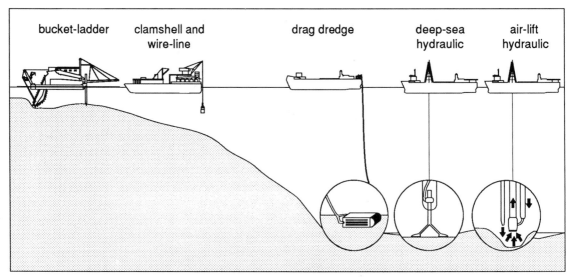

Fig. 8–11. Technologies commonly used for removing minerals from the seafloor (Source: Adapted from Satellite Planning Committee, *Marine Minerals: Exploring Our New Ocean Frontier*, 1987.)

QUESTION

12. What damage to the ocean environment might be caused by
    a. placer mining?
    b. manganese-nodule mining?
    c. crust removal?

FURTHER INVESTIGATION

Read library references and report on these topics:

a. laws and treaties governing rights to minerals on continental shelves and the deep seafloor
b. new technologies for discovering and recovering minerals from the seabed
c. experiments using chemicals, electrical fields, and other methods to precipitate materials from seawater
d. methods for recovering materials from the seafloor (see Fig. 8–11)
e. the location and extent of oil resources on the continental shelf
f. predictions of developments in the offshore oil industry
g. environmental benefits and problems related to offshore oil
h. the importance of sea salts throughout history

UNIT 5
TRANSPORTATION

"They're mad. They propose to make a ship of iron? Iron can't float. The very idea is absurd." To the amazement of the scoffers of two centuries ago, iron became a principal building material of large ships.

Inventors of the past found their ideas met often with ridicule, rarely with financial success. But ours is an age of invention, an age in which we wait eagerly for scientific breakthroughs in laboratories so we can convert them into useful new technologies.

On this note we conclude our studies with a glimpse at the technologies that have turned the fluid earth into grand arteries of commerce—the technologies built around ocean transportation.

1. Ship Flotation

Buoyancy is the force that supports things in a liquid or gas. When a ship is floating in still water, the pressure of water on the boat below the waterline pushes upward, creating a buoyant force. See Unit 3, Topic 4.

Net buoyant force on an object is the difference between the ability of the liquid to support that object and the gravitational force tending to sink it.

- When the net buoyant force on the object is zero, the object **floats** and is **stationary**.
- When the net buoyant force is positive (+), the object **rises**.
- When the net buoyant force is negative (−), the object **sinks**.

The equation for the net buoyant force of a boat is

Net buoyant force = buoyant force − mass of boat

The buoyant force is equal to the mass of the water displaced by the boat. In this experiment we will use the unit of mass called the gram force (gf). One **gram force** is the force of gravity on 1g of mass at sea level. A kilogram force (kgf) is 1,000 times as large.

ACTIVITY

Determine the net buoyant force of materials used to construct boats.

Determine the effect of boat shape on cargo-carrying capacity.

MATERIALS (per team)

- 100 g oil-based modeling clay
- 100-g chunk of metal
- 100-g piece of wood
- centigram balance
- overflow displacement tank
- liquid detergent
- 250-mL graduated cylinder
- wax-paper square, about 10 x 10 cm
- 400 cc dry sand
- spoon

PROCEDURE

1. Obtain about 100 g each of clay, metal, and wood. Shape the clay into a solid sphere. Weigh each sample and record its weight (in gf) in Table 1–1.

2. Determine the net buoyant force for each of the materials.
   a. Obtain an overflow displacement tank. Place it at the edge of a sink.
   b. Fill it with water until it just starts overflowing. Add one drop of detergent to decrease the surface tension of the water. Start step (c) after overflowing stops.
   c. Determine the weight (in gf) of water displaced when each of the materials

Table 1–1. Net buoyant force (W)

Object	Floats or sinks	Weight of object (a) (gf)	Weight of displaced water (b) (gf)	Net buoyant force (b)−(a) (gf)
Clay sphere				
Metal				
Wood				
Clay boat				

Table 1–2. Hull design and carrying capacity (W)

A. Your hull

Carrying capacity (gf)

B. Hull with the greatest carrying capacity

Carrying capacity (gf)

is placed in the tank. Catch the overflow in a graduated cylinder and record the weight of the water in Table 1–1. (Since 1 mL water = 1 g water, the volume of water displaced can be converted to gf.)

d. Observe and record whether the object floats or sinks.

e. Calculate the net buoyant force in gf.

f. Repeat steps (b) to (e) using samples of other materials.

3. Compete with others in the class to design a ship hull that has the greatest capacity to carry a load of dry sand.

a. Shape clay into a hollow boat. Check to see if it floats. Sketch your design in Table 1–2.

b. Determine the net buoyant force for your boat and record it in Table 1–1.

c. Determine the carrying capacity of your boat. Insert a sheet of wax paper into the clay hull. Slowly pour dry sand into the boat until it is just about ready to swamp. Do not let it swamp. Weigh the sand in gf. Record the weight of sand as carrying capacity in Table 1–2.

d. Compare your ship hull design with other designs in the class. Decide which has the greatest capacity.

e. In Table 1–2, sketch the hull design of the boat found to have the greatest carrying capacity in the class.

Principle of Flotation

How can we explain that such objects as steel ships can float, even though the material they are made of is denser than water? To explain how steel ships float, we will use the principle of **flotation**:

• A floating object displaces a weight of liquid equal to its own weight.

Consider the 1 ft³ solid block of iron shown in Fig. 1–1. It weighs 204 kgf (450 lb). Placed in water, it rapidly sinks, displacing its own volume of water, which is 1 ft³. (A cubic foot of water weighs 28.3 kgf or 62.4 lb.) Thus we know that on this block there is a downward force of 204 kgf and an upward force of 28.3 kgf. The greater downward force causes the block to sink. Suppose the same iron block were reshaped into the iron bowl shown in Fig. 1–1. The iron bowl will displace a much greater volume of water than the iron block, but the bowl still weighs the same, 204 kgf.

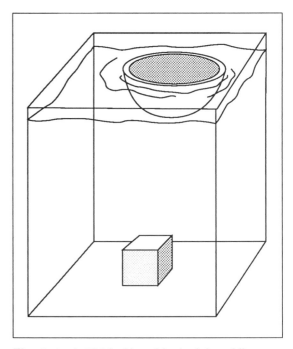

Fig. 1–1. A 204-kgf iron block sinks while a 204-kgf iron bowl floats.

If we place the bowl gently onto the surface of the water, it settles and floats. Now we know that the floating bowl has displaced its own weight of water. The iron bowl floats because it has an upward force of 204 kgf equaling the downward force of 204 kgf.

The principle of flotation, first discovered in 250 B.C. by Archimedes, can be demonstrated easily. Nevertheless, iron ship advocates were still being called fools in the late eighteenth and early nineteenth centuries. "Wood can swim; iron can't," old sailors would say. But in 1787 John Wilkinson's 70-ft barge *Trial*, constructed of iron plates, did stay afloat. This vessel was the forerunner of the steel ships sailing the oceans today.

QUESTIONS

1. Describe clay, metal, and wood materials in terms of their buoyancy.

2. In a calm harbor, gravitational force and buoyant force are the only two forces acting on a ship. These forces act in opposite directions.
   a. If the ship floats, are the opposing forces equal or unequal? If unequal, which force is greater?
   b. Explain your answer in terms of net buoyant force.

3. How does the flotation of a solid sphere of clay differ from the flotation of a clay hull? From this evidence, suggest an explanation of why metal chunks sink but metal ships float.

4. What relationship, if any, is there between the shape of a hull and its carrying capacity? How is shape related to net buoyant force?

5. Check your understanding of these terms:
   a. buoyant force
   b. buoyancy
   c. gram force
   d. gravitational force
   e. stationary

Ship Tonnage

Ship tonnage, a measure of what a ship can carry, can be confusing. There are five different tonnage figures. The two major categories are tonnage by weight and tonnage by volume. See Fig. 1–2.

Tonnage by weight, or **displacement**, is the weight of water displaced by a loaded vessel. This weight is expressed in metric tons. A metric ton is the weight of 1 m^3 of fresh water.

Tonnage by volume is based on the English system of measure of cubic capacity. In this system, 100 ft^3 is called a ton. It is equal to 2.83 m^3. For example, a ship that has a tonnage by volume of 1,000 tons can hold 100,000 ft^3 of cargo.

Ship Displacement

To gauge a ship's weight or its displacement at any time during loading or unloading, the ship's officers take the average of the bow and stern **drafts** (the vertical distance from the waterline to the keel).

Draft marks on a vessel's bow show the distance in feet from the keel to the waterline. An enlargement of the bow draft of the ship in Fig. 1–3 shows that the bow draft is 30 ft.

Look at the displacement curve shown in Fig. 1–4 for the ship in Fig. 1–3. If this ship were loaded to its 25-ft draft mark, it

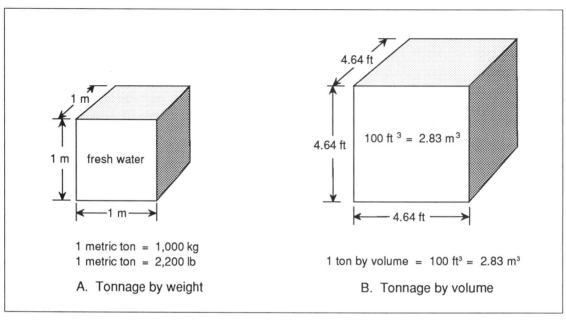

Fig. 1–2. Two categories of ship tonnage

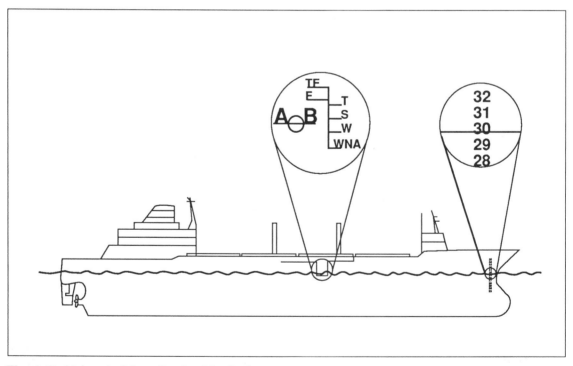

Fig. 1–3. Using draft to estimate ship displacement

338

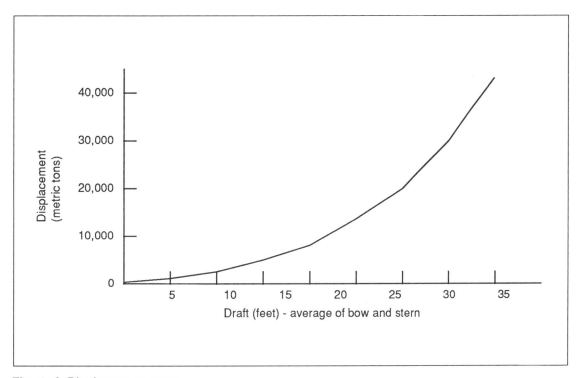

Fig. 1–4. Displacement curve

would have a displacement of approximately 15,000 metric tons.

Load lines, or Plimsoll marks, show the maximum depth to which a ship can be legally loaded in different zones and seasons. They are used for ship safety. Fig. 1–3 shows the placement of Plimsoll marks and draft marks on a ship. In the enlarged view of the Plimsoll marks shown in Fig. 1–5, the following abbrevations are used

TF	=	tropical fresh water
F	=	fresh water
T	=	tropical
S	=	summer
W	=	winter
WNA	=	winter North Atlantic

Because of bad winter weather in the North Atlantic Ocean, ships heading there during the winter are not heavily laden.

A B stands for American Bureau of Shipping, the agency that validated the ship's Plimsoll marks.

QUESTIONS

6. Why are summer load-line markings higher than winter markings? Explain.

7. Why are freshwater load-line markings higher than seawater markings?

8. Sailors refer to tonnage by volume more commonly than by displacement. Suggest a reason why.

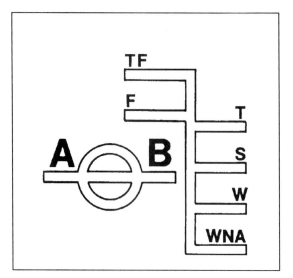

Fig. 1–5. Enlarged view of Plimsoll marks (also called load lines)

FURTHER INVESTIGATIONS

1. Using outside references, find out what kinds of construction materials are used today for building
   a. the largest supertankers.
   b. submarines.
   c. high-speed motorboats.
   d. racing sailboats.

2. Find out how the U.S. Postal Service and commercial airlines, buses, trains, and moving companies
   a. measure their cargo.
   b. set size or weight limits.
   c. charge their customers.

2. Ship Stability

Stability is the tendency of a floating object rolling from side to side to return to an upright position. Stability is vital in the design of a ship. A rocking chair on a floor has this kind of stability.

Stability can be achieved in two ways:
1. **Leverage stability** is achieved where there is a wide stance at the base. Examples of leverage stability are seen in the construction of barges or catamarans. See Fig. 2–1.
2. **Weight stability** is achieved by anchoring the base. See Fig. 2–2. A portable tetherball stand with its pipe cemented in a tire has weight stability. A hull with weight distributed toward its base has weight stability.

Forces Affecting Stability

Gravitational force and **buoyant force** operate in opposite directions and affect the stability of every ship.
1. **Gravitational force** (G) is the sum of the entire weight of a ship acting straight downward on its **center of gravity** (CG). The center of gravity of an object of uniform density is at the geometric center of the object. Fig. 2–3 shows the center of gravity as a dot. The arrow represents the gravitational force.

The center of gravity of an object not uniformly dense, however, tends to be close to the densest portion of the object. Notice the location of the center of gravity (the dot) in Fig. 2–4 as compared to the one in Fig. 2–3. Keep in mind that most ships are objects with unevenly distributed density.

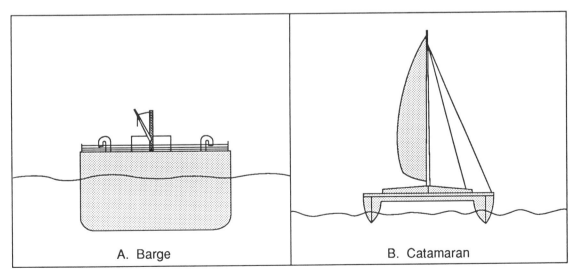

| A. Barge | B. Catamaran |

Fig. 2–1. Examples of leverage stability

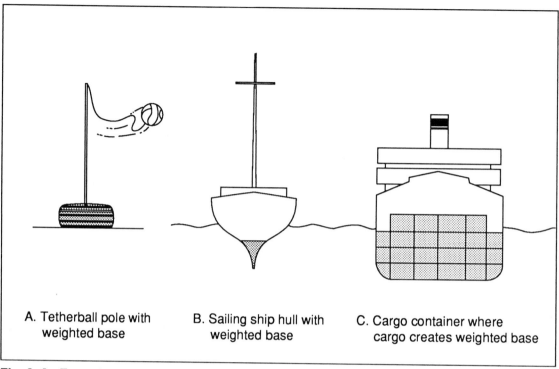

Fig. 2–2. Examples of weight stability

A. Tetherball pole with
weighted base

B. Sailing ship hull with
weighted base

C. Cargo container where
cargo creates weighted base

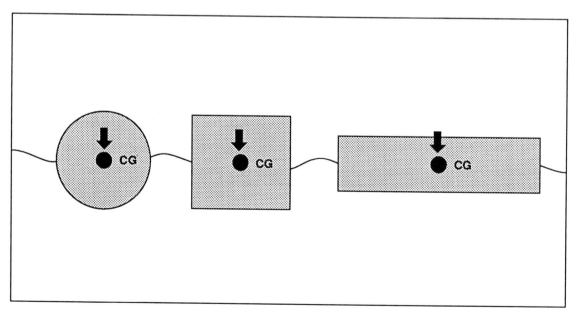

Fig. 2–3. Center of gravity in objects of uniform density

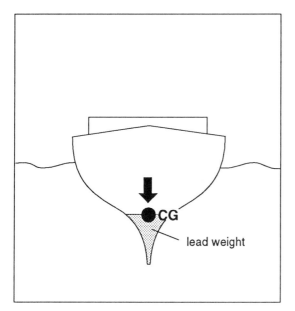

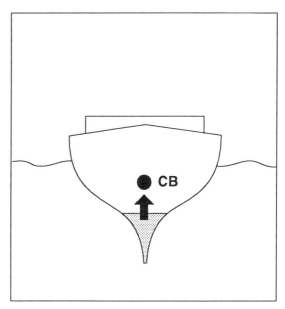

Fig. 2–4. Center of gravity in a hull of uneven density with weighted base

Fig. 2–5. Center of buoyancy

2. **Buoyant force** (B) is the force of a liquid acting straight upward at the **center of buoyancy** (CB) of the submerged part of an object. Fig. 2–5 shows the center of buoyancy as a dot. The center of buoyancy is always at the geometric center of the *submerged* part of a ship's hull.

Ship stability is determined by the balance between the forces of gravity and buoyancy. For a vessel in a calm harbor, the two forces of gravity and buoyancy are in a line and are balanced, as shown in (A) in Fig. 2–6.

A **stable ship** rights itself when tilted. In (B) in Fig. 2–6, the ship is stable. The center of buoyancy of the tilted ship is shifted to the right because the area submerged has been shifted. The opposing forces acting at their CB and CG will twist the ship back to an upright position.

An **unstable ship** will not right itself. It will continue to fall over, because the buoyant and gravitational forces act on the ship to keep it moving in the direction of list or tilt. See (C) in Fig. 2–6.

ACTIVITY

Using cross-sectional models, determine whether given ship designs are stable.

MATERIALS
• weighted Styrofoam ship cross-sections
• test tank of water
• pen
• 6-cm nail
• plumb line with weight
• Styrofoam (for plugs)
• knife or fine-tooth saw
• toothpicks
• 8 1/2 X 11-in sheet of blank paper

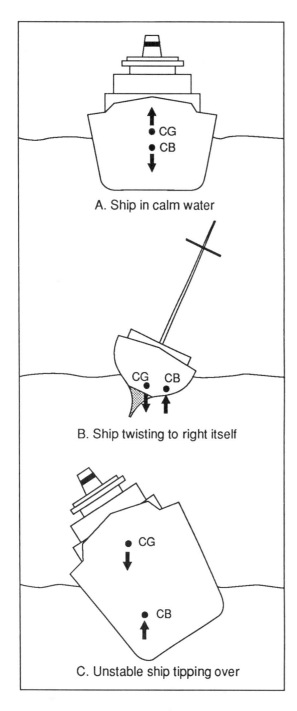

Fig. 2–6. Effects of the forces of buoyancy and gravity on stable and unstable ships

A. Ship in calm water

B. Ship twisting to right itself

C. Unstable ship tipping over

1. Obtain a Styrofoam cross-sectional model of a ship.

2. Tank-test the model for stability.
   NOTE: We are testing only for side-to-side stability. If a model tends to fall forward or backward, support it gently with your hands.
   a. Place the cross-sectional model in the test tank in a vertical position.
   b. Test to determine whether it is stable. Push down on one side so that the model lists about 30°. Release the model. See if it returns to an upright position. If it does, it is stable. (**List** means to lean or tilt to one side.)
   c. Again push the model down on one side so that it lists approximately 30°. Mark the 30° waterline across the face of the model. See Fig. 2–7.

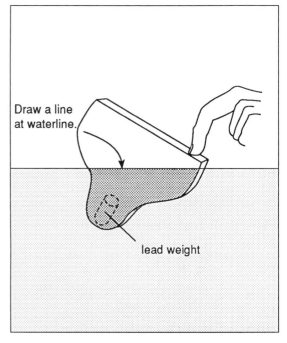

Draw a line at waterline.

lead weight

Fig. 2–7. Styrofoam model pushed to a 30° list

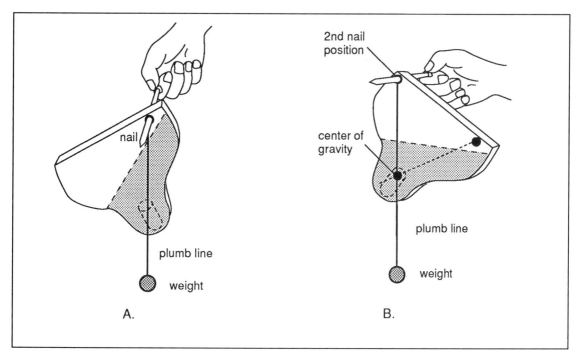

Fig. 2–8. Plumb line locating center of gravity

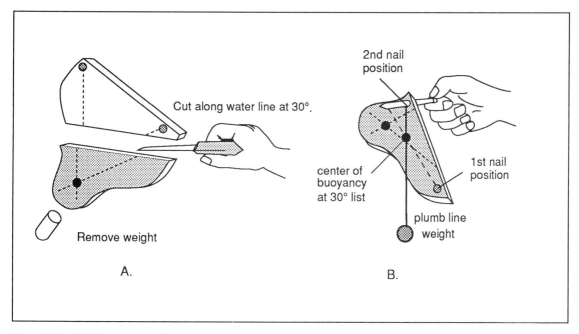

Fig. 2–9. Finding center of buoyancy at 30˚ list

345

3. Locate the center of gravity of the model. Do not use the test-tank as you carry out the procedures below.
   a. Place a nail through the cross-sectional model at any position close to an edge. Hold the nail so that the model swings easily. Enlarge the hole if necessary. See (A) in Fig. 2–8.
   b. Hang a plumb line from the nail as shown in (A) in Fig. 2–8.
   c. Draw a line on the model where the plumb line hangs. Repeat the above step, placing the nail near an edge and at least 5 cm away from its original position. See (B) in Fig. 2–8.
   d. Locate the point where the lines intersect. This is the center of gravity. See (B) in Fig. 2–8.

4. Determine the center of buoyancy of the model at approximately a 30° angle in the following manner:
   a. Remove weights from models and fill any holes with Styrofoam plugs.
   b. Cut each model in two along the 30° waterline. See (A) in Fig. 2–9.
   c. Using the section of each hull that was submerged, find its center of gravity. Follow the steps in Procedure 3. Since this section has uniform density, you are locating its geometric center, which is also the center of buoyancy. Mark the center of buoyancy. See (B) in Fig. 2–9.

5. Show the interaction between gravitational and buoyant forces on a sheet of paper.
   a. Reconstruct the cross-sectional model of the hull weights. Attach the two parts with toothpicks.
   b. On a separate sheet of paper trace the outline of the cross-sectional hull positioned at a 30° list.
   c. Locate and label the waterline, the center of gravity, the center of buoyancy, and the nail holes on the paper.
   d. Draw the buoyant and gravitational force arrows pointing to the centers of buoyancy and gravity. Show the direction of force. Recall that these forces are always straight up and down.
   e. Determine whether the two forces acting at their respective centers restore the ship to an upright position or capsize it. Draw an arrow in the direction the ship should roll. Is the ship stable?

6. Without placing your model in the water, predict the maximum list that it can have before it capsizes. Record your prediction and your reasoning in your notebook.

7. Restore the weight and test your prediction made in Procedure 6.
   a. Record in your notebook how you tested your prediction.
   b. Explain why you were or were not successful in your prediction.

QUESTIONS

1. Define *buoyant force* and *gravitational force*.

2. Define *stability* for a floating object. Use the terms *buoyant force* and *gravitational force* in your answer.

3. Describe two characteristics of a ship

346

that tend to make it stable.

4. Explain how the plumb-line technique finds the center of gravity.

5. A ship is considered **tender** if it slowly rolls back and forth to a stable position. It is considered **stiff** if it rights itself quickly, with little roll. What characteristics of the ship might determine whether it is tender or stiff?

6. Using diagrams, explain each of the following terms:
   a. leverage stability
   b. weight stability
   c. center of gravity
   d. a ship righting itself

FURTHER INVESTIGATIONS

1. Load a plastic model of a container ship with high- and low-density containers so that it has a stability of a stiff nature. It should be balanced **fore** (in front) and **aft** (in back) and loaded to its summer freshwater load marks.

2. Using references, look up and make a report on hull design and stability. Give a few examples of crafts that are tender or stiff.

3. Design and construct other hulls. Test them for stability. Use the procedures in this topic.

4. Read and report to the class about new hull designs such as semi-submersible platforms and fast racing hulls that are used in the America's Cup race.

3. Size of Transport Conveyances

Although we can readily visualize the dimensions of a Volkswagen, most of us cannot easily picture the size of a supertanker. A Volkswagen Beetle, for example, is 4 m long and weighs 643 kg (1,800 lb).

By comparison, some oil tankers are 350 m long (almost four football fields) and weigh 500 million kg (500,000 metric tons). Profiles of a supertanker and a Volkswagen Beetle are shown in Table 3–1.

ACTIVITY
Construct profiles to scale of various transport conveyances.
Compare the sizes and carrying capacities of the various conveyances.

MATERIALS
- 3 X 5-in index cards
- meterstick
- construction paper or poster board
- pencil
- sand
- centigram balance
- 250-mL graduated cylinder
- 1,000-mL beaker

PROCEDURE
1. Select one of the land, sea, or air transport vehicles described in Table 3–1, or choose another type that interests you.

2. Using Table 3–1 or other references, describe the size of the conveyance you selected. Record data on a 3 X 5-in card using the following terms or others that are appropriate:
   a. overall length (distance between extreme ends)
   b. greatest width (the beam of a ship)
   c. height (the distance from a ship's top deck to its hull bottom, including the keel)
   d. cargo capacity (either as weight or volume)
   e. speed
   f. cruising range
   g. fuel efficiency

3. Construct a profile to scale of your transport conveyance.
   a. Using the scale 1 cm = 2 m, draw the outline of the conveyance on poster board or construction paper.
   b. Attach a 3 X 5-in card describing the features of the conveyance.
   c. Post the profile on the bulletin board.

4. Demonstrate the cargo capacity of the conveyance
   a. by weight. Represent this by using 1 g of sand for every 100 tons of cargo. Display the sand on a piece of paper labeled with the name of the type of conveyance.
   b. by volume. Represent this by using 1 mL of water for every 100 ft^3 of cargo. Display the water in a beaker labeled with the type of conveyance.

Table 3–1. Conveyance statistics

A. Sedan automobile—Volkswagen Beetle

Length: 4 m (13 ft)
Width: 1.5 m (5 ft)
Height: 1.5 m (5 ft)

Cargo capacity: 35 ft³ (4 adults)
Speed: 138 km/hr (86 mph)
Cruising range: 423 km (262 mi)
Fuel efficiency: 25 mi/gal

B. Supertanker—S.S. *Ardshiel*

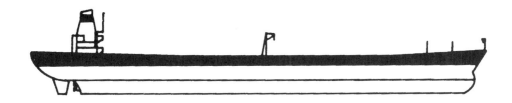

Length: 324 m
Width: 48 m
Height: 19 m draft

Cargo capacity: 9.1 million ft³ (256,000 m³)*
Speed: 22 km/hr (12 knots)
Cruising range: 31,000 nautical miles
Fuel efficiency: 0.006 statute mi/gal

*1 metric ton is 1.103 tons or 2,204 lb.

Table 3–1 (continued). Conveyance statistics

C. Airplane–Boeing 747

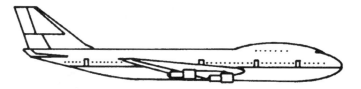

Built: 1967–1970
Length: 57 m (187 ft) internal
Width: 6 m (20 ft) internal
Height: 6 m (20 ft) internal

Cargo capacity: 6,190 ft³ cargo hold,
                            27,860 ft³ passenger compartment
Speed: 960 km/hr (600 mph)
Cruising range: 5,200 nautical miles (5,980 statute miles)
Fuel efficiency: 0.28 statute mi/gal

The 747s first went into service in 1970. They can carry up to 590 passengers and can fly around the world in 47 hours.

D. Containership—*Manu Kai* (Hawaiian for "sea bird")

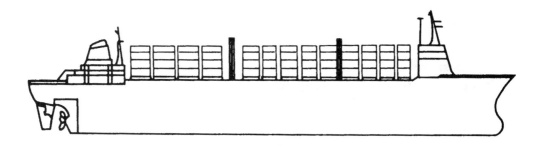

Length: 245 m (720 ft)
Width: 29 m (95 ft)
Height: 10 m (34 ft) draft

Cargo capacity: 1.8 million ft³
Speed: 41 km/hr (22 knots)
Cruising range: 8,400 nautical miles (9,660 statute miles)
Fuel efficiency: 0.02 statute mi/gal

Table 3–1 (continued). Conveyance statistics

E. Nuclear submarine—*George Washington*

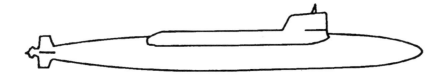

Built: 1959
Length: 131 m (430 ft)
Width: 11 m (36 ft)
Height: 11 m (36 ft)

Cargo capacity: unknown (displacement = 192,200 ft³)
Speed: 56 km/hr (30 knots)
Cruising range: limited mainly to endurance of crew
Fuel efficiency: unknown (nuclear-powered)

The *George Washington* is armed with 16 Polaris missiles that are 10 m long, 1.3 m wide, and carry nuclear warheads.

F. Fishing boat—*Anela*

Length: 30 m (100 ft)
Width: 8 m (26 ft)
Height: 4.5 m (draft 4 m)

Cargo capacity: 1,875 ft³
Speed: 28 km/hr (15 knots)
Cruising range: 375 nautical miles (431 statute miles)
Fuel efficiency: 0.43 statute mi/gal

This type of boat is used for tuna fishing. Individual fishers have their own poles and lines; they fish from a platform that projects all around the hull. Live bait is kept in tanks on the decks.

QUESTIONS

1. Compare the conveyances studied in class in terms of their length and volume.
   a. Which is the largest conveyance in the class?
   b. Which is the smallest conveyance?

2. How large is a supertanker? How many Volkswagens would you need to equal the size of a supertanker? How many Boeing 747s? Show how you arrived at your answers.

3. Some supertankers are so large that only a few harbors in the world can hold them. What possible advantages could there be in making supertankers so large? What disadvantages?

4. Explain the difference between a profile drawing and a cross-sectional drawing. Use a sketch of a ship in giving your answer.

5. Use sketches to explain the meanings of these phrases:
   a. a full-scale drawing
   b. a one-quarter scale drawing

6. Check your understanding of these terms:
   a. cargo capacity   c. fuel efficiency
   b. cruising range   d. speed

FURTHER INVESTIGATIONS

1. Construct profiles to scale of large marine animals. Include porpoises, whales, and giant squid. Compare animal sizes with the sizes of transport conveyances.

2. Make a study of the relative sizes and shapes of ships throughout history. Make predictions about the sizes and shapes of ships of the future.

3. As ships have become larger throughout history, how have their propulsion systems changed? What kinds of propulsion systems are likely in the future?

4. Ship Hull Design and Construction

A ship architect must design a ship so that it has the strength to withstand a combination of forces: the upward force of buoyancy, the downward force of gravity, and the powerful force of ocean waves. The ship must also be streamlined for speed.

For thousands of years, ships have been designed much like the bodies of vertebrate animals. The ships' ribs have been covered with a skin of hide, bark, planks, or metal plates. The skin not only made the ships watertight and buoyant; it also provided the necessary strength for their hulls. See Fig. 4–1.

Ship hulls were traditionally designed as small-scale models. The models were approved, then sawed into sections. Blueprint measurements were made of each section. These were mathematically enlarged when the ship was built to full scale. From the full-scale measurements, parts were constructed and assembled to build the full-sized hull.

Today computers are being used to design ship models and draw blueprints.

Fig. 4–1. Primitive animal-hide boat with skin stretched over wooden ribs (Tibetan design)

ACTIVITY
Design a ship hull; then make a blueprint of it. Construct a ship from the blueprint.

MATERIALS (per team)
- 2 sheets of 8-1/2 X 11-in graph paper
- ruler
- 250 cm³ oil-based clay
- knife with blade approximately 15 cm long
- scissors
- 9 X 11-in manila folder
- carbon paper
- 5-m length of 1/4-in or 1/2-in masking tape
- container of water

PROCEDURE
1. Draw a line down the center of a piece of graph paper. See (A) in Fig. 4–2.

353

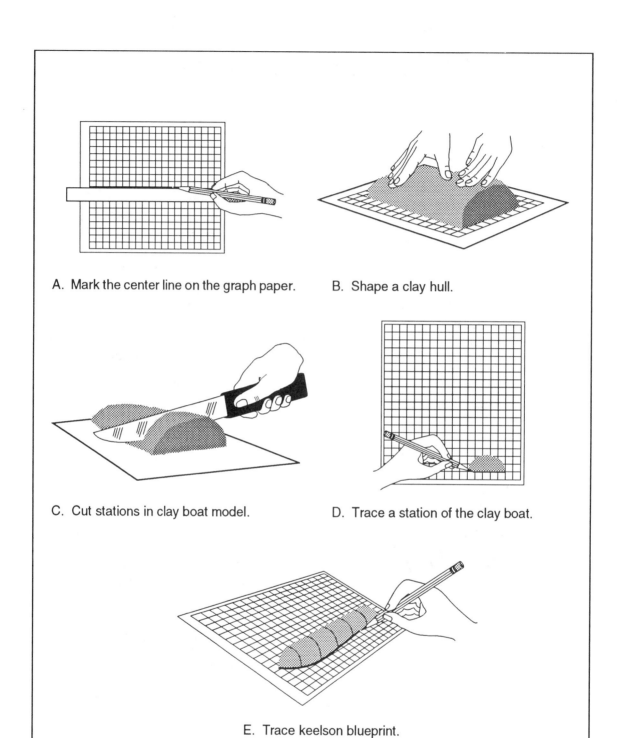

A. Mark the center line on the graph paper.

B. Shape a clay hull.

C. Cut stations in clay boat model.

D. Trace a station of the clay boat.

E. Trace keelson blueprint.

Fig. 4–2. Designing a ship hull

2. Shape a clay model of a ship hull that you think will be the fastest in the class.
   a. Place 250 cm³ of clay on your graph paper.
   b. Shape a solid ship with the hull facing up and the flat deck facing down. Use the graph paper to assure that your ship is symmetrical on either side of the center line. See (B) in Fig. 4–2.

3. Make a blueprint of the hull.
   a. Start at the **stern**, or rear, of the clay ship model. Cut stations (cross-sections) every 3 cm along the length of the ship. (A **station** is the nautical term for a cross-sectional drawing.) See (C) in Fig. 4–2. Use the graph paper as a guide in making the section cuts parallel. Use care in cutting the clay so as not to change the shape of your model.
   b. Trace each station onto a piece of graph paper as shown in (D) in Fig. 4–2.
      1) Place the aft section (**transom**) of the boat on the graph paper and trace it. **NOTE:** Not all boats have a transom; canoes, for example, are pointed at both ends.
      2) Number this station 1 on the graph paper.
      3) Follow the same tracing procedure with each station, numbering each consecutively.
   c. Reassemble the clay hull; then carefully cut it lengthwise along the center line.
   d. Place half of the hull on the graph paper as shown in (E) in Fig. 4–2. Trace the **keelson** onto the graph paper. Mark and number the positions of the stations as shown in Fig. 4–3.

   e. Label blueprint with student architects' names and the date as shown in Fig. 4–3.

4. Place the carbon paper under the blueprint, then trace the following onto half a manila folder:
   a. the keelson with station positions and numbers
   b. the stations with numbers

5. Cut out the keelson and stations. Stations numbered 2 through 6 will become transverse **bulkheads** for your ship. Bulkheads are part of the framework of your ship.

6. Cut slits in transom, keelson, and all transverse bulkheads (stations no. 2 through no. 6). See Fig. 4–3.
   a. On the keelson, cut a slit halfway down from the deck at each bulkhead position mark.

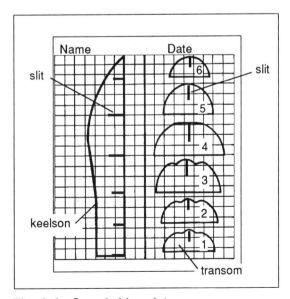

Fig. 4–3. Sample blueprint

355

b. Cut a slit in each bulkhead starting at the midpoint of the bottom of the bulkhead going halfway to the deck.

7. Assemble keelson and bulkheads upside down on a manila cardboard base as shown in (A) in Fig. 4–4.
   a. Draw a straight line down the center of the manila base.
   b. Position keelson along center line. Tape lightly in place so that it is perpendicular to the manila base.
   c. Interlock bulkheads on the keelson. Tape bulkheads lightly to the base, making sure that each bulkhead is perpendicular to the keelson.

8. Using masking tape for planking, lay planking over the hull by doing the following:
   a. Cut about 20 strips of masking tape about 6 cm longer than the hull.
   b. Lay the first masking-tape plank along the deck edge (**gunwale**) of the ship, sticking it tautly to the bulkheads and keelson. Repeat for the other side of the ship.
   c. Fasten a plank over the length of the keelson and rear bulkhead (transom).
   d. Lay the next plank parallel to and slightly overlapping the keelson plank as shown in (B) in Fig. 4–4.
   e. Continue planking on alternate sides of the hull. You can remove the ship from the base to make planking easier.

9. Test for leaky areas and repair them.
   a. Remove the model from the base if you haven't done so already.
   b. Press the planks together in areas where overlapping planks are not making contact.
   c. Test for leaky areas by floating the ship in a container of water.
      1) If there are a few leaks, dry the ship with a paper towel and patch it with additional tape.

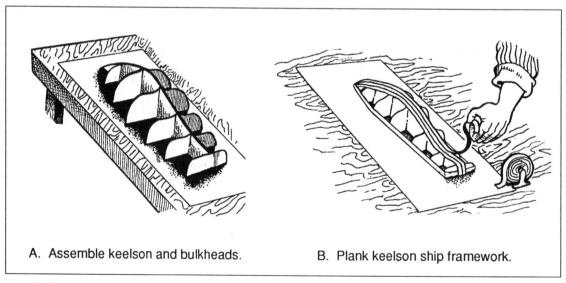

A. Assemble keelson and bulkheads.   B. Plank keelson ship framework.

Fig. 4–4. Ship framework construction

2) If there are many leaks, add a complete second layer of planking at right angles to the first layer.

10. Using what you learned in Topic 2, decide upon a method to stabilize your ship. This is an engineering contest. The winner will be the team that can produce a self-righting ship that will recover from the greatest possible list. A perfect hull would be one that cannot be capsized.
    a. Stabilize your ship.
    b. Plank over its upper deck. The ship should be waterproof.

11. Test the model in a container of water. The ship must float, and it must be stable; that is, it must return to an upright position (keel down) on its own.

QUESTIONS

1. Explain how the skin of a ship gives strength to the rib and keelson structure. What is your evidence?

2. What are the advantages, if any, of building bulkheads and keelson before constructing the skin (planking) of a ship?

3. Suggest structural similarities between a traditional ship and the following:
   a. a wooden frame house
   b. an umbrella
   c. a suspension bridge

4. Which ship designed in class was most stable? Suggest reasons why its design was the most stable.

5. Make a labeled sketch of the hull of a ship showing each of the following parts:
   a. bow and stern   d. keelson
   b. bulkhead   e. planking
   c. gunwale   f. transom

FURTHER INVESTIGATIONS

1. Look up and report to the class on how supertankers are constructed.

2. Find blueprints and building directions for a small boat of your choice. Talk to local boat owners or builders. Find out what kinds of boats they recommend for local waters. If possible, construct the boat or a model of it.

3. Take a Coast Guard Auxiliary boating safety course. Learn the nautical terms for parts of a boat and what each is used for.

4. Make a study of the relationship between the structure of a ship hull and its functions. Talk with knowledgeable boat builders or use references to find out how hulls are modified for such purposes as increasing speed, increasing cargo capacity, or making a ship more comfortable for passengers.

5. We still use the word *blueprint* for plans drawn by architects or designers, even if the drawings are not actually blue. Consult references to find out what made blueprints blue.

5. Ship Dynamics

Speed and fuel efficiency are extremely important when considering transporting materials by ship. In this topic we will examine the relationship of ship design to speed and efficiency. Let's first consider speed.

Speed is distance per unit of time. Most of us are familiar with car speeds expressed in miles per hour.

$$\text{Speed} = \text{distance traveled/time}$$

Efficiency is a measure of work done per unit of energy used. The less energy used to do a given amount of work, the higher the efficiency. Imagine a captain of a cargo ship carrying redwood from Oakland, California, to Honolulu. The captain has no arrival deadline, so he is not concerned about whether the voyage takes 5 or 10 days.

But the captain does want to complete the voyage (the work to be done) using the least fuel (the energy used) possible. To get the best efficiency, the captain must determine what speed will require the least fuel to complete the voyage. We face a similar problem in this activity. Remember that

$$\text{Work} = \text{force (weight)} \times \text{distance}$$

$$\text{Efficiency} = \text{work/energy used}$$

ACTIVITY
Test the speed of the ship models.
Test the efficiency of ship models at different speeds.

MATERIALS
- long wave tank, 2 m or more
- pulley device on ring stand
- model ships < 30 cm (from Topic 4)
- pencil
- centigram balance scale
- meterstick
- 5-m length of string
- paper clip or fishhook
- four 10-g weights
- paper cup
- stopwatch
- four 20 X 60-cm pieces of cardboard
- scissors

PROCEDURE
1. Assemble the tow tank shown in Fig. 5–1 as follows:
   a. Obtain a wave tank at least 2 m long. Fill tank with water to within 10 cm of the top edge.
   b. Set up the pulley device. Attach pulley no. 1 to the end of the tank. Attach pulley no. 2 to a ring stand.

2. Determine speeds of various ship models.
   a. Obtain four ships made in Topic 4. Sketch each hull design in Table 5–1.
   b. Measure the weight (gf) of the ship and record in Table 5–1. Measure the distance that it will travel in the tow tank from the bow tip to pulley no. 1.
   c. Beginning with the first boat, attach

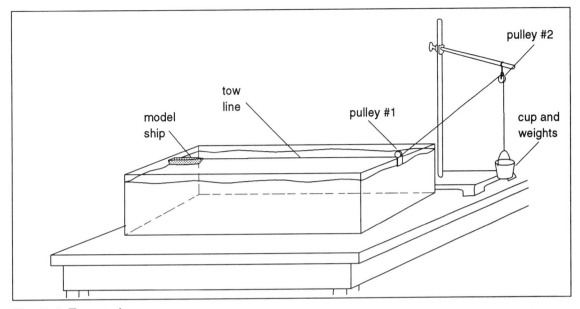

Fig. 5–1. Tow tank

the towline to the bow of the ship. Place two 10-g weights in the cup to serve as a **propulsion force**. Release the ship. Measure the time in seconds that the ship takes to reach the other end of the tow tank. Record the data in Table 5–1.

d. Compute the speed of the ship. Record the speed in Table 5–1.

e. Repeat steps (b) to (d) for each of the other ships.

3. Graph ship speed versus ship weight in Fig. 5–2.

4. Make a watermarked picture profile of the waves formed by the ship. Have one partner hold a sheet of cardboard out of the path of the ship. Just as the stern of the boat passes the cardboard, quickly dip the cardboard in and out of the **wake** (the waves formed by the boat). Immediately pencil in the wake profile. Label the cardboard with the powering force (in grams) and your name.

5. Repeat Procedures 2.c. and 2.d. using additional weights. Record the data in Table 5–2.

6. Determine the efficiency of your ship at different speeds.

a. Graph speed against powering force (in grams) in Fig. 5–3. Draw a smooth line connecting the data points.

b. Place an X through the graph where the efficiency is highest. **Efficiency** is greatest when speed divided by powering force yields the largest value. (This is where the slope of the graph is steepest.)

359

Table 5–1. Data on ship design and performance ⓦ

Distance (cm)	Time (sec)	Speed (cm/sec)	Boat weight (gf)	Force weight (gf)

Distance (cm)	Time (sec)	Speed (cm/sec)	Boat weight (gf)	Force weight (gf)

Distance (cm)	Time (sec)	Speed (cm/sec)	Boat weight (gf)	Force weight (gf)

Distance (cm)	Time (sec)	Speed (cm/sec)	Boat weight (gf)	Force weight (gf)

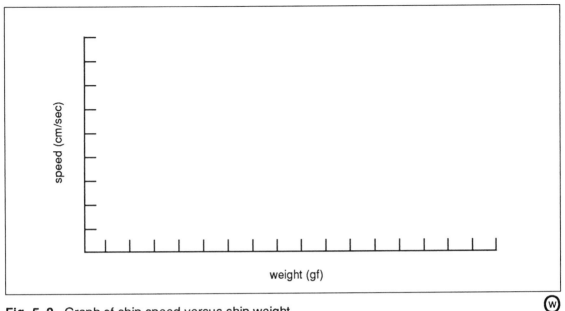

Fig. 5–2. Graph of ship speed versus ship weight Ⓦ

Table 5–2. Powering force and ship speed Ⓦ

Powering force (gf) (weight in cup)	Distance (cm)	Time (sec)	Boat speed (cm/sec)
10			
20			
30			
40			
50			
60			

7. Determine the effect of ship speed on wave size. The amount of water above and below the still-water level is a measure of wave size. It is also related to the energy in the waves.

  a. On each of the profiles you made in Procedure 4, draw a straight line across the paper midway between crests and troughs of the waves. Use a meterstick. This line represents the still-water level. Darken the areas between the still-water level and the crests and troughs with a pencil. See Fig. 5–4.

  b. For each profile, cut out the darkened area and determine its weight in grams. This is the **wave energy index** in grams.

  c. Graph ship speed against wave energy index in Fig. 5–5.

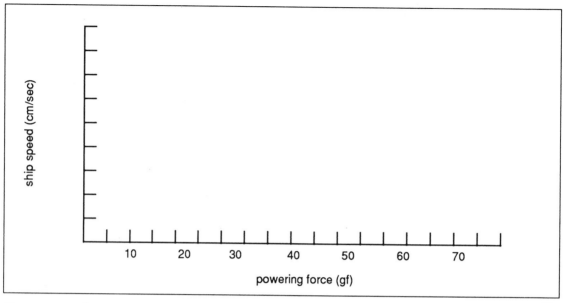

Fig. 5–3. Ship speed plotted against powering force ⓦ

QUESTIONS

1. Which of the four models traveled the fastest? How might you explain the speed of the fastest model?

2. What effect did ship weight and ship design have on ship speed?

3. Does ship speed increase constantly as the powering force increases?

4. As ship speed increases, how is the size of waves affected? Show examples.

5. At what speed does your ship travel most efficiently? Apply this information to the following:
   a. If you were building a small electric motor for your ship, what propulsion force would you have the motor exert to be the most fuel-efficient?
   b. Traveling at fuel-efficient speed is not always desirable in real situations. Comment on this statement.

6. The formula for **work energy** is

   Energy = force x distance

   Make a graph similar to that in Fig. 5–3 displaying speed (cm/sec) vertically and energy (gf x cm) horizontally.

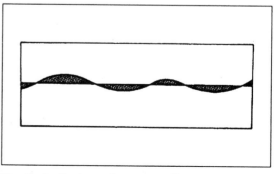

Fig. 5–4. Darkened wave profile

362

7. Compare this graph with the graph in Fig. 5–5. Explain the differences and similarities.

8. If additional force does not increase speed by much, where does the excess energy go?

9. Hypothesize whether there is a maximum speed that your ship could go. If so, what is it? How do you arrive at this speed? How could you test your hypothesis?

10. Compare the efficient hull speed of your ship with that of other boat hulls designed in class. What relationship, if any, is there between
    a. efficient hull speed and hull length?
    b. efficient hull speed and hull shape?

11. Make a list of the types of powering forces used on ships at sea today.

12. Imagine that you are a ship- or boatbuilder. Design an advertisement describing one of your ships. Use as many of the following terms as possible:
    a. design
    b. fuel efficiency
    c. speed (maximum speed)
    d. type of work or use
    e. stability
    f. cargo capacity (tonnage)
    g. powering force
    h. ship weight
    i. ship displacement
    j. length
    k. width (beam)
    m. price

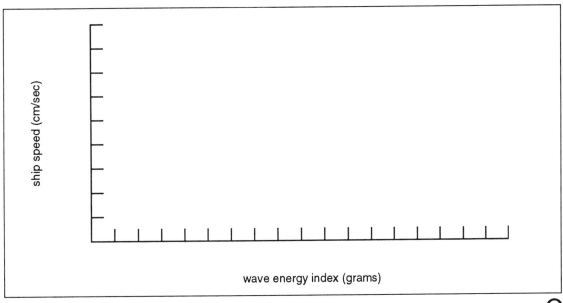

Fig. 5–5. Ship speed plotted against wave energy index

FURTHER INVESTIGATIONS

1. Compare shipping routes with maps showing patterns of winds, waves, and currents. Look for relationships.

2. Great circle routes are the shortest distances between two places on the spherical surface of the earth. Find out whether ships today follow great circle routes.

3. Read and report to the class about new technologies in boat design such as the Hovercraft and the hydrofoil.

4. Contact a shipping company and inquire about

   a. procedures for transporting goods.
   b. the time required to ship items from the U.S. mainland to Hawaii, Europe, or Japan
   c. costs of shipping goods by air, rail, and ship.

5. Interview people who work in the following fields connected with ships and shipping to find out what they do.
   a. marine technicians
   b. coastal and harbor pilots
   c. tugboat operators
   d. ocean engineers
   e. naval architects
   f. merchant marines

6. Navigation

Imagine trying to find your way around the open ocean in a small sailboat. How would you know where you are and which way to go? If you knew basic navigation and had a watch, a compass, maps, and tide charts, you could go wherever you wanted to.

Navigation includes methods for determining direction and speed, telling time, measuring distance, and fixing positions. Navigational techniques use many of the mapping skills from Unit 1, Earth and Ocean Basins. In this topic we will explore some of the types of instruments and devices used by navigators. We begin by constructing a simple floating magnetic compass.

ACTIVITY 1
Make a floating magnetic compass.

MATERIALS
- permanent magnet
- sewing needle
- paper cup
- water
- small piece of Styrofoam or cork
- Petri dish (top or bottom)
- protractor
- waterproof marking pen

PROCEDURE
1. Magnetize a sewing needle by pressing the south pole of a permanent magnet against the center of the needle and gently stroking the magnet four or five times toward the point. See (A) in Fig. 6–1.

2. Fill the cup with water to about 1 cm from the top.

3. Float the magnetized needle on the surface of the water.
   a. Insert the needle through a small piece of Styrofoam or cork.
   b. Place the needle-float assembly gently onto the surface of water to see if it floats. See (B) in Fig. 6–1. Adjust if necessary. When the needle floats satisfactorily, go to Procedure 4 .

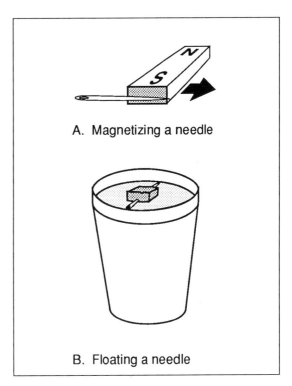

A. Magnetizing a needle

B. Floating a needle

Fig. 6–1. Making a compass with a floating magnetized needle

4. Mark geographical reference points on the cup.
   a. Locate **magnetic north** by allowing the needle to rotate until it stops.
   b. Determine the positions for the other **primary reference points**: south (S), east (E), and west (W). See Fig. 6–2.

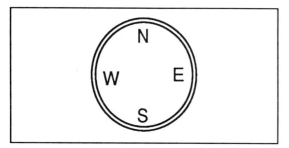

Fig. 6–2. Primary reference points

5. Make an indicator disk for the floating-needle compass.
   a. With a protractor, mark a Petri dish every 30° with a waterproof marking pen.
   b. Label the marks with degrees of the compass as shown in Fig. 6–3.
   c. Put the labeled Petri dish over the cup

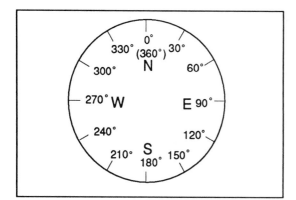

Fig. 6–3. Indicator disk for a floating-needle compass

with the 0° mark aligned over the point of the floating needle.

6. Use the compass to find **directions**.
   a. Hold the compass and indicator directly in front of you with the needle pointing forward to the north.
   b. Make a right-angle (90°) turn to your left.
   c. Read and record the number the needle is pointing to.
   d. Turn the indicator disk until 0°(360°) is over the point of the needle.
   e. In which direction are you facing—N, S, E, or W? What is the **compass bearing**—the direction in the number of degrees from north?

7. Practice using the compass to give directions.
   a. Write the directions for walking in a square 4 m on each side.
   b. Test your directions by having your lab partner follow them using the compass as a guide.

8. Repeat Procedure 7 for a triangle and for another geometric shape.

9. Locate your regular place in the classroom by **triangulation**.
   a. Sketch your classroom.
   b. Using your compass, locate the points on the walls that line up north and south. On your sketch, draw these points, connect them and label them.
   c. Locate two objects that are not along the same line of sight. Draw these objects on your sketch.
   d. Determine the compass bearing for each of these objects. Record them below the sketches of the objects.

e. Draw lines across your sketch along the bearing line for each object.

f. The place where the lines cross is your position. Mark this with a star.

g. Have another member of the class verify that your position is correct.

QUESTION

1. How could you use a floating-needle compass aboard a ship? What problems would you have to solve to make it practical? What modifications would you make?

Navigation Instruments

Navigation instruments include remote sensing devices that can detect distant objects such as other ships, **buoys** (floating navigational aids), islands, or coastlines, night or day, in clear weather or dense fog. A common remote sensing device is **radar** (**ra**dio **d**etecting **a**nd **r**anging), a rotating instrument that scans surrounding areas by transmitting high-frequency radio waves that reflect off objects they encounter. The reflected wave is picked up by a receiver on the ship, revealing information about the size and location of the object it bounced off. Compare the illustration of a radar screen in Fig. 6–4 to the section in the upper-right corner of the drawing of the nautical chart in Fig. 6–5.

Echo sounders such as the **fathometer** and **sonar** (**so**und **n**avigation **a**nd **r**anging) are instruments that measure water depth by using sound waves. Water depth is calculated from the time it takes for a sound pulse to travel to the seafloor and back.

Nautical Charts

Nautical charts are the road maps of the seas, used by sailors and navigators for

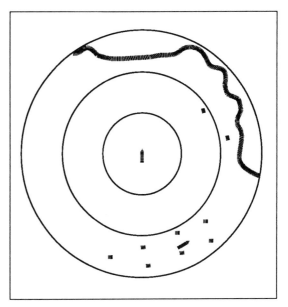

Fig. 6–4. A radar screen shows an outline of the coast and objects in the distance. Each ring represents 1 nautical mile from the ship that is the source of the transmitted radio waves.

locating positions and plotting courses. Examine the modified nautical chart shown in Fig. 6–5. Notice that the location of the area is given in degrees of latitude and longitude. Recall from Unit 1 that north is at the top, latitude scales are on the sides, and longitude scales are at the top and bottom. Grid lines indicate meridians of longitude and parallels of latitude.

The chart shows features that are important to navigators, such as water depth, shallow areas, navigation aids, hazards, and the coastline. On this chart the main ship channel and other important features are marked by buoys. The chart shows whether the buoys are equipped with lights, horns, bells, whistles, or gongs. A **compass rose** is included to show direction.

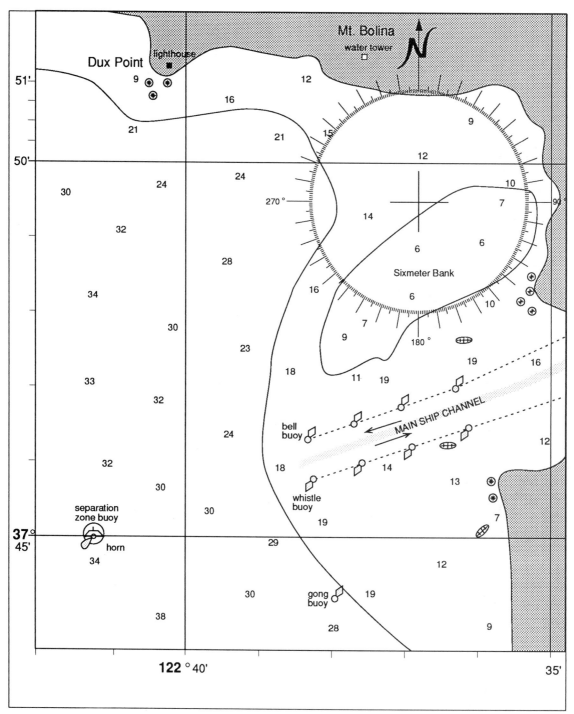

Fig. 6–5. Nautical chart with depths given in meters

ACTIVITY 2

Use a nautical chart to determine a position and plot a course.

MATERIALS

- 3 X 5-in index card
- ruler
- pencil
- scissors
- drawing compass with pencil

PROCEDURE

1. Imagine that you must use your nautical chart and navigation instruments to bring a ship into a busy harbor. You have a compass, a fathometer, and radar on board.

2. You take a compass reading on the Mt. Bolina water tower, which is at 60° relative to the position of your ship; the Dux Point lighthouse is at 350°. Using navigation triangles, locate the position of your ship on the nautical chart in Fig. 6–5.

   a. Make a pair of navigation triangles.
      1) Mark the longer sides of a 3 X 5-in index card with *X*'s and the shorter sides with *O*'s as shown in Fig. 6–6.
      2) Draw a pencil line diagonally across the index card. Mark the triangles *#1* and *#2* as shown in Fig. 6–6.
      3) Cut the card carefully along the diagonal line.
   b. Using navigation triangles, transfer the compass readings from the compass rose to the objects on the nautical chart.
      1) Align the edge of triangle *#1* on the 60° mark of the compass rose. The

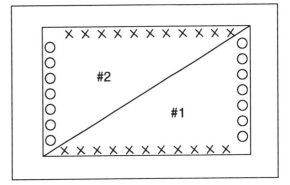

Fig. 6–6. Making navigation triangles

edge must pass directly through the cross in the center of the compass rose. See (A) in Fig. 6–7.
   2) Place triangle *#2* next to triangle *#1* with the diagonal sides touching and the sides marked with the same symbols opposite each other as shown in (B) in Fig. 6–7.
   3) Slide triangle *#2* along the diagonal until the side with the X's reaches the symbol representing the target object (Mt. Bolina water tower). See (C) in Fig. 6–7. If a target object is a long way from the compass rose, it may be necessary to move the other triangle as well. Always keep the sides marked with the same symbols opposite each other. Press firmly on the triangles to avoid losing the original reading from the compass rose.
   4) Draw a line through the target object (the water tower) and continue it across the chart. Label the line with the compass reading. See (D) in Fig 6–7. Your ship's position is somewhere along that line.
   5) Repeat Procedures (1) through (4) for the compass reading on the Dux Point lighthouse.

369

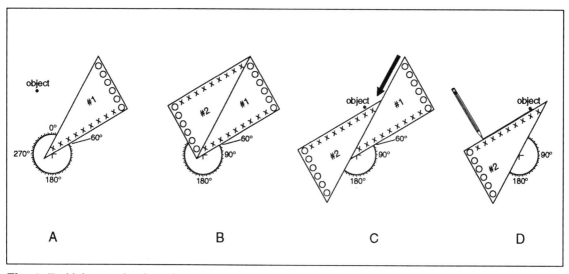

Fig. 6–7. Using navigation triangles to transfer a line parallel to itself

6) The point where the two lines intersect is your ship's actual position. Mark it with the letter A.

3. Verify your **position** by checking your fathometer, which reads 24 m. Does this reading indicate you are in the correct location?

4. What are the latitude and longitude of your position? Write these in your notebook.

5. Indicate the **course** (intended route) you want to travel.
   a. On the chart, find the buoys that mark the main channel.
   b. Mark the whistle buoy on the south side of the main channel with a B.
   c. Using a ruler, draw a straight course line from position B to position A.

6. Determine the compass bearing between the two positions.
   a. Line up one of the navigation triangles on the course line and move across the chart to the compass rose. This technique is the reverse of the steps used in Procedure 2.b.
   b. Draw a line from the exact center of the compass rose through the outer circle.
   c. Read the number of degrees from the circle. Count clockwise from zero degrees at the north.
   d. Write the compass bearing above the course line.

7. Determine the distance in nautical miles from position A to position B.
   a. Measure the length of the course line with the drawing compass or a ruler. See (A) in Fig. 6–8.
   b. Align the drawing compass or ruler with the scale at the edge of the nautical chart as shown in (B) in Fig. 6–8. To determine the number of nautical miles, use degrees of latitude. One minute of latitude (marked on the longitude line) equals 1 nautical mile.

370

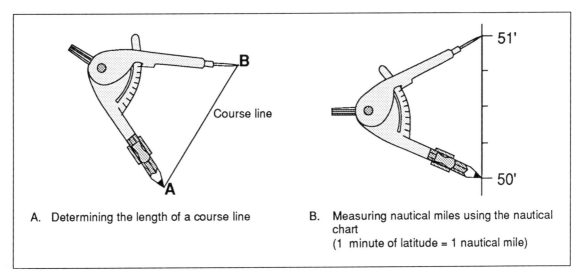

A. Determining the length of a course line

B. Measuring nautical miles using the nautical chart
(1 minute of latitude = 1 nautical mile)

Fig. 6–8. Using a drawing compass and the latitude scale (marked on the longitude line) on a nautical chart to measure distance in nautical miles

c. Write the distance in nautical miles below the course line.

8. Set a course and imagine that you are sailing toward position B. After about 45 minutes, heavy fog rolls in and a strong tidal current starts flowing out of the channel. You are sure you are off course because you should be in water a little over 18 m deep, but the fathometer reads 30 m. The radar screen indicates that the separation zone horn buoy is 1 nautical mile away and that the gong buoy to the south of the main channel is 3 nautical miles away. Determine your actual position.

a. Measure 1 nautical mile from the latitude scale on the side of the chart with your drawing compass.

b. Locate the separation zone horn buoy. Then put the point of the drawing compass on the buoy. Draw a circle with a radius of 1 nautical mile around the buoy. You are somewhere on that circle.

c. Do the same for the distance from the gong buoy.

d. The circles intersect in two places. Check the depths on the nautical chart to determine which is your actual position. Mark this position with a C.

9. Determine the **course made good** (actual direction).

a. Draw a line from position A to position C.

b. Determine the compass bearing of the course by repeating the steps in Procedure 6.

c. Write the compass bearing next to the line.

d. Use the steps in Procedure 7 to estimate how many nautical miles you actually traveled. Write the distance in nautical miles next to the line.

10. Set a new course to reach the main channel.
    a. Draw a line between positions C and B.
    b. Determine the new bearing by using the steps in Procedure 6.
    c. Write the compass bearing above the line.

QUESTIONS

2. List all the kinds of navigation information and aids shown on the nautical chart in Fig. 6–5. Which symbol represents a shipwreck? A submerged rock?

3. If there were no navigational aids such as buoys, foghorns, bells, whistles, or lighthouses along coastal regions, how could navigators find their way at night or in heavy fog?

4. What physical, environmental, or other factors could affect the accuracy of navigation?

5. Why is it not possible to use degrees of longitude along the parallels of latitude to determine nautical miles?

6. If the ship sails an average of 6 knots (nautical miles per hour), how much time should it take to get from position A to position B?

FURTHER INVESTIGATIONS

1. Test a variety of common metal objects and materials with a bar magnet. Use coins, paper clips, brass weights, aluminum foil, stones, steel washers, nails, bobby pins, and safety pins.
    a. What kinds of matter are attracted by magnets?
    b. What kinds are not attracted?
    c. Do any of the objects become magnetized and then attract other objects? If so, which ones?
    d. Wrap the magnet in cloth and test the objects. Record what happens.

2. Learn how to make a simple electromagnet from a nail, copper wire, and a battery.

3. Read and report to the class on the following:
    a. Micronesian stick charts used to teach navigators how to use ocean swells, wave patterns, and stars to find their way to small, remote islands and atolls in the Pacific Ocean
    b. Prince Henry the Navigator and the center he established to train Portuguese sea captains
    c. the explorers of the 15th century "Age of Discovery," including Dias, da Gama, Columbus, Balboa, Magellan, Hudson, and Drake
    d. Capt. James Cook's explorations and mapping of the southern oceans, Hawaii, Australia, and the northeast Pacific Ocean
    e. the history of development of the compass, the sextant, and the determination of longitude

4. A compass rose on an official nautical chart has two concentric circles each divided into 360°. See Fig. 6–9. The outer circle indicates **true geographical direction** and has a star at 0° (360°). True direction is used on maps and charts.

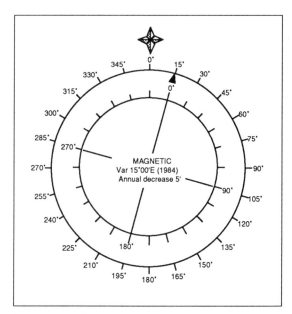

Fig. 6–9. Compass rose showing true geographical direction and magnetic variation

The inner circle on the example in Fig. 6–9 is turned at a 15° angle to the outer one and indicates the **magnetic variation** from true north for this chart. The magnetic north pole of the earth continually changes; the amount of variation differs in locations around the world. Nautical charts indicate the amount of variation and the yearly rate of change for these locations. Metal objects and machinery on ships affect compass readings. Each ship has compass corrections to compensate for these **deviations**.

a. Obtain a nautical chart of your local area or an area that interests you. Examine it to find the compass rose. What is the magnetic compass variation for the location?

b. List all the other types of navigational information that it contains. If possible, go to the area and find the navigational aids.

5. Learn to use parallel rulers on nautical charts to transfer a line parallel to itself. Devise a method for using a protractor or a pencil to determine a compass bearing on a nautical chart.

6. **Celestial navigation** is an ancient art that uses the positions of celestial bodies such as the sun, moon, or stars to determine position. This requires measuring **altitude**, the angle of a heavenly body above the horizon. The instrument commonly used to measure altitude is the **sextant**.

a. Learn to use a sextant to determine angles between objects and to triangulate positions.

b. Make and learn to use a simple **astrolabe**. Demonstrate for the class.

7. Consult your school counselor about training to become a ship or airplane navigator. What are the roles of the captain, the navigator, and the pilot?

8. Get more information about courses on navigation, boating operation, and safety from the Coast Guard or other local organizations. Take one of these courses.

9. Arrange to visit a boat or ship that uses modern navigation instruments. Visit the bridge and examine the compass, radar, fathometer, and other electronic navigational devices.

10. Read how satellites are used in open-ocean navigation. Make a diagram and explain to the class how satellites operate and the kinds of information they provide.

Appendix A. Symbols, Abbreviations, and Units of Measure

1. SYMBOLS

X	multiplied by
÷	divided by
<	less than
=	equal to
>	greater than
/	divided by or per

2. MEASURES

International System (SI) Units

mm	millimeter
cm	centimeter
m	meter
km	kilometer (1,000 m)
mL	milliliter
L	liter
g	gram
kg	kilogram
˚C	degrees Celsius

U.S. Customary Units

in	inch
ft	foot
yd	yard
mi	mile
oz	ounce (volume)
qt	quart
gal	gallon (U.S.)
oz	ounce (mass)
lb	pound
˚F	degrees Fahrenheit

3. OTHER UNITS

atm	atmosphere
psi	pounds per square inch
cal	calorie
kcal	kilocalorie (1,000 calories)
nmi	nautical mile
kt	knots

Appendix B. Formulas

1. CIRCUMFERENCE

square	4L	L = length
rectangle	2L + 2W	W = width
circle	$\pi d = 2\pi r$	π = 3.14
		r = radius
		d = diameter

2. AREA

square	L X L
rectangle	L X W
circle	πr^2
sphere	$4\pi r^2$

3. VOLUME

cube	L X L X L
solid rectangle	L X W X H
sphere	$4/3\ \pi r^3$

4. CIRCULAR MEASURE

1 circle	= 360°	(° = degree)
1 degree	= 60'	(' = minute)
1 minute	= 60"	(" = second)

5. OTHER UNITS

Density = mass/volume = g/cm^3 or g/mL

Joule (energy) = 1 newton/meter

Force = mass X acceleration = kg X m/sec/sec

Pressure = force/area

Appendix C. Scientific Notation

1. Numbers may be expressed in **powers of ten**. For example, 1,000,000 may expressed as 10^6, which means 10 X 10 X 10 X 10 X 10 X 10. In 10^6, the **base** is ten, and the **exponent** is 6.

one billion	=	1,000,000,000	=	10^9
one million	=	1,000,000	=	10^6
one thousand	=	1,000	=	10^3
one hundred	=	100	=	10^2
ten	=	10	=	10^1
one	=	1	=	10^0
one-tenth	=	0.1	=	10^{-1}
one-hundredth	=	0.01	=	10^{-2}
one-thousandth	=	0.001	=	10^{-3}
one-billionth	=	0.000000001	=	10^{-9}

2. Examples of converting numbers to powers of 10.

(a) 300 = 3 X 100 = 3×10^2
(b) 3,500 = 3.5 X 1,000 = 3.5×10^3
(c) 0.15 = 1.5 X 0.1 = 1.5×10^{-1}
(d) 0.05 = 5 X 0.01 = 5×10^{-2}

3. To multiply, add the exponents.

(a) $10^2 \times 10^3$ = 10^{2+3} = 10^5
(b) 10 X 10 = 10^{1+1} = 10^2
(c) $10^5 \times 10^3$ = 10^{5+3} = 10^8
(d) $(3 \times 10^4)(2 \times 10^{-6})$ = $6 \times 10^{4-6}$ = 6×10^{-2}
(e) $(4 \times 10^6)(2 \times 10^{-3})$ = $8 \times 10^{6-3}$ = 8×10^3

4. To divide, subtract the exponents.

(a) $\dfrac{10^3}{10^5}$ = 10^{3-5} = 10^{-2}

(b) $\dfrac{4 \times 10^3}{2 \times 10^{-6}}$ = $\dfrac{4}{2} \times 10^{3-(-6)}$ = $2 \times 10^{3+6}$ = 2×10^9

(c) $\dfrac{6.4 \times 10^{-2}}{1.6 \times 10^3}$ = $\dfrac{6.4}{1.6} \times 10^{(-2)-3}$ = 4×10^{-5}

Appendix D. Converting Units

1. LENGTH

Unit	cm	m	in	ft
1 cm	1	0.01	0.39	0.03
1 m	100	1	39.37	3.28
1 in	2.54	0.0254	1	0.08
1 fathom	182.88	1.83	72	6
1 mi	1.61×10^5	1.61×10^3	6.34×10^4	5,280
1 nmi	1.85×10^5	1.85×10^3	7.29×10^4	6,072

2. AREA

Unit	cm^2	m^2	km^2	in^2	ft^2	mi^2	nmi^2
1 cm^2	1	10^{-4}	10^{-10}	0.155	1.08×10^{-3}	3.85×10^{-11}	2.92×10^{-11}
1 m^2	10^4	1	10^{-6}	1,550	10.76	3.85×10^{-6}	2.92×10^{-7}
1 km^2	10^{10}	10^6	1	1.55×10^9	1.07×10^6	0.39	0.29
1 in^2	6.45	6.45×10^{-4}	–	1	6.94×10^{-3}	2.49×10^{-10}	1.88×10^{-10}
1 ft^2	929.03	0.09	–	144	1	3.59×10^{-8}	2.71×10^{-8}
1 mi^2	2.59×10^{10}	2.59×10^6	2.59	4.02×10^9	2.79×10^7	1	0.76

3. MASS

Unit	g	kg	lb	metric ton	ton
1 g	1	10^{-3}	2.21×10^{-3}	10^{-6}	1.1×10^{-6}
1 kg	1,000	1	2.21	10^{-3}	1.1×10^{-3}
1 lb (avdp)	453.59	0.45	1	4.54×10^{-4}	5×10^{-4}
1 metric ton	10^6	1,000	2,204.62	1	1.1
1 ton	907,184.7	907.2	2,000	0.91	1

4. VOLUME

Unit	m^3	cm^3	liter	in^3	ft^3	qt	gal
1 m^3	1	10^6	10^3	6.1×10^4	35.31	1.06×10^3	264.1
1 cm^3	10^{-6}	1	10^{-3}	0.06	3.53×10^{-5}	1.06×10^{-3}	2.64×10^{-4}
1 liter	10^{-3}	1,000	1	61.02	0.04	1.06	0.26
1 in^3	1.64	16.39	0.02	1	5.79×10^{-4}	0.02	4.33×10^{-3}
1 ft^3	2.83×10^{-2}	28,316.85	28.32	1,728	1	2.99	7.48
1 qt	9.47×10^{-4}	946.35	0.94	57.75	0.03	1	0.25
1 gal (U.S.)	3.79×10^{-3}	3,785.41	3.79	231	0.13	4	1

5. TEMPERATURE

Formulas

$$°C = \frac{°F - 32}{1.8} \qquad °F = (1.8 \times °C) + 32$$

Conversion table

°C	°F
0	32
10	50
20	68
30	86
40	104
100	212

6. TIME

1 day	=	8.64 X 10⁴ sec (mean solar day)	=	24 hr
1 year	=	8765.8 hr	=	3.156 X 10⁷ sec (mean solar year)
1 aeon	=	10⁹ yr (one billion years)		

Nautical time (expressed on a 24-hour clock)

Standard	Nautical
6 AM	0600 hr
9 AM	0900 hr
12 Noon	1200 hr
3 PM	1500 hr
6 PM	1800 hr
11:30 PM	2330 hr

7. SPEED

Unit	knots	mi/hr	km/hr	m/sec
1 knot	1	1.15	1.85	0.5
1 mi/hr	0.87	1	1.61	0.43
1 km/hr	0.54	0.62	1	0.27
1 m/sec	2	2.3	3.7	1

8. DENSITY

Unit	g/cm^3	g/L	kg/m^3	lb/ft^3	lb/gal
g/cm^3	1	10^3	10^3	62.4	8.35
g/L	10^{-3}	1	1	0.062	8.35 X 10^{-3}
kg/m^3	10^{-3}	1	1	0.062	8.35 X 10^{-3}
lb/ft^3	0.016	16.01	16.01	1	0.13
lb/gal	0.12	119.8	119.8	7.48	1

9. PRESSURE

Unit	atm	kg/cm^2	psi (lb/in^2)	in Hg	mm Hg
atm	1	1.03	14.7	29.92	760
kg/cm^2	0.968	1	14.22	28.96	735.56
psi	0.068	0.07	1	2.04	51.71
in Hg	0.03	0.035	0.491	1	25.4
mm Hg	1.31 X 10^{-3}	1.36 X 10^{-3}	0.019	0.039	1

10. ENERGY

1 cal	= 4.18 Joule	= 1.56 X 10^{-6} horsepower/hr
1 Joule	= 0.239 cal	= 3.73 horsepower/hr

Index

(Page numbers in **boldface** indicate figures and tables.)